Going Home

Kumar Pillay

In dedication to
my beloved
parents and wife

Going Home

Kumar Pillay

»Going Home«
Kumar Pillay

ISBN 978-3-00-052615-2

Printed and Distributed by Ingram Spark,
La Vergne, Tennessee 37086

© 2016 by Kumar Pillay, c/o BJ-Autorenservice.de
Gildehauser Weg 140a, 48529 Nordhorn

Photos on page 223 © Museum Associates/LACMA

Illustrations and Cover Photos © Kumar Pillay

Prologue

It was the warm season. Many an hour did I spend listening to her; the river. Here, on the roof of the world, the window to the stars, the home of the gods, was the holy river. Gentle was her voice, full of wisdom was her voice, cleanser of the heart, soother of the soul. I listened to the voices of the past, of voices to be.

There were moments when she was quick to speak and there were moments when she remained silent. It was in these silent moments I listened closer, letting it overcome me. It broke into a thousand voices, all speaking in unison, all voices becoming one, the one word, the word of all words, the 'OM'!

Allowing this single tone to carry me, floating on its vibrations, moving into higher state of awareness and finally arriving, finally being in the presence of the Enlightened Ones.

From the bottom of my heart I asked, 'I have searched you all my life.'

They spoke with great compassion, 'We have been here all along, waiting for you.'

1

True Happiness

It began a long time ago, or was it only yesterday? Some of us ask ourselves more than often whether we lived a good life. Was it a short or a long journey? Others would rather want to know if it was a meaningful one, one which made a difference. For mine I was thankful. There were difficult times, but again, what is life without its difficulties. Moments which challenge, moments which bring out either the best or the worst in us!

Don't we all deserve a chance to lead a fulfilling life? I believe so. But doubts and fears paralyze us from breathing freely. Though we are given chances, chances to spread our wings and fly to great heights. Changes in life are inevitable. So why ignore them? With change opportunity arises; the present will perish but it makes room for the future.

Again the tides have brought in new tidings. A new chapter to be written, the final pages. Now we will be taking leave from our beloved ones and from the home we have known. The time has come for us to move on. But before, we will tell Anna, our daughter, the whole story. About how it all began and about why we are here. Hence we have invited her, along with her husband Hira and his parents, for a get-together at our place.

It was a warm summer afternoon and I was waiting anxiously to see my granddaughter Ammu. As I heard her sweet voice outside in the garden calling 'Grandfather', I went out. She ran into my arms and I picked her up. As usual, I had only eyes for her. "How delightful she is!" With her curly hair and sweet smile she always manages to bring warmth into my heart. "My sunshine", as Indira refers to her.

Being a nice day outside, I went for a walk with Ammu. The streets were full with people greeting each other; all happy faces. As I walked down the road, I heard voices of peace. Life has changed. There was a scent of freedom in the air. For the first time in my life I felt hope, hope for the world, hope for humanity. It was great joy looking into the eyes of my granddaughter, knowing she'll be breaking into a beautiful future. And all will be well.

Our work has not only brought changes in Keajara, it also has spread like a cool breeze in a warm day, soothing the hearts of many around the world, changing the way men have been living, have been thinking. They are returning to their inner selfs.

Down the lane in front of a florist I met Togma, Hira's father. We came to a halt. A butterfly was swaying over the flowers catching Ammu's attention. The butterfly suddenly changed its course and flew directly at Ammu's pink flowered dress. Ammu laughed excitedly as the butterfly gently landed on her dress. Yes, it was one of the rare occasions in life, when time suddenly stood still. I couldn't help feeling nostalgic. Melancholy and joy arose in my heart. Yes, I shall leave only to return.

As I turned to Togma, I noticed the same emotions in his eyes. We have known each other since our early years, since I first came to Keajara. Over the past decades we have become brothers. Many were the ups and downs.

Togma laid his hand on my shoulders as he greeted me. 'Roger, nice to see you and Ammu enjoying the weather.'

I returned his greeting in the same way. 'Hello Togma, it's also nice to see you. Yes, it's a wonderful day.'

'I hope all is well with you and Indira?'

'Yes, all is well.'

'Have you spoken with Anna yet?' he asked a little reluctantly. Keajarans do not protrude into others' affairs. But this was a special case.

'No, not yet. We shall inform her and Hira today after dinner.'

'I see.'

'Would you and Aisha mind joining us?'

'We'll be very happy to.'

'That is settled then, tonight at eight.'

He nodded and we turned our attention back to our granddaughter, who was still very busy with her butterfly.

Around seven o'clock, Togma and Aisha arrived. The atmosphere in the cottage became merrier, one could say. Anna and Hira had just arrived from the outskirts

3

that day. Hira doesn't often have the chance to meet his parents, and naturally he was very glad to see them. Dinner was a happy event. Although the dining room was small, all of us found a place. Butter bread and rice was served, and traditional Tibetan vegetarian dishes with curry.

Anna and Hira were busy talking about their work and their travels. The new arrivals needed more medical attention, they explained. Both being practicing physicians, they traveled much within Keajara, and Ammu was always with them. Their traveling had not given me much chance to see her.

It was getting late and Ammu was getting tired. Anna brought her to bed, and we retired to the living room as we made ourselves comfortable. For some time now there has been an uncomfortable feeling in my heart. I had thought a lot about how to begin, but how does one say goodbye to those one loves. And so I had decided to tell Anna how it all started and had begun to write down my story; to leave it for my daughter and my granddaughter, as a legacy.

'We're very glad you could all make it this evening!' I began.

Anna replied, 'Naturally Papa, we hardly see each other, with our work and all. We're only too glad to be here – it's always nice to come home.'

When she mentioned the word "home", I couldn't help at looking towards Indira. I could sense her sadness. This "home" will soon cease to exist.

I checked my feelings before saying, 'You know, I thought it would be fun telling a story today evening.

Something we haven't really spoken of. It's a story about a young man meeting a young woman and how their lives changed forever.'

I ended the sentence with a smile. Anna became immediately attentive, and I could read the curiosity in Hira's eyes.

'It's now thirty-five years since it all began. Yes, it was a long time ago. Though it seems it was only yesterday I first met your beautiful mother.' I looked around the room and saw the dear faces waiting patiently for me to go on.

'Before we met, I was leading, how would you put it, a life of paradox. There was a great feeling of pride in me, for that what I had achieved in life. On the other hand there was also sadness, a gnawing pain. It had more to do with the results of my work than it did with the profession I had chosen for myself. Something was amiss in the world. There were many questions but very few answers.'

I saw concern in Anna's eyes as she asked, 'Papa, were you not happy when you were young?'

'I'm not exactly sure what my emotions were then,' I tried to console her. 'On the one hand my career was going on well, but on the other hand thoughts of those suffering constantly occupied me. The never-ending suffering in this world. No matter how much we worked, or how long, it never really made a difference. The victims were too many, and the resources to help them limited. Many a night was there a great burden on my heart, and the feeling of helplessness. There came a point questions such as, "Is there no permanent resurrection?",

"Is there no end to suffering?", "If God is merciful and almighty, why does he not do anything about the suffering on this world?" kept swirling in my head. There was one particular case which kept me awake many a night. It was a little girl. She was born in the slums of Mumbai. She lived and died at the age of four. I thought, "How could a merciful and lovable God allow this to happen? If by birth a soul is born innocent, why does this girl have to suffer and die in pain?" It did not make any sense.'

Pausing for a moment, I added, 'Looking back, I believe I was searching for not only a solution to the problems we face as humans, but also for answers as to why we were facing them.'

I opened my note book. 'There seemed to be no real logic to what we were doing to this planet. The suffering we impose on each other and that which we inflict on our environment. It's all so unnecessary. The earth gives us everything we need and there is enough for everyone. But we rather cause pain on each other than being satisfied and living in harmony. How can greed and hate be allowed to overcome compassion? The blindness of men's deeds has not limits.'

Stopping again for a long, deep breath, 'The answer came in the form of an old friend, but I'll begin at the beginning.'

2

Some thirty-five years ago

Opening my bedroom window, letting in the cool air of an early summer day as the sun was spreading out its warmth. Spring was bidding goodbye, and hope was in the air. The rain had stopped, and warmness was fanning out its wings. I took a deep breath thinking, "It would be a nice day spent outside!" But duty calls, and I was late for work.

'Breakfast is ready!' a cheerful voice piped up from the kitchen.

'I'm sorry! I don't have time, mom,' I answered and hurried down the stairs.

Walking into the kitchen I picked up the cup and swallowed down my coffee. 'Could you please send my other suit for dry-cleaning?' I asked. 'I had no time to do it.' I would normally do it myself, but I've been coming home late, lately.

She nodded with a smile as she straightened my collar.

Since my father, a marine lieutenant, died on duty, there has been only the two of us. I was eleven at that time. Being a strong person she managed to support me by herself. Always encouraging me to find my way in life! With her guidance I was able to excel in school.

This paved my way into Harvard Law School, after which I joined the UN. I returned to New York and moved back into my old room. Somehow, leaving my mother alone was no option.

I loved my work at the UN. As a lawyer for international human rights, I mostly had to do with cases of power abuse. Working there gave me the feeling of doing something meaningful, to make a small difference. As a kid I spent many hours letting my thoughts stray into faraway worlds, better places, where no one had to suffer. My mother used to call me a dreamer. I suppose she was right. The times I spent with my mother at the social security office were memorable ones. Every day after school, I would join her and help her to sort out the public contributions. We used to receive piles of clothes, food and so on, and to distribute them to those in need. Moments which shaped my destiny! Maybe I was young or too naïve, but I believed that the world required more people to lend others a helping hand. This experience helped to form my future.

'Take care, and take time for lunch! Promise me,' my mother said bringing me back to the present.

Before leaving, I took a final look in the mirror.

"I look a little different now," I thought. During high school it was another story. They were not the best of days – being a tall and skinny nerd. Not really an attraction for the opposite sex! For some reason this changed. I began using the school gym; started to jog and swim. It made a difference. Girls began to take notice, and I made new friends. After that, knowing a lot seemed to help. "Strange is this world!" In those days, like every other

8

teenage kid, jeans and T-shirts were my attire. Every-thing changed after me joining the UN. Dark business suits replaced casual wear, but I liked it.

'How do I look, mom?'

Examining me she said, 'I rather you change that tie. Why don't you try that light blue one, it suits the color of your eyes?'

She was right but I was already late. I hurried back to my room, changed my tie and left the house.

I had always liked our home. Sure, it wasn't very big; a two-storey, two-bedroom terrace house with a small garden. But it served its purpose. And the subway was only two blocks away. Driving into New York was no option for me. I hated the hustle, and the traffic only got my nerves up. The public transport system on the other hand was convenient. It gave me the chance to mentally get prepared for work, and the opportunity to "get in touch with the world".

Putting on my sunglasses I strolled down to the sub-way. I used to love days such as that, when the sun spread its rays over the city, like a golden blanket of goodness. Everything about the early morning hours was full of freshness. There seemed to be a sense of new beginning, new chapters to be written. The world had its flaws, but a morning such as that gave hope!

In my work it is not often that problems are resolved. A solution is complicated and involves many stake-holders, each having a personal agenda. And mostly issues are not settled, rather put "on hold". But there are those special moments when things do get done, and these moments cause great satisfaction, even if it was only a drop in the ocean.

Arriving in Manhattan, I walked out of the subway station, passing the book shop at the corner, stopping for a minute or two to look into the window for new arrivals. "Maybe I'll spend some time this evening looking in," I thought before moving on. From my place to my office it normally takes half an hour, plus five or ten minutes to get through security and to the eighth floor, the Department of Human Rights Law.

As I walked into my office, Amanda, my secretary, looked up and gave me a smiling 'Good morning, Roger!' while pointing towards my desk. 'There's an envelope on your table, delivered early today. It seems to be important.'

On my table laid a sealed envelope addressed to Roger Cane personally, with a familiar handwriting. It had been some time since I last saw this handwriting. Just before I could open it, Amanda walked in and gave me a quick update about my appointments for the day.

Two years ago she began working for me. She being reliable and efficient, I was grateful to have her as my assistant. There were rumors about us, her being a very attractive young lady, blonde with blue eyes and all. But we knew we weren't each other's type. We paid no attention to the rumors. Moreover, I knew of her liaison with a young medical student; a high-school love story.

As soon as she left the room, I turned my attention to the envelope. I must admit I was surprised to hear from Richard. It has been a years since I last seen him. "To be precise..." I recalled "...the last time I saw him, it was in

Harvard, after my law degree. Eight years have passed since then!" After which I had practically lost any contact. It was said he left without any word for the Himalayas and there were even been rumors about him being no more among the living. Somehow the whole thing struck me strange at that time. It was so unlike him, to make spontaneous decisions.

Richard had inspired me in those days. He gave me guidance I needed. In fact, he was the one who helped me to choose my major. There had been a time when we would spend nearly every evening discussing about it. A couple of times Richard had visited us in New York. During his stay at our place, my mother would also join in. Sometimes she would just shake her head with a smile, saying, 'There's a difference between reality and Utopia.' Richard would then reply, 'Yes, ma'am, but all good in the reality has its source in Utopia.'

I remember being disappointed, when Richard turned down my request for him to be my doctoral advisor. He gave no full explanation instead said, 'I'm very sorry, Roger. Believe me, I would be honored, but I stand now at crossroads.' More he wouldn't want to say. The cut was deep. But seeing my interest in human rights, he persuaded me to choose a topic at the UN. He made sure I was chosen for the doctoral programme, and a colleague of his at Harvard supported me as my doctoral advisor. That was how I ended up starting my career in international human rights here, so "all well end well".

Opening the envelope, I withdrew a mall note. The familiar scribble undoubtedly belonged to him. It said,

'Need to see you! Today, 10:00 a.m., in your office. Regards, Richard.'

After all these years, he was in New York! He wanted to meet me that very morning. For some reason I was a little nervous, at the same time I must admit I couldn't hide my curiosity and there was this feeling of silently joyful to meeting him. I glanced at my watch and thought "Time to hurry up, Roger!" Nostalgia overwhelmed me as I walked over to Amanda.

'Amanda, could you please postpone my appointments for the morning?' I ignored her surprised look and continued, 'And please inform the front security desk about the arrival of Dr. Richard Conners, at ten o'clock.'

'But the department meeting...' objected Amanda '...and the deadline for the report!'

'I know, but this is rather important. Please collect Dr. Conners at the reception and escort him to my office when he arrives. We'll also need some coffee. Thank you, Amanda!'

I turned and left her visibly astonished and irritated. But there was no time to explain. Going over to my desk, I grabbed the project report. "Have to finish my review before Richard arrived. That would give me some free time for him," I thought.

An hour later, Richard walked into my office.

'Richard,' I exclaimed, 'what a wonderful surprise!'

'I too am happy to see you Roger. Indeed it has been some time now.'

Obviously overwhelmed he hugged me like old friends do. Although time had passed, seeing him took me back to the days at college.

He looked a little older, but there was an air of contentment around him, as if he was at peace with the world. He still had his tweed checked jacket on, even in summer, with the well-known jeans and white shirt.

After helping him out of his jacket, he remarked in his usual fatherly manner, 'I heard you've done well, and your superiors are very proud of the work you do.'

I raised my eyebrows, wondering how he knew my superiors. He smiled and rubbed his hands, as he used to do, before answering a question. 'I know the Secretary General.'

"Of course," I thought, "who else?" I cleared my throat and replied, 'Thank you, Richard, coming from you it's a big compliment. I do my best and I'm not alone – my team also deserves the praise.'

He nodded and followed my invitation to take a seat in one of the convenient armchairs in the corner of my office.

'How's your mother, is she well?' he asked courteously.

'Very well, thank you. We were both rather surprised, hearing of your disappearance, without saying anything. There were rumors, but no one knew anything concrete.'

'I'm very sorry,' he said reluctantly, 'but it's this which has brought me to you today. I need your help.'

At this point Amanda walked in with coffee and biscuits. While she was serving them, Richard remained silent and seemed to wait for her to leave the room. He proceeded after Amanda had closed the door.

'There was a very good reason for me to leave silently. I couldn't say anything about it. It was a mission. I've been involved in this matter ever since.'

'A mission?' I asked. 'That sounds official.'

'Well, it is. The Secretary General personally had asked me to oversee it.'

"A mission from the Secretary General?" I wondered, instead of interrupting him I chose to hear him through and waited for him to go on.

He took a deep breath before speaking further. "This was new," I thought. There was definitely something different about him. 'Roger, listen, it's a matter of paramount importance. That's why I'm unable to say much, I apologize for that. I know it is unorthodox, and I know I'm asking much of you, but I can't think of anyone else who is more suitable and more qualified for this task.' His tone had changed, he sounded mysterious and that made me feel uncomfortable. 'All I'm asking is for you to trust me in this, and to accept the offer you will be given.'

I raised my eyebrows, repeating, 'The offer?'

He nodded. 'A meeting is scheduled with the Secretary General and other persons in the next few days. Knowing the Secretary General well, I assume he would ask you to think about it before accepting. The reason for me to see you first is that, I believe you would not regret taking this assignment.' He paused and smiled seeing the confusion in my eyes. 'The brave pave the way.' He then proceeded with an earnest expression. 'Again, he'll be inviting you, he will be offering you the position, so please don't hesitate to accept it. In this meeting all will

14

be revealed, including the reason for me disappearing some eight years ago.'

Apparently I couldn't hide my astonishment. Richard laughed and shook his head.

'Don't worry, son! I believe a great adventure is waiting for you. So embark on it, and don't look back. I did, and have never for a single moment regretted it. For now...' he took a look at his watch '...let's take leave. Time is running. I'll see you soon!'

Although I felt overrun, I tried to put on a smile and hide my irritation. I passed him his coat and hat.

All I could say was, 'Richard, thank you for your confidence. I must admit you have raised mixed emotions in me, of confusion and insecurity. But at the same time you have made me curious.'

Without giving me any answer, he waved me goodbye and left.

While I watched him leaving, my body remained motionless. I wasn't very sure I understood what had just taken place. The only thing I had was the sentence 'A matter of paramount importance!' "That was some clue!" I thought a little irritated. To think of it, he didn't really tell me anything. All I could think is, 'He appears out of nowhere, after all these years, asks me to trust me, tells me nothing and leaves.'

Feeling a little indignant, I sighed deeply and went back to my desk. Checking my calendar I realized I had a lot to do. Not wanting to waste any time speculating, I decided to leave the matter at rest for the time being.

As soon as Richard left, Amanda walked in. She must have noticed my bewilderment.

'Everything OK?' she asked.

'Well, I'm not very sure. I hope so.'

'You need anything?' she asked.

'No, I suppose time will tell.'

I had the impression, she didn't really know what I was saying but seeing me not wanting to answer she offered, 'Would you like some time or would you like to go on as scheduled?'

'No, no, it's alright. Let's go on.'

She nodded and left the room.

The rest of the day just slipped by.

A few days later, Amanda forwarded a call. The Personal Assistant of the Secretary General asked me to attend an appointment at the Secretary General's office the next day, at 8:00 a.m., and advised me to keep it confidential. The only piece of information I had was that the Secretary General, Richard, the Under Secretary, and one Miss Indira Yogini would be present at the meeting. The reason would be disclosed at the meeting itself.

That night sleep avoided me, left with no choice but to wander through the house, from my bedroom to the living room and to the kitchen, where I ended up having a piece of delicious chocolate cake. It brought back childhood memories, uncomplicated happy days, when I used to do homework in the kitchen with the radio on until late in the night or read a book in quietness. How time flies!

The next morning at breakfast my mother asked, 'Honey, is everything fine?'

'Yes, mom,' I replied, forgetting the visible rings under my eyes.

'I heard you in the kitchen late last night,' she persisted.

That was the only problem with this house; one hears every movement. 'Oh, it's only work,' I said downplaying the matter. I couldn't tell her about Richard, not before I knew more. For the moment I would keep it to myself.

She nodded and poured me another cup of coffee. That was her way to show me her sympathy. There is something about the fragrance coffee in the morning; it is like sipping down new expectations, another day, a new beginning.

In the early hours hardly anyone was around in the office and I normally enjoy the silence. Today it was different. The silence made me nervous. I went to the window and allowed my gaze to stray for a while. The weather has been sunny the whole week. "Maybe, it is a good sign?" I thought, trying to encourage myself. A meeting with the Secretary General is an important matter. I only wished I knew what it was about; I could at least be prepared. As Amanda knocked on my door, I was startled. She noticed this, and apologized.

'Sorry, Roger,' she said softly, 'I think it's time.'

I nodded and grabbed my jacket. 'Thank you.'

I normally take the stairs today but I took the elevator. I didn't want to appear breathless at his office. As I entered the waiting room, a friendly voice greeted me and asked me to take a seat. My eyes followed her into the Secretary's room. "What great men," I thought with an odd feeling of respect, 'have sat in this office! How destiny works in strange ways. Many decisions impacting the world were made in this room. History was written here,' I sighed. There were those decisions of hope, of good things, but also those compromising the needs of many. A deep sadness arose in me, thinking of those many events which had brought suffering, those problems which were left unresolved. Nevertheless, the room was dedicated to those who serve the purpose of mankind and humanity. They serve this planet, defying all odds to ensure that the needs of so many are secured.

My thoughts were interrupted by a friendly voice, 'Dr. Cane, would you please follow me?'

I stood up and followed the young lady into the Secretary's office. Now, the moment I had been called for was here, my heart was beating faster. Entering the office, I could feel an awesome atmosphere. The room was large, but, to my surprise, it was very pragmatically furnished. My gaze settled on the conference table. The meeting seemed to have already started. The friendly assistant guided me to my place. I nodded, thanking her, and sat down quietly.

The Secretary General welcomed me to the meeting in an unexpectedly cordial manner and introduced everyone at the table. He then handed over to the Under Secretary, Mr. John Stevens, a tall, slim man dressed in a well-fitting dark blue suit, with a matching tie. He came from Oxford, if I wasn't mistaken, and was in his mid-fifties.

'Dr. Cane.' He addressed me formally in his British accent. 'I'm glad you could come in at such short notice.' His deep voice did somehow not suit his appearance. 'You come naturally with high recommendations,' nodding towards Richard. 'Indeed, this is a very important meeting, actually one of a kind in the history of the United Nations.' Pausing, he stressed, 'I can't begin without first emphasizing the urgency and the confidentiality of the issue. With due respect, I have to remind you of the clause of confidentiality which you're bound by.'

I signaled my understanding by nodding. Mr. Stevens confirmed this with a smile of satisfaction. Then he looked at me and proceeded. 'We believe you're the perfect candidate for this assignment. Not only with you being a lawyer, but also one who is specialized in international law. A bonus point for us is you being an employee of this organization who is familiar with its processes and procedures. We believe your experience and qualifications would help us to steer the issue at hand in the right direction.'

The Under Secretary turned towards Richard, saying, 'Dr. Conners is highly regarded by us. He has worked with us on this topic for the last few years. He strongly recommended you for this assignment.'

Richard nodded in agreement.

'Thank you very much,' I responded, impressed by the formal wording of Mr. Stevens. "He carefully chooses his words," I thought, "and he knows always to make the correct assertions." I now understood why the Under Secretary had a reputation as a competent diplomat.

'Well, I think we can start the briefing then,' Mr. Stevens suggested.

The Secretary General agreed with a short but clear nod. He seemed to be pleased.

'Dr. Cane.' He looked at me directly, and spoke without blinking his eyes. 'This is the situation, when China enacted Tibet, which was – personally speaking – a great tragedy, and – according to international law – a breach of law, the Chinese made a mistake. Unintentionally of course, if I may stress. China overlooked a part of Tibet, a region in the far middle-west known as Keajara. For some reason China did not claim this small piece of land. It remains unclaimed and unnoticed until today.' He paused and passed a piece of paper to me, showing a map with a highlighted area.

'As you can see,' he continued, 'the red point indicates the position of Keajara City, whereas the blue circle indicates the position of Keajara.'

I couldn't help thinking, "This information is astonishing, I can't believe it." I surveyed the sector on the map at the westernmost region of Tibet, shaped in the form of a flower and being vanishingly tiny compared to Tibet or the whole of China. "How could China miss a piece of land? It was too crazy to be true!" Mr. Stevens waited giving me a moment to evaluate the information. I was trying to digest it all. I wasn't prepared for a question. I needed more information, so I decided to listen further. He took my silence as a sign to continue; changing his tone from businesslike to a more narrative one, with some emotional aspects.

'This fact wasn't noticed at first. Only by and by did the people of Keajara begin to realize it. The result being them deciding to act. They also knew this realization had to be kept secret. Try keeping something like this quiet. I believe it is the most best kept secrets in history.' For a moment I noticed a new expression on his face, followed by a smile. It was admiration. 'They began quietly establishing things. A government, key agencies such as intelligence agencies, foreign relationship agencies and so on. But in everything they did, they ensured that a low profile was kept. They did not want to alert China. It was their hope, one day, when the time was right, when it was favorable, that their region, their land be given a chance to be recognized as a sovereign state by the United Nations.' As I frowned, Mr. Stevens paused for a moment.

'To keep such a thing a secret would be very difficult, to put it mildly,' I responded.

He nodded, taking a sip out of his glass of water. 'You're right. It was and still is no easy matter! Especially when rumors are spread and the paranoid ears of the PSB never rest. No, it has been very difficult to conceal the matter from the Chinese. But thanks to the many dedicated people who were willing to sacrifice their lives for the sake of something bigger than themselves, we have been able to keep it under containment. We only hope it will remain so until the final hurdle is overcome.'

'The PSB never sleeps, Mr. Stevens. They have people everywhere,' I noted.

'Of course you're right Dr. Cane. The Keajaran Government has had great foresight in this respect. It began very early with preparations to infiltrate the PSB in Lhasa.'

'You've someone in the PSB in Lhasa, an informer?' I asked a little astonished. 'Its recruiting requirements are very difficult.'

'Yes, it was difficult, but the Keajaran Government managed it. More I cannot say. The Prime Minister and the High Lama of Keajara are the only ones who know of his identity. We would like to keep it that way.'

I nodded thinking, "The less people who knew, the better kept is the secret." At the same time, for some reason or maybe it was the fact that Miss Yogini was one of the most attractive women I had ever laid my eyes upon. I noticed I couldn't stop taking my eyes of her. I kept asking myself, "Who was she? An official representative of Keajara, maybe!"

Apparently the Under Secretary had noticed my curious glances. He took it on to himself to say, 'I beg your pardon, Dr. Cane. Where are my manners! I should have done it at the beginning. Yes, please allow me to introduce Miss Indira Yogini. She is an official representative of the government of Keajara. Should you accept our offer, she'll be working with you closely.' I nodded towards Miss Yogini, she answered with a smile.

After the introduction he continued, 'Where was I? Ah yes, since 1959 the Tibetans have not only lost their home, but also a chance to practice their identity and their culture. We don't seem to have much alternatives or means to resolve this situation. We have come to the point where we have to do everything possible to turn events around.'

I concurred by saying, 'I can only agree.'

'I'm glad you do. We think the time has come for this to happen. The sympathy and the understanding the world exhibits for the Tibetans is enormous; we believe this is the time for the people of Keajara to proceed with their application for a sovereign state. For this reason, we were looking for the right candidate who would be able to manage and complete the application process, which Dr. Conners had begun. We believe you to be the right person.'

John Stevens reminded me at that moment, more of a general who was preparing his officers to go to war. His expression showed resoluteness. I knew that the moment had come for me to react. But I was still unsure of what to say. I ran my fingers through my hair. I was hoping no one noticed my nervousness. I couldn't help to once steal a glance at Miss Yogini. I believe I noticed a little smile on her lips. Not being sure what it meant, I just smiled back.

The tragedy that befell the Tibetan people was great. In the face of a wall of ignorance and brutality, they fought back with compassion. Many have fought this battle of freedom. A battle driven by hope and the strength in their faith, yet success has avoided them. "Would I be successful, would we be successful?" I asked myself. But at the same time, I remembered Richard's words, "...Don't worry, son! I believe a great adventure is waiting for you. So embark on it, and don't look back. I did it, and have never for a single moment regretted it..." All the time I had known him, Richard has never advised me unwisely. This was a chance for

23

me to change something important in the world, to do something more meaningful in this life.

Richard must have understood my reluctance for he said, 'We do know this is a difficult endeavor. But you will have all the help you need and you need not start from scratch. I together with Indira have been working on it for the last few years. She is born and bred Keajaran. Her knowledge of the matter is deep. All this will help you to conclude what we had started,' from his tone it was clear he spoke more as a paternal friend than in an official capacity. He rubbed his hands and seemed to collect his thoughts before continuing, 'My adventure started eight years ago, when the then tribal head of Keajara approached the Secretary General and discussed the issue with him. I and his son, Mr. Ngapoi Jigme, knew each other from our days in Cambridge, England. Upon which the Secretary General contacted me. He smiled a little mischievously and went on saying, 'At that time, my work had become routine and deep inside I was looking for a change, a new challenge in life. One lead to another and of I was to this new and wonderful country.'

"That must have been the time I asked him to be my doctoral advisor," I thought. At last I knew the reason for his disappearance.

'By and by we assisted Keajara to establish a government. Jigme's father was elected as the first Prime Minister. I remained in Keajara as contact person to the UN and as consultant in many other issues.'

'How does one reach Keajara? I assume there are no official entry points,' I asked being curious.

He seemed to have expected this question; I saw it in his eyes, I couldn't help smiling. 'Keajara is about 7,000 square kilometers and situated between the 78.5 and 97.5 longitude and 32.0 and 32.5 latitude. One has to take great precautions to reach Keajara. A route does exist, but it's only known to a handful of people.'

I was holding the document Mr. Stevens had given to me earlier. Based on the information on it I walked over to the world map hanging on the wall and tried to pin point the area. "It lies more to the west of Tibet," I thought. Still searching for the exact location Richard said, 'A little more to the left.'

'Ah yes! There it is.' I placed my finger at the spot.

'It's a region not very populated,' said Richard.

I couldn't help wondering, 'I'm still a little confused as to how the Chinese Government could have made such a mistake. This piece of the country lies within Tibet?'

'So are we,' responded Richard. 'We can only assume that some bureaucratic failure took place. Whatever it might have been, we are very glad of it.'

I was not really contented with the answer, but apparently there was no other. 'I assume you have a strategy on how we are to proceed forward?'

Richard and Mr. Stevens nodded simultaneously.

'It was planned that Miss Yogini remains in New York until the application process is completed,' as Mr. Stevens explained. 'Her insight would be of great value. At the same time Dr. Conners is planning to return to Keajara. From there he will ensure the communication between the teams.'

I did feel a little overrun as Mr. Stevens recommended me to visit Keajara as soon as possible. 'The visit would give me the opportunity to witness and evaluate the situation, and I would be able to meet the necessary people,' he said. In just a few seconds, my mind had imagined all the things one would face in such a journey; high altitude, dangerous hiking treks, breaking the law, and so on. For some strange reason I did not object. Besides that, I was excited to be responsible for such a sensitive diplomatic mission.

I believe the Secretary General must have sensed my indecisiveness as he tried to ease my confusion. 'I apologize, Dr. Cane, for giving you the impression that we need your answer today.' I had not personally met the Secretary General until now, but I liked him. He had an aura of compassion around him. 'As you see,' he continued, 'we are all very enthusiastic to proceed forward. We know it is not an easy task. I understand if you need time to think this through. The fate of 1,500 people is at stake; not to mention the fate of the Tibetan Culture as a whole. All will depend on your efforts to being successful.'

"That didn't really help me," I thought. I returned to my chair and chose my words very carefully. 'I would like to thank you for this opportunity and for giving me time to think it through. But before we proceed, I do have a few questions.'

'Of course, please do ask.'

'Well I was wondering, what is the timeline for completion and what actions have been taken so far? Most importantly, how am I to engage in discussions, when I'm to keep the whole matter confidential?'

The Secretary General responded understandingly, 'As Mr. Stevens mentioned, the present positive political climate speaks for our course and we are a little concerned about the PSB; the more the reason for us to move as quickly as possible. We are of course aware of the need for you get acquainted with the subject matter, nevertheless we would like you to work on the proposal as soon as possible.'

'You are of course right; the timing is important, but I would need my time to speak with the respective ambassadors, to do onsite evaluation of the situation and to finalize the affidavit.'

'Dr. Cane what is your estimation?' asked the Secretary General.

'Sir, I believe I am speaking of at least three months.'

Richard added, 'Mr. Secretary General I can only concur.'

'Well if that is the case, we have to rely on the best guess and proceed forward.'

'Sir, do you have an idea as to how the UN General Assembly would vote. China is a major trading partner in many of these countries.'

'Yes, it is. But I do believe in providence. I believe that the UN General Assembly will approve our application. I will go further Dr. Cane. With you at the helm, I believe even the UN Security Council would agree on with our proposal.'

'Even China?'

The Secretary General looked Indira in the eye when he said, 'Something tells me, China will finally succumb.'

I didn't want to sound impertinent, but I interrupted him by asking, 'Sir, if I may; I am sure, you are aware that a state has to fulfill certain criteria according to international law, such as having a recognized national territory, a population and a legitimate government. Is this given?'

Mr. Steven interrupted by saying, 'Dr. Cane, I understand your concern. The fact is we fulfill only two out of the three criteria. We have no other choice but to proceed with what we have.'

I assumed from this remark that a decision had been made, and there was no room for discussion.

He continued by saying, 'As you know, the membership in the organization must be in accordance with the Charter of the United Nations. Them being "...It's open to all peace-loving states that accept the obligations contained in the United Nations Charter and, in the judgment of the Organization, are able to carry out these obligations.".'

'Yes,' I said.

'States are admitted to membership of the United Nations by decision of the General Assembly upon the recommendation of the Security Council,' he commented.

'But,' I objected, 'the recognition of a new state or government is an act that only other states and governments may grant or withhold. It generally implies readiness to assume diplomatic relations. The United Nations is neither a state nor a government, and therefore does not possess any authority to recognize either a state or a government.'

Mr. Stevens nodded. 'Naturally, but as an organization of independent states, it may admit a new state to its membership or accept the credentials of the representatives of a new government. In the case of Keajara, I believe this prerequisite is given.'

'We have done our utmost to fulfill the preconditions,' Richard added shortly, 'but some things are just not possible at this moment.'

They were right, of course. As soon as another nation recognizes Keajara as an independent state, it will be in the media. The secrecy of the whole thing secrecy made it difficult to make it public. I simply added, 'Naturally you are correct, but it had to be mentioned.'

Mr. Stevens answered, 'We understand that. So how do we go on?' He didn't wait for a response, 'As soon as the application is finalized, Keajara would submit it to the Secretary General with a letter formally stating that it accepts the obligations under the Charter. The application will then be forwarded to the Security Council for its recommendation for admission. We require an affirmation by 9 of the 15 members. If the admission is agreed upon by the Council, it will then be presented to the General Assembly for consideration. From which, as you know, we need a two-thirds majority for admission as a new member state. As soon as the admission is adopted, the membership becomes effective.'

'Do you have any information on how China would vote?' I asked Mr. Stevens; not really wanting to offend the Secretary General, but I needed a second opinion.

'It is hard to say, but considering the present world sympathy for Tibet, I would say we have good reasons

29

for optimism. I know China would tend to veto against this application, but at the end, they would be persuade by the external pressure. I believe we should move forward optimistically and trust in the good judgment of those responsible.'

The Secretary General stood from his chair and walked over to his desk. He was looking for something. He returned with a thick folder in his hand. Handing it to me he said, 'As we have elaborated, these are reasons for timing and speediness. This is the draft we have worked out, which we would like you to evaluate.'

I simply answered, 'Thank you.'

'In the last few decades,' he continued, 'meaning even before Keajara officially approached the UN, they have done a lot of work on preparing the country for this application. They have built schools, and improved the country's infrastructure and standard of living. With the installation of a democratic government and a constitution, they have fulfilled one of the three criteria's. You will be witnessing this personally during your visit.'

For a moment the room was filled in silence, it was as if he wanted to stress the importance of what he was about to say next. 'Yes, as you have correctly recognized, we do have things to do. Despite these activities, we need to keep it all under lock and key until the final talks begin with the Chinese UN Delegates. As soon as the submission takes place, we shall not waste any time in submitting it to the Security Council for its recommendation and to the UN General Assembly for its approval. Your talks with the ambassadors are important to ensure we have their support for our course. We need you to use your good relations with them and to convince them to vote for this petition. I can't stress this point strongly enough. Confidentiality has to be secured until the talks begin with the Chinese ambassador.'

I was thinking at the same time about my strategy. "Of course, I would begin with everyone else first and postpone my talks with the Chinese Ambassador to the last. Naturally, the Secretary General has to be kept at a distance from all this to ensure impartiality; but honestly I was not sure how this would be possible. Nevertheless we had no other option."

'Mr. Secretary, I must admit, it is a little overwhelming. The importance of this assignment is very obvious and the chances of success hangs on a very thin tread. I do have my doubts. But at the same time, the fate of the Tibetan People is on the line. Furthermore, you're right in saying that the independence of Keajara is a move in the right direction. Through it we would be sending a positive message to the world and supporting the values upon which this organization was formed some sixty years ago, to represent the interests of this world.'

After a short pause, I added, 'The world is going some very difficult times. War, sickness, poverty are increasing and hope is diminishing. Just maybe, the independence of Keajara is what we need in these futile times. Just maybe, it might restore humanity on this planet. I always stood for the right for freedom, for equality and for peace. I will do my best to uphold these values; the reason for me to accept this assignment.'

There was a short moment of silence, then I saw relief and satisfaction in the faces around me.

The Secretary General rose and took my hands saying, 'Dr. Cane, I think, I speak for all of us, when I say we are very pleased to hear this. I would like to welcome you to our Task Force!'

'Thank you, Sir!' I said accepting his warm handshake.

'I'll be promoting you to the status of Special Delegate of the UN, beginning immediately. You will be relieved of all other duties.'

I swallowed a little when he said, 'You will be relieved of all other duties,' slowly realizing what it meant. I'm no more a Department Head! No regular working hours, no large team to support me. Instead it meant special projects and field work. I loved my job, but on the hand this was an once-in-a-lifetime chance, and I would be a fool not to take it.

The Secretary General, assuming the issue to be closed, excused himself and left for another meeting. The rest of us left the office and walked towards the elevator. On our way down, Richard suggested going out for lunch to celebrate this moment. We decided to try out a vegetarian restaurant in the West Village of Manhattan.

It was a small restaurant, with a teak-wood frontage, modern furniture and a friendly atmosphere. I ordered vegetarian lasagna with a glass of mango juice, and a chocolate pudding for desert. It was the first time for me trying out vegetarian food, I mean, pure vegetarian food. It taste was surprisingly delicious.

Needless to say we were all in high spirits. While having lunch I couldn't stop myself from on-and-off glancing Miss Yogini. She was sitting opposite to me.

And she possessed one of the most enchanting smiles I had ever seen. The sunlight made her dark, shoulder-length, thick hair glow. Her dark blue shoes matched the color of her dress; a western-like summer outfit reaching her knees, emphasizing her slim figure.

Richard and the Under Secretary were occupied with the topic on hand as I silently enjoyed my food and listened in. As we were having desert and cappuccino, John Stevens changed the subject.

'Miss Yogini, how do you find New York?'

She answered with one of her flighty smiles, 'It's an exciting city. I believe one could undertake a lot of interesting things. I personally, however, prefer a quieter environment.' The sound of her voice was soft and melodious.

'Younger people, I had assumed, prefer such exciting places?' he commented laughingly.

'That might be true,' she replied smiling. 'But some of us "young people" would prefer less exciting places.'

'Would you mind telling us a little bit about your country? I'm sure Dr. Conners is familiar with it, but I and Dr. Cane aren't. I would imagine it's very beautiful.'

'I believe the world itself is a beautiful place; it depends what men do to ensure this,' she said simply. 'About five thousand meters above sea level and very secluded; my country is a peaceful place to live in. There are four seasons, with a comparatively long winter and a long summer, the other two seasons are quite short. During winter we hardly go outside. Many of us use the time to study Dharma and to meditate. It is the time for indoor activities; we spend time sewing new clothes and repair-

33

ing old ones. We even make shoes, books and other things we need. The streets are quiet mostly; sometimes you see children playing.

After a long winter everyone is happy to begin a new cycle. They plough the fields and plant the seeds. Spring is normally a very busy time. Every man, woman and child is outside. You see life busting. Our summers are warm, and for the next five months you see sunny faces everywhere. The time for festivities, the time to enjoy the wonders of nature! The meadows and forests are green and the streams are full with fresh water. I love the summer,' she confessed with a shy smile. 'And then you've autumn; nature shows itself from a colorful side; gold, brown and red dominate the landscape. The sun has difficulty getting up. It is time to reap what we have sown; it is time to prepare for winter. Autumn's stay is short, it vanishes without much ado.'

'I haven't heard the seasons described so poetically before,' Stevens admitted with a smile. 'I suppose it comes from your awareness and respect for nature.'

Instead she said, 'Our problems are men made, it can be solved by men. Peace everywhere and at all times can only be reached from within. We breathe the same air, wish well for our children, and share this tiny planet as a home. Why don't we set aside our differences and work towards a better world!'

34

3

The Beginning of the End

This narration is based on Colonel Yang's personal diary, which he entrusted to me at our first and only encounter.

Colonel Yang was a very slim and tall man. After absorbing the military academy with distinction, he had the opportunity to choose any career line he wanted. But he chose military intelligence, being particularly interested in Tibet. He wasn't the usual military man; there was something different about him, something that always kept him at bay. He never really mixed with his comrades. There was this thin line that no one crossed, maybe partly out of fear and partly out of respect. He liked it so.

He has had many successes in curbing uprisings and other "incidents". Another one in his place would have enacted unnecessary casualties, mostly on the side of the Tibetans. He always tried to avoid this.

Peking, on the other hand, was only interested in reducing political agitation. His efforts to do so won him friends in the party. His dedication to ensure peace and security in Tibet was the reason for his progress and advancement up the military ladder, finally becoming the head of the PSB in Lhasa. His unorthodox methods helped to save not only many Tibetan lives, but also those of Chinese soldiers.

About twenty years ago, he then was a captain in the PLA Special Operations Forces, he came to Lhasa. The most distinct building structure in these days was the Potala Palace, for centuries the formal residence of the Dalai Lama, the worldly and spiritual leader of Tibet. Surrounded entirely by mountains and having a surprisingly rich flora, this city had preserved at least some flair of the bygone era. When Lhasa being the seat of the Dalai Lama, when Tibetan culture and religious traditions dominating the town, and when a journey to the home of the Dalai Lama, their Living Buddha, was an essential for the many nomads. But over the many years Col. Yang spent in Lhasa, he witnessed the fading of the once mystical characteristics. Today it looks more like any Chinese town. One finds skyscrapers, fast food restaurants, hotels and large shopping facilities; Lhasa has been turned into a commercial center. Military control and political propaganda have replaced the peaceful and spiritual atmosphere. The spiritual warmness has given way to the cold charmless streets of capitalism and communist terror. Pilgrims do continue to visit Lhasa, but you see in their faces confusion. Their beloved holy city has become a strange place, as if their eyes are playing tricks with their memories. As if their past cannot accept the present. Torn between yesterday and now! Their search for salvation is disturbed by the world of contradicting values. As they stare up at the Potala Palace, one of the most inspiring buildings on the planet, they are remembered of this bygone world of peace and tranquility. The Palace has become a museum; his age-long evolving construction, beginning in 1645, ended in 1959.

Today a sterile and hostile atmosphere lingers over it. The Pilgrims nevertheless seem to find some comfort seeing it, visiting it. As if holding on to a last piece of happiness of yesteryears, a line of rope connecting them to days whence all was well, all was pure. The Potala Palace reminds the Tibetans of the absence of their spiritual leader, but it has become even more; It is now a symbol of the resilience of the Tibetan people.

Col. Yang witnessed this and much more. Tibet becoming a police state which denies the Tibetans the chance to live freely according to their belief. A form of containment established which allowed neither Tibetans to leave the country nor foreigners or the foreign press into the country. Many Tibetans, including the 14th Dalai Lama, forced to flee to live in exile. Relocation and resettlement programmes tearing the people from their homes and families. Continuing suffering of a folk, that has become strangers in their own land. But there was nothing he could do, except to prevent.

Aiming for influence Captain Yang gave his best. Some years later, now being a highly decorated officer, he was assigned as the Senior Military Intelligence Officer for Lhasa. He was responsible for investigating and analyzing the validity of rumors and information which were directly or indirectly acquired. It was during this period when he first heard of rumors about a mysterious region known as the "Land of Paradise". Many travelers spoke of this place in the west, hidden in the mountains. It was mostly the Chinese travelers and traders who enthusiastically told this story. But none had seen it directly. Although the PSB took measures to investigate the validity of these rumors, by sending agents to seek and find this place, they returned without any success. Many went out to seek proof of its existence. They found none. All endeavors were in vain. Captain Yang had not shown any interest then, and Col. Yang shows none today. He finally concluded the rumors to be pure humbug, and reported them to Peking as such. He described it as a myth comparing it to another well-known legend, "Shangri-La". His arguments were supported by the unsuccessful attempts of many. All official investigations in regard to the "Land of Paradise" were subsequently stopped.

The present PSB Bureau lies in the vicinity of the Potala Palace. It is a highly secured complex; an unassuming building from the outside, but equipped with the most modern and sophisticated surveillance systems. In additional to that, it is guarded by elite military personnel. It is the nerve center of military intelligence for all of Tibet. Col. Yang's office is where all this information comes together.

Col. Yang was assigned a young PSB officer, Lt. Chan, as his adjutant recently. Like any young ambitious man, he was looking for a chance. He was looking for an opportunity, and so he left no stone unturned. The rumor of the "Land of Paradise" did not leave him any peace; he began to dig into the old files. It was a great opportunity for a quick advancement up the ladder. Despite his many attempts to awaken Col. Yang's interest on the topic, he remained unsuccessful. The reaction of his superior was not logical. Somehow the whole thing did not make any sense. The rumors were many, and the rumors continued until today. "How could it be?" he thought. "So many rumors and no evidence; unless," it occurred to him, "of course, someone was manipulating the information. Someone must be filtering the information coming to Lhasa!"

Hence he would take the matter into his own hands; he decided to conduct his own investigations. As for his superior: "He was a lazy old man waiting for his retirement". Silently Lt. Chan began to divert resources to a so-called "Special Project", and recruited people sending them to seek proof.

One evening, Sgt. Choo, a loyal and long-serving soldier, walked into Col. Yang's office.

'Sir, the Lt. has begun activities, just as you had predicted. What will be our next move?' he asked.

'Alarm our people,' said the Col. calmly.

He walked over to the wall facing his desk, where a portrait of Mao was hanging. Removing it a safe with combinations appeared. It opened after a set of numbers were punched onto the lock combination.

The Col. removed a stack of bank bills and handed it to the Sgt., simply saying, 'Sgt., ensure he has no success.'

Sgt. Choo turned and left the room.

The Col. closed the safe and hung the portrait back on the wall, walked to his table and took out a hand phone, one with a non-traceable sim-card, and dialed a number.

'The birds will be flying west.'

'Very well,' said the voice at the other end.

He hung up. "Soon," he thought, "soon I will be going home."

4

On the way to salvation

It was still early but mom had already turned in for the day. Couldn't tell her, had to postpone the matter. Poured myself a glass of milk and sat in the kitchen. Spent time thinking about what had taken place that day; so many unexpected events in such a short time. Richard had called on me and offered me this opportunity, I was grateful for that. By and by, questions were popping up. I wished Richard was there for some answers, but he was going to leave early the next morning. "Well, I'll just have to speak with Miss Yogini then," I thought.

The following morning I knocked at her apartment door. I heard a somewhat calm voice saying, 'Coming!'

Miss Yogini opened the door a little shyly. 'Please come in and make yourself at home, I was just getting ready, would you like something, I've just prepared morning tea from home, if you would like some.'

'Thank you, that sounds great!' A little too much enthusiasm in my voice, trying to cover it, I added, 'I understand you've a very exotic mixture.'

'I don't know if it's exotic, but we do have quite a variety, although you too have various interesting mixtures in the US.'

As she disappeared into an adjacent room, I noticed unpacked luggage in the corner. The apartment, although not very luxurious, had all the comforts of a hotel room, and the view of the George Washington Bridge was breathtaking.

'Is this your first visit?' I asked.

'Yes. As a matter of fact, this is my first trip out of Keajara.'

'In that case, I would make the following suggestion, that we transfer our work "outdoors" whenever possible. In that way you would not only be able to see New York but also enjoy the summer. Agreed?'

She came back to the room and nodded with a smile. Obviously she was ready to go, so we left the apartment, got a taxi, and drove directly to Central Park. Considering the nice weather, we decided to spend the day in the park and not in one of the restaurants. We walked to a nearby supermarket, got some French bread, olives, cheese, fruit, and two large cappuccinos. With the shopping bags in the hand, we returned to the park and occupied a bench in the shade of a large tree.

'Have you been working very long with Richard?' I asked as we were sipping our coffee.

'Yes,' she said. 'I met him first about eight years ago. I was only seventeen at that time, and he's been very kind and helpful in our purpose. I've learned much from him.'

'Richard Conners is an extraordinary person. His family, paternal side was English emigrants and his mother was a German lady. His father, an American diplomat, met his future wife while working at the

American Embassy in Germany. They fell in love and got married. Due to the nature of his father's job, Richard never really went to school. He had a private tutor. He didn't mind this, he once told me, in fact he was fascinated by the many countries he grew up in, and enjoyed the company of his parents.'

She nodded. 'I see. I understand now how he was able to describe a country so well; you know, little things one doesn't normally know of.'

'Being a single child,' I continued, 'Richard enjoyed all the privileges his parents could afford. He went to Cambridge, England, to do law, and later to Harvard to do his PhD. In Boston he found a sort of home, but I always had the impression that he wasn't at the end of his journey yet.'

'How did your roads cross?'

'My friendship with Richard began in Harvard. Maybe it was the fact that I didn't have a father and maybe it was the fact that he didn't have a family, or maybe it was the fact that we somehow got along. Whatever the reason, we both hit it off from the start. We used to share many hours discussing the law, and enjoyed very much our whiskey and cigar evenings in his study. We would dive into the world of Aristotle and Plato, or debate on the purpose of religion. He's a brilliant man with a very sharp mind.'

She smiled saying, 'Wow. I'm sure he would say exactly the same about you!'

I realized I had turned red. 'Wouldn't you want to travel and see the world?' I asked, trying to divert her attention.

'I know that the world has many interesting places, but I'm very happy where I am. I don't wish to travel around the world,' she answered charmingly.

'You can't see yourself living anywhere else then?' It was a little difficult to hide my surprise.

'No. I can't imagine living anywhere else. I believe Keajara gives me all I need, it is my home.'

Somehow I envied her simple words. To know where one belongs must be very fulfilling. I like New York, but I always had a feeling that there was something missing, something I might find somewhere else. Somewhere I could call home. But instead of saying how I felt, I replied, 'I haven't been to Asia, let alone to the subcontinent or the Himalayas. For Westerners it's a different world, magical and unknown. I for my part am eager to see it.'

She nodded. 'I can imagine that ours appears to be a different world to Westerners, and even to other Asians. I feel the same about your world.'

'And yet we're all human beings, with the same needs, and aspirations. But how is it that our way of living has developed into so many varieties?'

'I suppose all of us adjust our lives according to the place we live in. But at the end of the day, we all have similar wishes in life. We just take different paths in fulfilling these wishes. We might be different on the outside but we share the same common values. We all want to be happy, we all have dreams and hopes in life which we would like to fulfill.'

She looked at me for a moment; her expression was that of uncertainty, as if she had crossed a certain line.

Her eyes however revealed calmness. 'The sad thing is, we allow fear to influence our lives. Fear which corrupts the way we think and act. Where I come from we have great trust in Dharma or the teachings. Dharma allows us to be courageous. With Dharma we manage to overcome fear and choose to lead a simple and peaceful life. Our time in this world is best used by "being" and not by "having". Our conviction of happiness has more to do with the realization of inner peace rather than that of material consumption.'

'What about modern education, career, modern living comforts?' I asked.

'Your question implies that our sole purpose of existence is to aim for a modern education, and for building a career which aims at possession, earning a lot of money, and achieving social status.' She gazed at me with her soft eyes.

'Isn't that what is propagated from the cradle to the grave?' I asked.

'We too have schools but we learn to prioritize differently. Of course we learn to survive in this world, but our education is focused on how to develop and practice compassion and how to achieve wisdom, in short how to create the basis for experiencing inner peace.' She paused and looked into the sky. 'There is more to the "Book of Life" than just the urge to satisfy one's worldly needs.'

I nodded thoughtfully. 'I suppose you speak of religious views.'

'Actually, no, I'm speaking about the secret of life.' She smiled and looked at me mischievously.

I took a deep breath and contemplated a few moments, before answering, 'Are you saying you've discovered the secret of life, the secret to our existence?'

'It's not something new, you know. It has always been there for those who are willing to see. Like everything else, this also begins with a journey,' she went on with a smile. 'Why are we here, why birth and death, what is the purpose of our life? Questions we ask. The answers can't be found by exploring the stars or matter. This is only the beginning of an important journey.'

I protested by saying, 'Yes, but many believe to have found the answer. It's just not the same for everyone. Some believe in science, some believe in an almighty God, some believe in the laws of nature and so on. Whatever it might be, they consider it as something precious. So much so, that it's practiced and protected with complete conviction.'

Her eyelids closed for a moment and she smiled softly, a smile so serene, as if I was looking into a Buddha's face.

'In the course of time, ours is but a brief existence,' she whispered.

'You still have not answered my question,' I reminded her.

With equanimity she answered, 'According to Dharma, one's mind, or as it's known in the west, "the soul", travels from one body to another, from one life to the next. This has been happening since beginningless time. We call it "uncontrolled birth and rebirth". This cycle continues until one chooses to leave it. The leaving is also known as "liberation". In order to achieve liberation from this cycle we believe one has to experience the union of bliss and emptiness, also known as "enlightenment". This state of consciousness can only be achieved by practicing Dharma and through the state of single pointedness in the meditation. Now, to answer your question...' she gazing into the horizon, as if searching for something '...the secret of life is to achieve liberation from this cycle, also known as "Samsara". That is why this life as human is so precious. The rebirth as humans is very rare. One could compare it with this metaphor; it is like a corn of sand on a beach of sand.'

'What do you mean by the rebirth as humans being rare?'

'Our mind or "the soul" has been traveling since beginningless time. It has created infinite actions, which in turn will cause infinite reactions. The results one can witness everywhere. Unfortunately we do more harm than good. Thus the rebirth as humans is seldom.'

'Is this a universal fact?'

'Yes.' She looked at me and added, as if it was the most normal of things, 'It's up to each of us to change our destiny. Dharma applies for everyone.'

'If that is so, why are the Tibetans suffering?' I tried to understand.

'I can ask the same question in regard to other believes. It's one thing to be shown a path, and it's another thing to follow it.'

I concurred as she continued.

'I believe everyone has the right to live according to his or her wishes, as long as one doesn't hurt another being. And if a spiritual path is perfect, it would not give way for misuse.' She obviously hesitated to go further.

'Please do go on,' I encouraged her.

'I was only going to say, if a spiritual path is perfect, it would not hurt any being.'

'You mean physically?'

'I mean in any way. It will not cause any pain or suffering to others or to oneself. Rather it would lead one out of pain and suffering.'

'Don't all religions do this?'

'I can't speak for other religions or dogmas, I don't know well enough about them,' she said avoiding to answer.

I thought about my daily work and tried to find a reference point. 'If I interpret you correctly, punishment is wrong?'

'I would have to explain much to answer that question. Another time perhaps, but for now let me just say, neither punishment nor violence reduces suffering or pain. In the infinity of all that is life, both are unnatural.'

'I would like to know more about it,' I pleaded. Of course violence wasn't ethical, I agree completely. But how can it not be part of human nature? Does she mean deep inside we are not capable of violence, or of that which is not good? Is she saying we are pure, deep inside? I was somewhat perplexed.

She smiled and evaded once more. 'I require more time to explain; another time.'

I reluctantly had to admit that she was right. A bird which was flying very low caught our attention. It was soaring between the high trees, flew into our direction, over us and away. I couldn't help thinking how attractive this young lady was. She was only in her mid-twenties but she impressed me. She had more sense about what is important in life than the most people I knew. She obviously had deep philosophical knowledge, which I very much wanted to learn about. "What is true happiness?" a question which had always been with me. Could it be that this person had an answer? I suddenly became impatient, "This she must explain this to me!"

'Material gain,' I started, 'you were saying it doesn't bring true happiness, but this concept is regarded very highly and practiced by most human beings.'

She nodded. 'Yes, you're right. Men seek material gain. You see it around you. Man believes in the accumulation of material objects. He believes it would bring him happiness. But it is also common knowledge that matter is perishable. It's something unstable. You don't need scientific proof for this. You see it everywhere, matter decays. But we believe this will give us ultimate happiness. We value it and protect it at all cost. We equip buildings with alarm systems for safe guard and create laws to ensure the right of possession. At the same time it is a paradox.' She shook her head. 'It's up to us to realize that the true answer to happiness lies elsewhere.'

'I understand when you say matter would be unable to give us eternal happiness. But people have a very different interpretation about what is meant by "true happiness". There is salvation through God, having a family, achieving knowledge, leading a quiet life, making new discoveries, helping others, and so on. Are you saying there's only one form of "true happiness", or is it an individual concept?'

'I believe in "true happiness" or "eternal happiness". I also believe it can only be achieved through something lasting. The world we live in is not lasting.' She underlined her statement by pointing to the flowers in front of us. 'Of course, there is the concept of an "almighty God".'

I waited for her to continue, but she did not elaborate on the last point. Instead, she closed her eyes and leaned back. Again, she was holding something back. I decided to not give in. 'Do you mean to say that there is no "almighty God"?'

She gave me one of her sweet smiles. 'It's not for me to question the convictions of others. As I already said, I think that everyone has a right to live according to what he or she believes in.' And after a pause, as if wanting to make an emphasis, she added, 'But I strongly believe, they should cause pain or suffering on to others.'

"Strange," I thought, "she didn't want to discuss the question" – for the moment I conceded. We had finished our little picnic, and began to walk along a jogger's lane.

The paths were a little wet from the rain the night before. In the shades they didn't dry up so fast. I suggested we walk on the grass, it was drier. She politely refused and so I led her carefully, with her hand on my shoulders, out of the area. It was nice to walk in the shadows. They offered a little coolness in the heat of the midday sun. She seemed to enjoy the walk. At the same time, I noticed her watching children playing. There were people listening to music, reading a book, having picnics, or just lying around. The sun invites people to enjoy the day outside, to feel the warmth, and to take a step backward in this busy life for reflection.

'It is good to know that people have not forgotten nature, even if one is living in a city such as this. It helps one to reflect,' she said.

I understood what she was saying. I had spent many hours here during the summer and some of them with my mother. "How time flies," I thought. We were quietly strolling down the park. It was now about 33 degrees Celsius and I was beginning to feel thirsty. We walked over to a stall selling water.

While I was paying, she spoke, more to herself than to me, I think. 'You know, the conventional education system prepares one for this world. A certain occupation leads to the "creation of income", which leads to "spending". One buys a house or a car. People then have children, and the children go to school, and this also requires spending. The children, too, go through a similar form of education. Then there are the other expenses such as holidays, all forms of entertainment, and naturally material consumption, paying taxes, paying for insurances, and planning for a retirement. That is the cycle of life of the conventional modern world.' She made a pause, noticing that I had a question.

'A conventional world?' I asked.

'Well, generally speaking, a conventional world is one which is ruled with conventions.'

I raised my eyebrows as I looked at her, 'You're speaking of the world we know, this world that we live in, right? Or are you speaking of other worlds?'

'There is only one world which is free of conventions, all others are not. As you know, conventions are made of values, norms, rules, or globally accepted views. Conventions vary based on time and space. For instance, natural laws existing on earth are not applicable in open space. And conventions have an important function. They grant harmony, or balance. Due to the ever-changing environment, conventions change and adapt.'

'You mentioned a world free of conventions. How is this possible, since all worlds need some form of rules to co-exist?' I said, a little unsurely.

She ran her fingers through her beautiful hair. 'In this life, we know that all things are subjected to change, and all things are transient. The only constant in life is change. Be it time, space, matter, the universe, or life itself, nothing remains forever.' She paused, and somehow I had again a feeling she was holding something back. Nevertheless, all things she spoke thus far made sense. She looked at me and smiled before answering my question. 'There is a world without conventions. Deep in us is a world where no doubts exist, where perfect clarity reigns. Here, in the realm of oneness, one needs no conventions.'

'Is that why meditation is needed, to reach this realm?' I was eager to know.

She appeared a little surprised. I saw it in her eyes. 'Yes, very good. You've been paying attention,' she replied laughingly. 'With meditation and contemplation,' she answered softly, 'one can achieve this state of consciousness.' Reluctantly she added, 'But as long as we believe that matter, time, and space to be the ultimate truth; we will be bound by uncontrolled changes. We will depend on conventions. This is what we call "Samsara".'

I raised my eyebrows asking, 'Samsara?'

She smiled again. 'I'm sorry; I should have explained it earlier. Samsara has many names. It's known as the World of Maya, the World of Illusion, the World of Suffering, the Conventional World, or the World of Impermanence.'

I nodded eagerly to show my interest to know more.

'According to Dharma, all the things we see around us will disappear with time. Sooner or later everything will be replaced by something else. Most of us prefer to ignore this fact. We learn from an early age that material accumulation could secure us against material poverty. It would give us the possibility to lead a comfortable life. We concentrate our energies and efforts on piling up material goods, with the hope of not falling into poverty.'

'Is that a bad thing?'

'I'm not saying it's bad or good,' she protested. 'In life it's about choices we make, and about living with them.'

'I don't think that a little girl in the slums has many choices,' I came back to my daily work issues.

'You're right; it is easy to speak of choices when one has the possibility to make one. For a child in the slums, living under hunger and ailment, it is a different world. Some of them do not even live beyond the age of five. Theirs is about having the next meal, or to not become ill. It pains me only to think of such a situation. The more the reason for those who have the ability and the possibility to make choices to choose to help those in need!'

I was still thinking of a child in the slums of Mumbai. How hopeless is her world!

Tears were rolling down her cheeks; she stopped and sat down, looking into the distance. 'At the end, it is up to us, not only as an individual, but also as a collective, to help!'

'We should learn to choose wisely.'

'Yes.'

I sank onto the bench beside her. We were silent for a moment. "I am slowly getting it," I thought. It is not only about helping yourself but others. By helping others you help yourself. It's spiritual. Their fight for an independent state has more to do with sustaining the spiritual path. Inner peace begins with the act of love for the wellbeing of others. What the Keajarans call universal compassion. One does not require enmity, wars, or conflicts in life. All these are just obstacles towards happiness, towards inner peace, towards helping this little child in the slums! All of us could do this, here nothing stopping us but ourselves from striving towards a higher purpose. By helping someone in need, one overcomes one's ego, one's selfishness. Self-centeredness, greed, hate, jealousy, and fear disappear, the turmoil in us subsides, contentment takes their places, inner peace resides.

At that moment it occurred to me why Richard was so taken with this world. I realized why he had said, "…go forward and don't look back…" I believed he had found his peace of mind. I remembered our evening discussions; he used to wish for a place where he would feel at home. Somewhere being happy and contented wasn't a crime. He has found his sanctuary and had decided to stay. "Would I do the same, is this a chance for me?" I asked myself, and left the questions unanswered.

The people in the park; go through time, unaware of the reason for their existence. Her explanations made sense, but could centuries of other religious ideas be misguided? Were these doctrines really different; perhaps misinterpreted! It has happened, things have been misunderstood, it happens even today, every day. Why not over centuries?

There were times when knowledge was passed on verbally through generations. One false sentence and the whole content would have been another. Is that what happened? A misunderstanding?

She had been reluctant to speak about it, but I wanted to know. 'Why is it,' I asked, 'that so many people belief in God without one moment of doubt?'

'There is nothing to say against believing in a higher instance; any path leading us to spiritual practices of compassion is commendable. If one is happy with one's path, why change. But if one is unhappy and seeks a new one, Dharma could be a choice for them.'

'So, you're saying one should leave his family and friends, the whole system, behind, and go to a lonesome hut in the woods or mountains to meditate?'

'For some people this might be the way. But no, I do not speak of this. In Keajara we have found a way to live together in a society, having nice private homes and a happy family life, we live a happy and contented life, in a peaceful community.'

I looked at her. 'Fine, but what is the key message here?'

She said patiently, 'There are many, but an important one would be "lead a modest life, a spiritual life".'

'But to make such choices, it would be a new way of living.'

'You've a proverb; "Rome wasn't built in a day".'

'Yes, but the barriers in thinking are difficult to tear down,' I objected.

She gave me one of her sweet smiles. 'The walls we build are no more than bygone dust.'

In that moment I realized why her smile was so different. It showed open-mindedness! 'Rules are there to be broken!' I thought out loud.

'Humans tend to hold on to almost everything, in some cases even to pain,' she continued. 'The reason is the so-called "self-grasping mind". Out of fear, we refuse to let go. Fear is a powerful emotion. It makes one do things which we normally wouldn't. The reason for fear is insecurity. We feel insecure due to the changes which keep repeating, and we feel powerless.'

'One can eliminate insecurity through accumulating knowledge, through learning and qualifying oneself,' I countered.

She answered, 'Yes, you're right. But many of us are not capable of doing this. The reasons are many; poverty, mental ability, personal tendencies, discrimination, social problems, political instability.'

"Of course, she is right, I see it every day at work," I thought.

'Not all knowledge leads to spiritual wisdom,' she continued. 'In an ever-changing world, humans are continuously occupied with learning new things. Without this one would be out of the system; naturally leading to social problems, poverty, suffering. That is the conventional world. On the other hand; the strive towards spiritual wisdom reduces dependency on this changing environment, increases peace of mind, and develops the path to no more learning.'

'What you are saying makes sense. There is no permanent means to remove fear in a temporary world, the fear of the unexpected remains and steers our course in life!'

'We cling to the belief, that matter would save us, not understanding that this is a fatal illusion.'

'And we continue living chained down by fear.'

Up to this point of our discussion, it was a matter of intellectual brain storming; but for some reason I began to feel a little uneasy. Suddenly the whole foundation of my life was beginning to sway.

Presumably I was able to conceal my emotions. She seemed not to have noticed anything as she said, 'Yes. But we go further. Greed sets in. We willingly perform activities which might harm others. We become blind to the essential part of life.'

This left me with even less foundation to stand on. At the same time I knew she was speaking the truth. I experience it every day in my work. The many cases coming in from around the world, people looking for hope and salvation! We do what we can, but in most cases our hands were tied. We were not able to solve their problems. Politics were made by those intend to keep their interest intact. Those guided by the fear of losing what they possess and nurture their greed for wanting more.

'This is known as the self-grasping mind,' she continued. 'Maybe you know it as "the ego". This is a state of mind which is ruled by ignorance. If one doesn't practice attentiveness of the mind, the ego would motivate us to act only according to its own personal interest.'

It is a well-known fact, but I couldn't help thinking how selfish the ego is. In its attempt to concur for more; in its attempt to satisfy its unrelinquishing hunger, it bulldozes everything in its part.

'If we were to observe the flow of our thoughts, we would become aware of what is really going on. That we are continuously jumping from one thought to another. Trying to solve one problem after another, we are seldom in peace.'

'Due to the craving we have for "things" and the fear of losing them,' I said.

'Constantly in search for answers which lead not to any ultimate solution but only to more questions.'

I nodded. 'And not realizing the futility of our deeds in Samsara.'

'The futility of going after material gain, going after things which are not really substantially important,' she added.

'It is not enough only to realize that we are on the wrong track. Isn't it?'

'Correct! We need to train our mind every day to make a difference. In the course of the day we are preoccupied with various activities. We tend to be distracted. To remain focused, one needs practice. Meditation is the method.'

'To remain focused, to be attentive of the manipulation through the ego.'

She nodded. 'One needs to possess courage to perform virtuous actions. But how can there be courage when one is preoccupied with fear!'

I sank my head between my hands, realizing the magnitude of the problem. 'So we perform non-virtuous actions, day after day, life after life. And all these actions have their consequences for others and for ourselves.'

I thought I saw a spark of approval in her eyes as I continued, 'And because we don't control our ignorant mind, we perform acts which might do damage to other beings. And that's why we suffer, in this and the following lives.'

'The law of karma is universal, independent from time and place. Non-virtuous actions cause non-virtuous experiences; one is caught in a cycle of suffering, unless one decides to "awaken" from ignorance.'

'Awaken?'

'Actually, it's also very logical,' she said.

I raised my eyebrows, expecting her to go on.

She took out a small blue note book and sketched a diagram. When she had finished, she gave it to me.

I saw her drawing while she explained.

The Conventional World

Continuos change of conventions leads to continual learning

Inability to learn leads to Ignorance

Which leads to lack of self-confidence

Somewhere down the line, spiritual growth becomes less important.

Fear begins to take the upper hand

Ego or selfishness begins to rule

'Due to the continual changes in the conventional world,' she began, 'we continuously learn to survive. But not all of us have the possibility or the ability to do so. This leads to ignorance and creates insecurity, which is fatal in an ever-changing world. One would not be able to keep up. In due course fear occupies one's life. One begins to have difficulty in surviving and one begins to become selfish. In the end, the ego wins the upper hand.' A glimpse of reality for me. 'Most of the systems in this world are based on non-altruistic conventions. To survive in these systems we need to have many things, good education, good looks, or cleverness, or a certain skin color, or a certain cultural background or, or, or. The necessities are endless in a system which promotes materialistic objectives.'

'On one side,' I countered, 'you speak of things one needs to do well in this world, and on the other side you speak of things which cause discrimination.'

'On one hand we have conventions and on the other the results arising through them. Conventions are based on views, half-truths and opinions. We judge based on these conventions, creating barriers and cleavages. We train our senses to register the discriminations and pro- grammed reactions which cause pain and suffering, not only to others but also to oneself.'

'And our senses are only capable of understanding what our mind interprets,' I said. 'As long as we keep feeding incorrect information, we can only expect incor- rect results.'

'The mind's capability to process information has to do with its state of consciousness,' she explained. 'The deeper this state, the clearer we are.'

'You speak of the depth of understanding,' I suggest- ed.

She nodded. 'Yes. The knowledge one learns in school has more to do with survival in this world and not with liberation from this existence.'

'Are you speaking of dying?'

'No, of course not!' she said seriously. 'I speak about moving deeper into a profound state of consciousness. Death is not a friend, it hinders our spiritual develop- ment.'

I noticed the sun was lower, moving towards the hori- zon, throwing a large shadow onto the world. My watch, to my surprise, said it was four o'clock. Must have lost track of time. The discussion was phenomenal! At the same time hunger was calling. "How impolite of me!" I thought. "She must be hungry too."

I apologized and asked her if she wanted to join me for a late lunch or an early dinner. She smiled, apparently relieved. We rose from the bench and walked back to catch a taxi. I knew a place, an Italian restaurant, between 6th and 7th Avenues, pretty much modern, with creative cooking and very delicious. Lately I had been there quite often, and I knew the chef, an exceptionally gifted young lady called Julie. She was the owner too. Only because of that, we managed to get a place without a reservation.

'Hi, Roger, how are you doing this evening?' Julie Rossini said in her sweetest voice.

'Very well, thank you, and how are things with you?'

'All good,' she answered with a charming Italian accent and added, gazing at my companion, 'I hope you will enjoy your meal.'

I hoped Miss Yogini had not noticed her hint. I distracted Julie by saying, 'I always enjoy your creations. They're simply delicious.'

'Thank you for the compliment!' She smiled and made a small bow.

'I would like to introduce a working colleague, Miss Indira Yogini,' I said. 'Indira, this is Julie Rossini, the owner and chef of this little piece of Italy.'

Both ladies politely shook hands and exchanged a few words. We were both hungry, so we ordered vegetarian food, but not from the menu. Julie was kind enough to make a few suggestions. Miss Yogini decided to have a vegetarian pizza with mushrooms, cheese, onions, and olives, along with a mango juice. I ordered fried brinjals, braised paprika with tomato sauce, and garlic bread, and with it a glass of my favorite red wine, a merlot.

'Oh, I'm sorry,' Julie said suddenly, 'I have to go!' I saw her hurrying back into the kitchen. I guessed she had forgotten something on the stove.

'I believe she likes you,' Miss Yogini said with a smile.

'I like her too, but only as a friend,' I replied a little irritated by her suggestion.

She said no more. After the intensive discussions that day, a strange silence hovered over our table. As usual my mind began to stray. I noticed that, although it wasn't lunch or dinner time, the restaurant was full; unusual, especially when it was the middle of the week. The food was very good. The restaurant critics had only good things to say about the place. It's a relatively new place; it started four years ago and has been winning one prize after another. Suddenly it occurred to me, whether Miss Yogini had any plans during her stay – that is, other than work. With all the people around, I thought it would not be a good idea to discuss work.

'If I may ask, do you have plans during your stay, in your free time?'

'No, Roger, actually not.' She must have realized she had addressed me by my first name, because she turned red. 'Oh, I'm sorry, I don't do it normally, it sort of blurted out.'

'No, not at all. I was going to propose it anyway. Please let's keep it informal.'

'In that case,' she said sweetly, 'I'm Indira.'

I smiled. 'You were saying you've not planned anything, right?'

She nodded. 'I didn't have the time. It all happened suddenly. I was asked only a couple of days earlier, if I would come.'

'I understand.' I didn't, but knowing Richard, it's possible. 'Well, allow me to plan something.'

'I'll be very grateful, thank you.' She smiled.

When the food was finally served we began to speak of the UN and my earlier projects. From there we were suddenly in the middle of my life in New York, my days at Harvard, my favorite books. Indira was enchanting and charming the whole time through. She laughed when I was speaking of my "philosophical-brandy-cigar-evenings" with Richard.

'How time flies,' I sighed as I was chewing on my fried brinjals.

'Strange,' she said laughingly. 'Although time is non-existent, we personify it.'

I nodded. 'You said something about beginningless and endless time this afternoon?' I mused. 'What does that mean?'

'For the modern human, time is important. He uses it as a measurement unit. He measures all sorts of things – age, distance, speed, performance, and so on – and by doing so imputes an importance to it. But the assumption that time is linear and can be measured is an illusion.'

'How's this?' I asked, astonished.

'Actually, there's neither a beginning nor an end. Per se! Time exists only in the material world. Without matter, there is no time, therefore no beginning and no end.

In our present mental state we have difficulty understanding this concept.'

'Do you understand the concept of beginningless and endless?' I was very curious to hear her answer.

She avoided a direct reply and said smilingly, 'Imagine a world without matter.'

'There would be no you or me, no nature, no planet, no universe.'

'What is left?' she asked.

'My soul?' I proposed questioningly.

'Only that?'

'A consciousness?' I said uncertainly.

'Anything else?'

'God?' I said, still unsure.

'Interesting that you didn't mention time, isn't it?' She removed a strand of hair from her face as she smiled at me.

'Yes, that is interesting,' I admitted, and added skeptically, 'How can that be? Every aspect of our lives is defined trough the concept of finite time; an end and a beginning is a prerequisite. How could I have missed it?' I was a little baffled.

She smiled at my bewilderment, as would a master at a student, I thought a little indignantly.

'There are many things we don't understand,' she started to explain. 'But one does not need to understand the molecular composition of oxygen to know of the importance of breathing. We know as a child many things instinctively; a sense of danger, the importance of food, the need to be loved.'

'So you're saying we don't possess the capability to understand the concept of "no time".'

'No, I'm saying, we do have the capability, but many aren't aware of it,' she replied calmly.

'How would one achieve this capability?' I wanted to know.

'The modern man believes science would help him to do this.'

'But not you, I assume?' I laughed and took a nip of my red wine, as I watched her reaction. She wasn't going to be caught off-guard. Perfectly calm and focused.

'Science could help, but to really understand time, one has to go deeper; where science doesn't look, at least not yet.'

'Because it concentrates on matter?'

'Yes,' she said with a satisfied expression in her face. I believe she was contented with the progress I was making. 'You've been listening.'

'What is deeper?' I wanted to know. 'And is spiritual practice the only way to overcome these boundaries?'

'The deepest part of us is not made of matter; it's a divine state of consciousness called the "very subtle mind". Although it's called the "mind" it does not refer to the brain or something solid. I speak of a state of mind. It is all knowing and all understanding. It's pure clarity. To reach it, one needs to abide in a state of oneness for an unlimited period.' She looked at me and answered my question even before I could ask it. 'Oneness is a state in which only a single thought prevails. The meditation is the only known method to do this.'

'What if science would find a method to do this?'

'I would gladly welcome it.'

'I see. But don't you think it would be difficult to make people understand this. It's a complex topic.'

'It's not about convincing the world. It's about understanding oneself. We are not here to help liberate others. A task only Enlightened Beings; Buddhas and Bodhisattvas are able to fulfill. We can only decide for ourselves if we choose to follow this path, if this is what we want. It's a personal decision.'

'What about other people? Do we leave them in Samsara?'

'Just as you came to me for answers, others will seek when they find the need. It is an individual decision. We can't force someone to believe, it will only lead to more pain. We can give answers when asked, we can be role models, and we can even help others who seek assistance. But we don't intrude.'

"It's a peaceful path, a path with great strength and wisdom," I thought.

It was getting dark outside and we had finished our meal. We spoke some more as we were having our coffee and tea. I told her of other things in my life and life in the US in general. I found the evening an enjoyable one.

It was late as we left the restaurant. We took a taxi to her place. I dropped her off at her apartment and went home. We agreed to meet the next morning, at about eight at the entrance to the UN building.

5

The Heart works in strange ways

I couldn't sleep that night, but this time it wasn't my job. I was thinking about her. I got out of my bed and went downstairs, as quietly as I could. "A glass of warm milk might help," I thought. I was about to heat it up when I heard my mom coming down.

'Let me do it, honey.' She took away the pot from my hand.

'Thanks mom. You don't have to do it, you know. I'm sorry I woke you up.'

'Don't worry about it. Anything disturbing you?' she frowned as she was watching me. I knew this look; it meant she was worrying about me.

'Oh, I don't know. It's just too much stuff rattling up there,' I said pointing to my head.

She nodded understandingly as she watched the milk bubble and waiting for the exact right moment to take it off the hot plate. With a smile mom set the glass of warm milk on the dining table saying, 'Sometimes, writing down things, brings some order into chaos.' I thanked her with a smile. She knew I had understood and went back to bed saying, 'Good night, dear.'

Sipping the milk, I thought, "That's a pretty good idea." I always felt comfortable sitting in the kitchen late at night. It brought back old memories, the good old days. "OK," I thought. I went back to my room and grabbed my laptop, returned to the kitchen, turned on the radio to my favorite broad-caster, and began to note down some of my thoughts.

'Time, space, matter, the mind, somehow all these entities are interconnected,' I wrote. 'On the one hand, we know we live in an impermanent world; on the other hand, we continue to strive towards permanency. Why the paradox? When we observe the world around us we see nothing that lasts forever. Might it be that deep inside, we believe in a permanent existence? Is that why we cling on to permanency, despite the impermanency of our existence? Is this something new? Do other religions speak of it? In some way they do. But they speak of a finite time on earth and an infinite time in paradise or in hell. But how many of us do actually believe it? Most of us are focused on surviving this life. Very few of us contemplate on an afterlife. We prefer to concentrate our efforts on extending the present one.'

I pressed the enter key, to open up a new paragraph for the next topic that came into my mind. 'Is there something such as eternal happiness? Is there something "bigger", a higher power, a higher wisdom, or even a higher state of consciousness? The Oneness! What is this that we call "oneness"? What is this that is called the "ultimate wisdom"? How can this exist when all things are relative? What is right or wrong? What is normal? If there is such a thing as "oneness" or "ultimate wisdom" then there has to be something called "ultimate truth"; and this is an indisputable truth, something not challenged, something which is not relative. Yes, that made sense. But what is this, this ultimate truth? This one thing which answers all questions erases all doubts. I don't know.' I stopped writing for a moment and thought, "I have to ask her about relativity!" Then I continued with my notes. 'Yes, everything else is only doctrines and conventions. How do we reach this "ultimate truth"? Have we forgotten the path to it?'

I suddenly remembered the last two lines from "Invictus" by William Ernest Henley; "I am the Master of my fate, the Captain of my soul." While incarcerated at Robben Island Prison, Nelson Mandela recited the poem to other prisoners and was empowered by its message of self-mastery.

I drank the rest of the milk, thinking. I don't know whether Henley had meant this, but those two final lines say much about what Indira spoke of today. Perhaps that is the key to achieve a higher stage of existence. Probably it's courage that we need, to go forward to that uncharted land of "peace and tranquility".

Such were my thoughts that night. Tired, and with a little less rattling in my head, I went to bed.

The next morning, Indira was waiting for me. She looked stunning. She was wearing a light brown business suit and a white blouse with black shoes.

'No high heels today?' I joked.

She smiled as she passed by me taking the lead. We had various appointments scheduled for today. Our first one was with the US Ambassador. While we briefed her, we could see clearly her astonishment. When Indira finished her report, the Ambassador stated, 'The little bees have been silently busy.'

'Madam, you do have to understand,' Indira pointed out, 'the matter had to be kept secret. It required great efforts of confidentiality. We as one people have been struggling for the last fifty years. We have had no support from anyone. We practically are fighting alone, in peace.'

'I know the situation, Miss Yogini. You've our understanding,' said the Ambassador.

'Madam, we need more than that. We require your support. We have come and gone with nothing else than good wishes and promises, and that is not sufficient. The time for justice has come. We need our friends to act. It's now and it's by supporting our application.'

'Miss Yogini, China is a major trading partner. The US must try to maintain a relationship based on common understanding.'

'Madam, with due respect, we are not speaking of a strategically important region. It's a very small part of Tibet, hardly more than seven thousand square kilometers. A region which wasn't enacted by China, still independent and free! Technically speaking, the application should be seen as only a formality.' Indira became passionate as she proceeded, 'The world kept quiet when injustice was done to the people of Tibet. Will the world repeat history? Will it again stand aside and not do anything?'

'Miss Yogini, it's a complicated issue.'

'No ma'am, it's not. It's a very simple one. One that we tend to forget! Deep down we are very clear in our choices. It's about the basic right for freedom. The freedom of choice, to choose a certain way of living. Is that not what the Constitution of the United States stands for? Is it not what this organization stands for?'

Indira straightened herself and looked the Ambassador directly in the eyes before starting to recite a part of the Declaration of Independence by heart. "...We hold these truths to be self-evident, that all men are created equal, that they are endowed by their Creator with certain unalienable Rights, that among these are Life, Liberty and the pursuit of Happiness. That to secure these rights, Governments are instituted among Men, deriving their just powers from the consent of the governed, that whenever any Form of Government becomes destructive of these ends, it is the Right of the People to alter or to abolish it, and to institute new Government, laying its foundation on such principles and organizing its powers in such form, as to them shall seem most likely to effect their Safety and Happiness..." Indira took a deep breath as she came to an end.

'Is that not so, madam?' she insisted.

And all I thought was "Wow. She doesn't cease to amaze me." The last two days, she was easygoing and appeared to be unaffected. With a charming smile and patience she answered my questions. I suppose I was lucky. For the first time I saw her in action. She was a lioness protecting her cubs. A passionate advocate representing her case. Not afraid of heated discussions, and ready to fight for her cause.

There was a moment of silence before the Ambassador spoke. She was apparently impressed. 'We are forgetful indeed,' she said. 'You're right; perhaps the time has come for your people to finally gain their right to a free "Life, Liberty and the pursuit of Happiness...".'

No more needed to be said. The meeting adjourned a short while later. We left with the assurance that the matter would be supported.

Needless to say, I was very impressed by how Indira had handled the meeting. She had managed to convince our most important partner to support the course. One done and three more to go.

I had arranged meetings with the permanent members of the Security Council. Our next meeting was with the Ambassador of Russia, and followed with those from England and France.

Indira also did splendidly during those talks. She was indeed very well versed in the diplomatic arena. She had a talent for it. I understood now why Richard had confidence about her capabilities.

The day somehow just slipped by and it was already evening. Seeing she liked Italian food, we went to another Italian restaurant for dinner. We were lucky to get a table on the upper floor, with a view overlooking the Central Park. We were still discussing the highlights of the day as dinner was served.

'You were great, you know,' I commented.

'I was fortunate to have good teachers in my life,' she said simply.

'That might be; nevertheless I believe you would be a good lawyer.'

She laughed and said, 'You're not the first one to say that.'

I asked, 'Richard?'

She nodded, and we both broke into laughter. I could picture it. Richard there, painting the virtues of law and encouraging his sheep to follow him into his world of rules and regulations.

'That's not for me.'

After the main meals, I ordered a cappuccino, whereas she ordered an Earl Grey. The sun began to set and we were quietly enjoying the marvelous view. It had only been a couple of days since I had met her, yet I felt closeness, a familiarity unknown to me. I didn't want the day to end. "It seems that happiness and suffering are two sides of the same coin," I concluded.

After the second coffee, the evening was coming to an end. The way home was unavoidable. We left the restaurant and were making our way to her apartment. Arriving at door, I waited at the doorstep for a moment. She quickly turned around and kissed me on the cheek. She then turned, entered the room and quickly closed the door behind her. I was still standing there a minute later, wondering what it meant. I hoped she wasn't watching me through the keyhole.

Slowly I left the building. It took me the whole way back to our house, to realize that I had fallen in love with her. It was very unlike me. I mean, to have such feelings for practically a stranger! But at the same time, it was as if I had known her all my life.

I was up early the next morning, and waited at the entrance of her apartment building. It was not long before she walked out, dressed in a pretty white dress, knee-deep, wearing sandals. It seemed she was expecting another beautiful sunny day. I believe she was pleased to see me. Seeing her made my day. I grinned from ear to ear.

She returned my smile. I wasn't sure if she was surprised to see me. She hinted nothing. I had no idea how, but I knew I wanted to talk to her about us. But there were things speaking against it, and things speaking for it. I was torn apart. I could clear the air or complicate the working relationship. If she didn't share the same feeling, I could be jeopardizing our relationship as colleagues; but at the same time, I couldn't help wanting more.

Somehow I ended by deciding to speak to her about it, and so we ended having breakfast at a café nearby.

I began by saying, 'Indira, do you think that it's possible, that two people could come close only after a couple of days, after meeting for the first time?'

To my utter surprise she asked, 'I believe you're speaking of us?'

Were my feelings for her so obvious? I nodded slowly and repeated my question. 'Do you?'

She lifted the croissant from her plate and took a bite, placed it back. A moment later she answered shyly, 'Yes, I do,' and hesitated before going on. 'I'm a little confused about my emotions. This hasn't happened to me before.'

'Do you mean...' – I had to clear my throat – '...you feel the same way?' My hands were shivering a little and I had to put the spoon back on the table, to prevent it from falling down.

'Yes,' she said with the most charming smile she had given me since we met.

I took a deep breath. 'I'm a little confused about my feelings, too. But I'm happy having them,' I admitted with a shaky voice.

We both smiled and looked into each other's eyes. Then we kissed for the first time, a long and soft kiss. It felt right. As we looked at each other again, I whispered, 'I think it was meant to be.'

'I believe,' with a heavy breath she said, 'everything is meant to be.'

She looked at me with those warm brown eyes. I bent forward and kissed her again, a long tender kiss, and it was as if time stood still. We spoke no words; I touched her hair and felt its tenderness. We held each other's hands for a long time; until the waitress walked to our table interrupting the silence.

She wanted to know if we would like to order something else. Realizing the "now", I looked at my watch. It was time to go. We had an appointment that morning. I paid and we left the café, holding hands, and remaining silent until we reached the UN building.

The sky was bluer and clearer that day, the birds were singing and the fragrance of love was in the air. I liked the music life was playing that morning. It was of hope, of happiness. People were laughing and the flowers were blooming. I would have rather spent that day with her alone, breathing in the endless love we felt that day, that moment. It was as if I had waited for her all my life; she had shown me how to love unselfishlingly. I felt I couldn't love someone more.

If I had to live my life without her, I knew my days would be empty and the nights would be long. Nothing would change my love for her. The world might change but I shall carry her in my heart. I would always be there for her. Our dreams might be young but I knew it would take us where we wanted to go. I realize today, I owe her all I am. She is my life.

With a heavy heart, I went back to work. Before we noticed it, we already had been in three different meetings that morning, two in the afternoon, and lunch had to be skipped.

As we finished our last meeting, I took a deep breath watching Indira organizing her papers. Her light brown eyes were scanning through the documents, and her slim, tender, soft hands were sorting them efficiently; at the same time the twilight highlighting the little things about her which I seemed to be discovering. I could have watched her for hours.

She looked tired. I offered to help her. She declined gently, but asked me to organize dinner. Us being exhausted, I proposed we order something in. She agreed with a smile. I wasn't quite sure about that smile. Was she smiling about me, thinking I had a specific intention? Or did she like the idea of a romantic dinner in her apartment?'

On the way, we stopped at an Indian restaurant. I knew the place. They were fast and the food was good.

We ordered dhal, rice and potato curry. A few minutes later we were sitting in a taxi driving towards her apartment. She leaned over and whispered with tears in her eyes softly into my ears, 'You are my heart, my love, my soul.'

'I can't imagine living without you,' I said and took her into my arms. 'I can't imagine my world without you.'

At her place, Indira took the food directly to the small kitchen and unpacked it onto plates, and she prepared tea. Meanwhile I went to the big glass front facing the southside city view. I loved the skyline at this time of the day. From the corner of my eye I noticed a paper on the table. It looked like Indira's handwriting. Unintentionally I began to read it.

'What holds us back, to love or to live freely? Is it the fear of being hurt? The insecurity and uncertainty we carry in us. Ah, fear, why are you in the way, why allow not courage to help? Are you not alone, are you not living in darkness? Allow a little light into your life and ease your pain. Allow your friends to share your burden. Would it not free you, would it not free us? Allow happiness to shine and lay down your unwanted load. Would it help us to walk upright again? Would it not help us to see the world?'

The words penetrated the deepest part of my heart. I sank into a chair and gazed out, into the twilight, the late summer sun rays touching the rooftops of the city.

A moment later I continued to read.

'Fear, let us be friends, allow me to lead you away from the dark corners you find yourself. You and I have lost touch with our inner strength making everything a daily fight. Life could be painless. One needs inner awareness. Outer peace needs inner stability, it needs balance and contentment; the road to inner peace, the secret to eternal happiness. Fear, let us be partners and share the burden we carry.'

I smelled food. Indira had entered the room. 'Ah, I'm sorry, I didn't mean to... I started and before I could realize it, I had read it through.' I felt as if I was seven and had been caught doing something mischievous.

She smiled. 'You should see the expression on your face – cute!' And she added with a friendly wink, 'I don't mind.'

I took a breath and relaxed. 'When did you write this?'

'Yesterday,' she said as she walked over. I gently took her into my arms. She kissed me tenderly; I wouldn't let her go and held her tightly until she whispered, 'Dinner is ready.'

The food was delicious and I was happy, because Indira liked it too.

That whole day had been tedious. Our meetings with the non-permanent members of the Council went well. We managed to secure their support. It was difficult convincing them. As expected, the ambassadors were at first a little irritated and surprised. The same question repeated, 'How did China miss this?', but eventually the atmosphere eased off as they began to listen to our reason, our course.

All of them reacted with the usual jargon about how sad they were about the whole issue, and about China being an important partner. They spoke of economic and political risk. No, they didn't make it easy for us, and no, they didn't spare us with their questions. But together with Indira's argumentation skills and the commitment we had from the four permanent members of the Council, we were able to win them over. It had been a good but tiring day.

The important part of the work having been done, I began to relax.

I was curious about where this chapter, this part of my journey was taking me. What did the future have in store for us? Has she thought about it, or was she just as much unsure? Or should we leave it to destiny? Should I ask her, maybe it's too early to speak of it. But my curiosity did not let ease, questions kept popping up. At our day in the park, Indira had told me that she was happy at home and didn't want to travel anywhere else. But my life was here. What would we do? Maybe I was making a big fuss over nothing, and just maybe everything will be settled when the time comes.

Such were my thoughts as Indira was speaking of how she had first met Richard and how her life had changed since then. Somehow she didn't speak about us. I remembered her once saying, "Things will happen as they should, so let them come." Maybe she was right.

Maybe we should wait and see where the tides would be taking us. But I'm not a patience person. I'm used to doing things otherwise.

As we came to dessert, my favorite; sweet milk rice with cashews; the doubts and uncertainties had disappeared, at least for now.

Indira prepared a fresh pot of tea. We made ourselves comfortable on the sofa and looked out at the skyline. We spent the rest of the evening thus enjoying each other's company. When I looked at my watch again, I realized it was already half past eleven. Indira looked at me sideways and said, 'You're welcome to put up for the night here, if you like.' Jumping on the sofa, testing it, laughing, she added, 'The sofa is very comfortable.' The matter was settled, I was spending the night on the sofa. I laughed, as walked over to her and lifted her from the sofa, and gave her a soft kiss to wish her a good night.

Watching the city in the moon light, my mind was wondering hither and tither. Many were the thoughts occupying me. Many were the questions I had about my future. Slowly I became tired and fell strangely in a dreamless sleep.

Early the next morning my hand phone rang. It was Mom.

'Honey, is everything fine?' she asked, with a sorrowful voice.

'Mom, oh, I'm sorry for not calling you last night. Yes, everything is fine.'

'I'm glad to hear that, honey. I understand.'

'Thank you mom, could I call you later? I have something to tell you.'

'Of course, honey, see you then.'

'Bye.'

I got up and walked to the kitchen, following the smell of coffee. I heard Indira in the shower. I poured myself a cup of the hot, delicious brew. The cup had been next to the pot. It seemed Indira had set it there for me. With the coffee I walked back to the sofa and sank in. The day showed all the symptoms of another sunny day. I literally breathed in the sun's rays; it felt good. This was a perfect start for a day!

The clock on the table showed 7:00 a.m. Ten minutes later, Indira walked out of the bedroom and entered the kitchen. I followed her and pulled her gently into my arms. As I kissed her she giggled. She carefully freed herself from my embrace. She looked so young and so innocent. Her luggage must have been extensive; she was wearing a different outfit today, an elegant, light blue twinset which looked like cotton, with long white striped pants and white ballerina shoes. She must have been on a shopping spree before coming to New York. I believe I made her so uncomfortable, scrutinizing her that way, that she flushed and urged me to take a shower.

Coming back into the kitchen, there was scrambled eggs and toast with butter and jam on the table. As we were having breakfast, I remembered wanting to ask her something.

'You know,' I began, 'I wanted to ask you about relativity. What does Dharma say about it?'

'Why relativity?' she asked, as she took a bite from her toast.

'Well, if, as you say, everything in life is perceptions, it would mean that everything depends on how someone sees it. And would that not lead to the assumption that everything in life exists in relativeness to each other? That ties in with Einstein's theory of relativity, doesn't it? At least I think so.'

Indira nodded and put down her coffee, with her hands holding the cup. 'Well, I'm not so sure about Einstein, I didn't pay much attention to science at school,' she said with a shy smile. 'But I'll try to explain it from a spiritual point of view. What, for instance, might be "good" for some people, might not be "good" for others. It depends on where, when, and in which situation these people live in.'

'That would mean it is difficult to give someone something, because it might not be good for the other person?'

'Helping means giving. But one should help with wisdom. It has more to do with what a person needs, and not what the giver thinks is right. Our lives are based on convictions, which could be valid in some places but not everywhere. Our values and beliefs, our laws and rules, our opinions and judgments are all relative in time and space. But we regard them as the ultimate truth.'

'That might be, but one needs rules and regulations in a world to secure peace and social harmony. Without it we would have anarchy,' I replied.

'Yes, you're right. In a world such as ours, in this world, one needs all this to secure a peaceful and safe

82

life. I'm not questioning them. I'm just saying that not all conventions are applicable everywhere and at all times.'

'We have managed to develop global values; basic human rights, international see laws, etc.'

'Yes, that is true, nothing to say against it. Only, they too are conventions. The fact is, we live in a world of versions. In a world of contradictions, there is no ultimate truth. It is a world of half's, of parts, of views. A world created by dependencies, formed by conventions and demarcations. The ultimate truth has no versions.'

As I listened carefully, a thought came up, 'You're saying that every opinion or belief is just as true and valid as any other?'

'Yes.'

'If that be the case, there cannot be anything such as good or bad, right or wrong, can there?'

'Yes and no.'

'What do you mean?'

'In a world of conventions, it is important to obey and live according to laws and regulations. The spiritual path on the other hand begins to reach out to one's inner self. This is a different world one treads. The closer one gets to one's inner self, the lesser is one dependent of the conventions of Samsara.'

'Worldly conventions become meaningless as purer and virtuous guidance takes over.'

'Once reaching this world of oneness, a world without conventions, there is no good or bad, no right or wrong.'

'What is left?' I asked.

'Something above all this!' She smiled with a cheeky expression.

'And what is this "something above all this"?'

'The state of "Oneness".'

I took another sip out of my cup, expecting the discussion to get complicated. 'How can I imagine this state of "oneness"?' I asked.

'It's difficult to explain,' she sighed. 'Sometimes, when one tries to explain something, it sounds strange.' She was playing with her cup.

'Please, I have to know!' I pleaded.

'I shall try.' Taking a deep breath, 'It can be seen as a state of utter unison, the realization of state of singularity. All things are reduced to a single clarity, a clarity gained by allowing compassion to overwhelm you. A state where no phenomena exist independently from each other; we are all interconnected, we are all bound. Infinite beings united as one consciousness.'

She was right, it did sound strange. But I was glad she had made the attempt. At least I was beginning to have an idea of what it meant. I have always been curious about death and thereafter. Questions about things which had always interested me as a youngster. "What was there before this universe began, and what will be there after this universe ends? Where are we going after this life? What is destiny? What is life?"

Everything Indira spoke of seemed to make sense, especially the part about the non-existence of conventions; I also couldn't deny the fact that Karma, the interconnectedness between our deeds and our experiences, does explain the "whys" of life. The Teachings or Dharma does seem to offer an explanation on how all facets of life correlate. "Everything is connected with each other," she had said. Take the weather, for instance; global warming is a good example. Even the most isolated regions of the world are affected by it. It's irrelevant, who is causing the pollution and who is not. The influence of the global weather system is felt everywhere, from the highest mountains to the deepest oceans. Apart from the weather, there are other things, which also play an important role in the cycle of life, which our senses don't perceive, but they are there.

It seems we are all bound in a unique way. I don't yet know how exactly, but I'm beginning to understand, at least intellectually. I smiled and took her hands into mine and kissed them, saying, 'Thank you.'

The next weeks proved to be busy ones. We spent a lot of time in meetings. Putting our feelings aside wasn't easy. We did spend the evenings in a more romantic atmosphere. During the day, however, we worked and tried to keep our feelings a secret. We were having conference calls with Richard on a daily basis to discuss our strategy and our next steps. Meanwhile we were preparing the application. Although well formulated it still had some missing points, arguments I hoped to have after my visit in Keajara.

One afternoon, a week before me leaving for Keajara, my mom called me at work and asked me if she could speak with Indira.

'It's my mom; she would like to talk to you. Is that ok?'

I saw the nervousness in her eyes as she nodded uncertainly. I passed my mobile phone to her. 'Mom, you're on the speaker,' I announced.

'Hello, Mrs. Cane,' Indira said.

'Hello dear. How are you?' my mother replied.

'I'm fine, ma'am. How are you?' asked Indira a little shyly.

'I'm fine too, dear. I've heard a lot about you from Roger. I was wondering if I could meet you for dinner?'

Indira saw me with a frown and said, 'I would be glad to, if it's fine with Roger.'

'Oh, don't mind him, dear. It is set then, we'll meet this evening for dinner.'

'Well, ok Mrs. Cane,' confirmed Indira a little timidly.

'Could you please pass the phone back to Roger, thank you dear, and see you this evening. Bye.'

'Thank you, bye,' said Indira, and gave me the phone.

I took it back with a confused look and turned the speaker off. 'Mom.'

'Please don't be late, honey. Seven o'clock. Bye.'

'Bye mom.' I hung up. 'Well, that's set then.' I whispered somewhat overrun.

The evening came and, to be honest, I was a little nervous.

'Come in, my dear,' my mom welcomed Indira with a heartily smile. 'At last I meet you! Roger is very particular about who he brings home.'

'Mom, please,' I tried to interrupt her.

But she ignored me and added, whispering, 'In fact, this is the first time he's brought a girlfriend home.'

'The pleasure is all mine, Mrs. Cane,' Indira responded politely.

'Call me Martha, and I'll not hear any objections to that!'

Indira smiled and nodded. I closed the main door behind us and gently guided her to the living room.

'You do have a very charming home,' complimented Indira.

My mother was apparently pleased to hear the compliment. 'Thank you dear. You look wonderful in your dress,' she returned.

A little shyly, Indira answered, 'Thank you, Martha.'

She, indeed, was looking extremely beautiful that evening, in her red summer dress and her shiny hair spread over her slim shoulders.

My mother signaled that dinner was ready and we moved to the dining room. I poured Indira a glass of water as my mother disappeared into the kitchen. It was the first time she had cooked vegetarian. I noticed that she too was a little nervous. A few minutes later, I could smell basmati rice. It was served with tomato fried in onions, brinjals baked with garlic and cheese, pumpkin cooked in olive oil and onions and curry.

Well, I don't know Tibetan food; it tasted more like Indian food with an American touch. It was delicious all the same, and Indira enjoyed it too. My mother was very happy about it. I suppose that is what mattered.

It came to me a bit of surprise, the interest my mother showed. Not really knowing this part of her, her being aware of the state of international affairs. She began by speaking about Tibet and about Dharma. She wanted to know more about it. She was so involved. Indira answered all her questions patiently. She also gave my mother a general explanation of Dharma.

At one point my mother gently interrupted Indira. 'Please don't misunderstand my questions, my dear. I was born and bred a Christian, but there came a time in my life in which my faith wasn't able to comfort me. It could not answer my questions. John, my husband, died in the war, a war which I saw as senseless.' At this point my mom became quiet, she rose from her chair and walked over to the old brown wooden cabinet we had in the living room. Something she refused to give up, something she and dad once found in a garage sale, when she was still full of hope, when she still used to laugh.

She continued, as she withdrew a small box from the second left hand drawer, 'It was a difficult time for me, for us. Roger was very young back then.' Opening the box, she retrieved a pile of letters. The hand-writing, it was my fathers. There was a clout in my throat. I walked over to her and took her shaking hands into mine as tears rolled down her cheeks. We embraced each other.

Moments later, I released her as she wiped her cheeks with the tissues Indira handed over. I looked up into Indira's soft brown eyes; it is the moment I realized I loved her.

'John wrote to me every day, from Iraq. He was torn apart, between duty, the love for his country, and the course it had taken.'

She started reading from one of his letters. "The people are suffering; they live in fear and in poverty. Children don't have anything to eat; it is so difficult for them; fathers and brothers endangering themselves for their loved ones, facing sharpshooters, mines, bombs, and us; just for a piece of bread, a bottle of water. One sees love, one sees courage. Without weapons, without fear, facing all odds, they walk through the streets of Baghdad in search of basic necessities."

My mother opened another letter. "I see so much suffering on the streets, and in all this chaos, I see humanity." She jumped to another page. "Something happened to me, I was on patrol. In a small alley, between all the ruins and the smell of destruction, appeared a little girl, hardly three years old, so thin, only bones and skin was on her. She stood up, shaky and freezing, to her feet. With such dignity and courage she approached me, with much difficulty, she moved her hands to mouth, asking me if I had some food. At this moment I fell to my knees, the load of sorrow in my heart just overcame me. I picked her up and held her in my arms, with tears in my eyes."

Indira embraced my mother, as both sobbed for a small eternity. It was as if, my mother was finally speaking her heart, finally freeing herself of her sorrow. If there were no words, no way to speak, the heart would still know what to say.

My mom went on a few minutes later, 'When his father had died, I had difficulties explaining the situation to Roger. How could I? I was myself not certain about what had happened or why. Lost and unsure I tried to go on with life. Many were the unanswered questions, they taunted me in my dreams, they wouldn't go away.' She slowly raised her head and said, "Why me, why us?" I asked myself. "What had we done to deserve this? Why was God not there to help my husband?"

She paused a moment and smiled. 'Don't misunderstand me, I wasn't lamenting. Deep in my heart it didn't make any sense.' She took a deep breath. 'One morning on the way to work, I saw a poster with the following words written on it; "Doubt me and doubt my teachings". It was an announcement for a Buddhism session. My curiosity was awakened, I decided to go there. Some more visits followed.'

My mother's confession took me by surprise. She obviously noticed my astonishment. 'Darling, I just wanted that you find your own way in life.'

'You never told me,' I said, a little accusingly.

'Oh honey, I didn't want to confuse you. You were still too young. You had enough to deal with. And later…' – she paused – '…well, it didn't seem important as you had found your own way.' She looked at me with apologetic eyes.

'But you could have talked to me,' I said.

'I know, I know… But honestly, it wasn't so much a secret; it was only me trying to find some answers for myself. How could I talk to you about something which already had caused you so much pain?'

'I just wished you had taken me into your confidence, despite my "problems with dad's death".'

She nodded apologetically. She stood up and hugged me. I thought about how difficult it was for her, and how well she mastered her life, and how thankful I was to have her. She was just trying to protect me.

I also realized she had been alone with her grief. 'I'm sorry, mom. I didn't mean it that way. It's just that maybe I could have been of help. But I understand. It wasn't an easy time for both of us.' I tried to console her as tears rolled down her cheeks. We stood thus for a few moments.

She wiped her cheek, simply saying, 'I still miss him, he was my soul mate.'

Some say time heals. I had been very young, a child, but I still remembered him, our afternoons in the park, playing baseball, going to the games, memories which don't age, joy and pain accompanying them.

In that moment I felt a light, but warm, embrace. Indira had joined us and embraced me, and my mother with one of her loving smiles. It brought us back to the present.

'As I was saying, I went to that event,' my mother went on, still wiping the tears from her eyes, 'I learned a lot about myself and the reasons for my situation. Although it was difficult for me to accept the explanations, I remained until the end. It was a three-hour session. There were many questions from the floor. People were asking about all kinds of daily problems. And I was surprised about the practical answers Dharma offered.' She paused again and said, 'Strange how everything ties.' She didn't elaborate but continued, 'I learned something important that evening. I needed to let go, to go on; not carry these unnecessary burdens with me. I bought a book that evening. It still helps me to overcome my difficulties in life.'

We realized the tea pot was empty. I walked into the kitchen to get some fresh tea. While waiting for the water to boil, I heard Indira speaking about karma. A few minutes later, I joined them with a full tea pot in my hand. Somehow, the discussion went over to our activities for Keajara. It was the first time I spoke of it with my mother, and I was somehow glad that she approved of my activities and saw the importance of preserving the Keajaran culture.

'Everyone has the right to fight for their home and for their culture, especially such a wonderful and old one as yours. We fought for ours against the British and the French. But...' – she paused with a sad expression – '...we enacted the Native Indians of their rights to preserve their way of life. We thought we knew better. We did it here and in other parts of the world. The Europeans have been colonizing the world and making all kind of blunders, suppression, slavery. I'm not saying that it's only the Europeans or the West, but to behave as if we were innocent is hypocritical.'

I was very surprised how passionate my mother was about the topic. I had not seen her speak out so clearly, not until today.

'Through the technological developments and the production of weapons we have only caused more pain to this world,' she continued. 'The many wars carried out in the name of democracy did more harm than good. With the industrial revolution, global warming was prepro-grammed. That is one of the reasons why it's important to help the Keajarans. Your people have shown the world what compassion means, that money and power has little to do with humanity and wisdom. Your peaceful endur-ance of the tragedy fallen on to you only mirrors your inner strength.'

Indira thanked her for her kind words. I for myself was very glad to see Indira and my mother hitting it off. As if they were old friends. As mom heard that Indira would be putting up at the diplomat's apartments, all alone, she wouldn't have it. She invited her to come and stay in our house. My mother can be persuasive when she wants to. Indira gladly gave in, and I didn't even start arguing about it. I knew it would be futile. And so we made up a room for Indira and she moved in, bag and all, the next day. I also arranged a daily taxi service for her, to pick her up and drop her back after work.

The next few days, we were very much preoccupied with our work and spoke most of the time about it. But I also noticed a change in my mother. She became more involved in what we were doing. She spent every even-ing with us, and contributed ideas and experiences. I liked how happy she was.

The evening before I left for Keajara, she confided, 'Honey, thank you so much for bringing Indira into my life! I know now how it is to have a daughter, a friend.'

Her smile gave me the confidence I needed leaving the women I love behind.

6

A search begins

The next day I was on the way to Keajara. It wasn't easy saying goodbye. They saw me off at the airport. I'd be seeing them in a few weeks' time. I had no idea what was awaiting me.

To avoid undue attention, the route was carefully planned. It was known only to a handful of people. My flight took me directly to Delhi, where I transited to Leh, in Ladakh.

Upon arriving in Leh, I took a taxi and checked into the hotel "The Ladakh". I felt right at home, had all the comforts of home. One could say quality accommodation and great service. It was not too far from the city center and 15 minutes away from the airport. The receptionist, thinking me being a tourist, recommended a few trekking areas, such as Zanskar Treks, Adventure North, or Overland Escape.

My room overlooked the garden, designed for escape and relaxation. Having jet-leg and being tired, I decided to take a shower and go straight to bed without dinner. A guide was supposed to meet me the next morning. I'd be spending a night here before continuing towards Tibet the next day. I had no more details.

The next morning, feeling refreshed and excited about my journey, I was up early. What was the day going to bring? Going down to the lobby, hardly anyone was around. Being famished I walked into the restaurant. The breakfast buffet was generously spread out. It was a mixture between continental and Indian dishes. Some were familiar. As I was in the middle of my breakfast, I noticed from the corner of my eye someone approaching me. Looking up I saw Richard.

'Good morning, Roger! I hope you're fine?'

'Richard, this is a pleasant surprise! I had not expected you here.'

His eyes were signaling me to be cautious. I became suddenly a little nervous, but I couldn't notice any uneasiness on Richard's face. I whispered, 'Is there anything wrong?'

'I hope you had a comfortable flight,' he said ignoring my question. 'The trip must have been tiring. What are you having? It looks delicious!'

I decided to play along and nodded.

He began to speak about Leh. 'Leh is a very old city, stretching back to the days of the Indus Civilization. That is about 3,500 years ago. It has a small population of about 27,000 people, and belongs to one of the highest populated regions on the planet. It once was under the rule of "Great Ladakh Kingdom", which stretched from the Holy Mountain Kailash up to Swaat. The Persians and the Chinese were trying to claim Leh in the seventh century. Over time Buddhism did become settled in Leh, what was significant in bringing it to Tibet. Until the independence of India, Ladakh was an independent state.

I thought we should travel to some of the holy and historical sites, if you're interested.'

Something was certainly amiss! Richard never liked visiting tourist sites. It was obvious he wanted us to leave the hotel. 'What do you have in mind?' I asked, trying to be interested.

'The Dropa areas are quite interesting; we could visit one of the villages still populated by the Dards, such as Dha Biama. The Dards are considered to be the last remnants of the lost folk of Aryans. These villages have great importance as anthropological sites. As a matter of fact, we are lucky. This is the time of the Chhopo sRbla, an important festival in these areas. It's considered to be rare and eventful. The villagers dress in their traditional colorful costumes and celebrate the festival in high spirits.'

I nodded, pretending to be excited, and finished my coffee. We stood up and left the dining room. Richard seemed to have already arranged a car with a guide. The man was waiting for us at the hotel entrance. As we drove away, Richard gave the guide a hand signal. The young man made a sharp turn at the next junction and began to accelerate. He made a second sharp turn into one of the side streets. Shortly after that a third and finally a fourth one, before disappearing into a small courtyard. The heavy steel doors closed behind us. With his finger on his lips Richard signaled me to be still. I noticed I had been holding my breath the whole time. I began to breathe; amazed that we made it through those narrow and busy streets without a single scratch.

We sat quietly, not moving. I could hear my heart beating. The minutes passed. Suddenly the car doors opened and two men ushered us from the courtyard into what looked like a barren building. From what I could see, it seemed to be a storage room, stuffy and dark, with flour sacks stacked to the roof. Another door opened, letting in light. Two men rushed in and winked to us to follow them. We found ourselves in a narrow back alley. An old pick-up was waiting. The men asked us to get in and keep our heads down. At this moment I noticed my luggage. They closed the doors and the pick-up drove away. It sped up, making innumerable zig-zag maneuvers. I had no idea where I was being taken to. If it wasn't for Richard, I would have probably taken the next flight home.

We stayed in this position for the next hour until the truck came to a halt. I was pretty shaken up. My back was killing me. Looking at Richard's face I could see he didn't look all that well. The guide who was squatting with us in the truck asked us to step out. I took a deep breath and tried to calm my stomach. Obviously we were not in Leh anymore. It was barren country, a stone desert to be precise. A four-wheel-drive was waiting for us. The driver and our guide exchanged keys and transferred our luggage. We hurried in, happy about the small improvement of not having to squat again. Our guide spoke a few words with the driver. I didn't understand anything. Then he joined us in the car, gave us a smile, turned on the ignition and drove away towards east.

With an upset stomach and disturbed nerves, I opened the window. Tried to breathe in fresh air and calm down.

We were still moving fast but the roads were better, making the journey smoother. I closed my eyes and began to rest, leading me to doze off. An hour later, the car began to slow down. Looking around I noticed the landscape had not changed much; we were still in the middle of the Himalayas.

Richard must have noticed me opening my eyes. 'In two hours we would arrive in a small town called Kumdak,' he announced.

Sometime during midday, we arrived in what looked like a sleepy town. Hardly anyone around, a typical Tibetan village, from the serene sky-framed mountains to the prayer flags fluttering in the wind, depicting at the same time the daily life in a remote Himalayan village. Its bright colors livened up the environment and made it mysterious. A sanctuary embedded in the beauty of the Himalayas.

'Everyone in the fields, harvesting time,' said the guide and walked away.

We stepped out and began to walk around, stretching ourselves. Slowly I was feeling better again. My stomach was signaling hunger and, as coincidence would have it, the guide was coming back with plates of steaming rice and hot vegetable curry spread over it. Behind him followed another man carrying a couple of chairs.

'This is delicious,' I said shuffling the full spoon into my mouth.

'Yes, homemade,' said Richard with a grin.

'Do we have to be careful here?'

'Yes, but we are in friendly territory. No need to worry for now.'

Finishing our food we returned the plates. As Richard was speaking with the guide I looked around. Did not imagine my first trip to Keajara would lead to an adventure. To think that Richard had done this several times! I was impressed.

But little did I know that the true adventure would begin after lunch! We took the so-called "secondary roads" from Kumdak to Thangra. The first ninety minutes were a bone-breaking experience. There were moments I wished I had not eaten anything.

We would spend the night at a guest house. As the weather had suddenly changed, dark clouds and heavy rain had appeared out of nothing within a few minutes, we could hardly see anything. The few houses in town were dimly lit. It did help it being late night as we finally. Nevertheless it was a relief.

The few houses in town were dimly lit. I noticed dogs roaming around. Richard beckoned me to be careful and make a big bow around them.

The compound of the guest house was fenced with a stone wall. Entering the courtyard, I noticed that the house was built in a crescent. All guestrooms were facing towards the courtyard. The "lobby" was in the middle of the building, whereas the rooms spread to left and right of the yard. The courtyard was decorated with various plants, bushes, and pebbles.

We crossed over the courtyard heading towards the lobby armed with torchlights. I accidently stumbled over a stone and began to cough intensely. The other two men gave me a concerned look. But I assured them all was fine.

In the lobby the guide had organized soup, chapattis, and black tea for us. At least it was hot. To my amazement, there were other people around, Chinese tourists mainly.

'We should not draw any attention,' whispered Richard.

"It would be difficult, being the only Americans around," I thought.

Back in the room after dinner, I looked around; the room had no real flooring. Cement floor, two beds with raspy yak wool blankets and used pillows; neither cupboard nor chair. I took a warm shower, brushed my teeth, and went directly to bed. Sleep wasn't possible, my thoughts were swirling around. The air was cold, dry and stuffy. The humming of the generators in the distance disturbed the silence. But suddenly around eleven o'clock; the generators went dead and with them all the lights. At least silence returned, and with that slowly peace returned to my mind.

The next morning, there was a knock on the door. Opening the room door, which made a loud squeak, I saw two young men with a large grin and tea pots in their hands, shouting, 'Herbal tea, sir, hot tea!' Before I could answer, the boys asked, 'Sugar, no sugar?'

Still a little sleepy, I answered with half closed eyes, 'No sugar, thank you!' and took a cup. I assumed it was the morning "room service".

They then moved on to the next room. The warm tea felt good after the sleepless and cold night.

Despite the fact that the rooms were equipped with a small bathroom, a few guests came out of their rooms and began to brush their teeth. For some reason I joined in and Richard did the same.

'How did you sleep?' he asked.

'Well enough,' I said tiredly.

He seemed to know why, 'It has to do with the height. We are climbing slowly. So it is only normal to have some difficulties sleeping as the body is getting accustomed. Not to worry, if you show any symptoms of height sickness, I will know.'

'OK,' not knowing what else to say.

Ten minutes later, the two young men appeared again on the scene. This time with chapatti and gravy, "Breakfast Indian style," I commented.

Richard seemed not at all disturbed. In fact, he found my reactions amusing, saying, 'Spoilt by the comforts of the modern world.'

I on the other hand found the whole thing not very amusing. I asked myself what other surprises this journey had in store. I missed my morning coffee, by the way! I went back into my room and ate sitting on the bed.

Richard was leaning on the wall and seemed to be enjoying his third or fourth cup of tea, when I walked out again. He whispered, 'I apologize for not explaining what happened yesterday. There was no time, and I didn't want to disturb you unnecessarily. The information reached me two weeks ago in Keajara, upon which I decided to take precautions and to escort you personally to Keajara. I arrived in Leh only one day earlier to your arrival; met our informer, the guide, who is accompanying us. He is working in Lhasa for the Chinese. I don't know if you noticed, but there were people observing us in the hotel.'

'No, I hadn't,' I admitted.

He continued in a low voice, 'We know for some time, that the Chinese are investigating. They are not sure about Keajara's existence but the rumors continue. The PSB is always on guard. They follow all hints, even if there are no concrete proofs. To be on the safe side, we take precautionary measures.'

'But the rumors make them nervous?' I asked.

'For a long time, they believed Keajara to be a myth. At least, that is what the PSB officially communicates. The rumors describe Keajara as a paradise and some even consider it as the long lost city of Shambhala or Shangri-La. However, the PSB does not take things for granted and is very careful in regard to the internal security of Tibet.'

I shook my head. 'Since they considered it as a myth, why the investigations?'

'It has to do with a sudden change of personnel at the PSB Office in Lhasa. There is a new guy. He has re-opened the case. He has also posted people everywhere, at hotels, airports, and so on. One can't be careful enough.'

'I see.' Richard was right. This could hinder the application process. All the work done until now could become futile.

'The word came to me they are controlling movements of foreigners in Leh. As a form of counter intelligence, we let information slip to the Indian authorities, saying Chinese agents are active in Leh. We hope the authorities would investigate it...'

He left the sentence unfinished. I knew what that meant. It meant, if the Indian authorities begin to look into the matter, the Chinese agents would be too preoccupied to look for them. A diversion!

Richard continued quietly, 'We are trying to avoid anything which might jeopardize our enterprise. Moreover, I didn't want to put your safety in the hands of strangers.'

'I appreciate it very much!' I replied. 'How much does the PSB really know?'

'They are pretty divided regarding the issue. Some believe it to be a myth; but there are others, who believe, there are enemies in every corner. For the moment we are out of danger. We still have some time, but we must speed up the whole endeavor.'

I nodded feeling somewhat relieved.

When Richard proceeded; his voice became softer, full of reverence, 'Apart from our informant, we also rely on the Great Oracle of Keajara. He has not given us any reason for concern, at least not until now, that's why we are proceeding ahead as planned.'

'We ought to consider that we have only one shot at this; this application has to work the first time.'

'The more the reason for us to be careful without being hasty!'

'I understand.' If we were caught without any official permits in Tibet, we could be arrested as spies and imprisoned, or even executed. It wasn't what I had in mind as my first field experience.

Richard left me with my thoughts and went over to speak to the guide. He returned a few minutes later, saying, 'We have to go now. It's time to leave.'

He led us to the back alley. Our guide was waiting there with our backpacks. Richard nodded and we began to move. In that moment I realized we would be traveling on foot. Richard obviously had forgotten to mention that point.

Before even realizing it, we were on our way to Hanle, a hundred kilometers away. It would take us at least two days to arrive there! My nervousness increased as we traveled land inwards. We were at 4,000 meters above sea level and walking was difficult. Every single step was exhausting. My body needed a lot of motivation. My heart was beating fast and my breathing was hasty, almost desperate.

It was somewhat irritating to watch the others not having the same problems. They were practically waiting for me every single mile to catch up. By noon we had 16 kilometers behind us. We stopped for a small break; the guide cooked ready-made noodle soup and tea for us. Half an hour later we continued. At some point I gave up asking how much further we had left to travel. One gets the same answer, 'Only a little further, sir.' And so I dragged myself step by step forward. The altitude was killing me, my feet were aching, and my back was hurting. I have never walked so far in life. My pulse was raging and I wasn't in any constellation to enjoy the beautiful and majestic landscape. By night fall we arrived at a small village with hardly four houses. We put up in one of them.

The next morning, I heard people moving around in the room. Opening my eyes, I saw the guide preparing breakfast. The smell of tea began to penetrate my nostrils, but my body was somehow reluctant to move. Finally my stomach managed to persuade the other parts of my body to sit up. The guide brought me tea. Richard's bed was empty.

'Where is Richard?' I asked still a little sleepy.

'Mr. Richard outside sir, having breakfast.'

I walked outside, and saw a vast plateau, high snow-topped mountain ranges. Nested between the hills and steppes was an immense lake. I joined Richard at the table and breakfast was served.

'That is a beautiful lake,' I commented.

'Good morning,' said Richard.

'I have heard that some of them give birth to many of Asia's mightiest rivers. I know now why.'

'Some of the big rivers, such as the Yarlung Tsangpo which cuts through the Himalayas to become the sacred Brahmaputra in India, or the Nu also known as the "Black River" which later turns into the Salween and flows through Myanmar and Thailand, are only some of the examples. Even the Mekong and the Yangtze which rush down hundreds of miles of precipitous gorges to rice fields of China and Indochina have their origin here. They feed more than a quarter of humankind.'

'The main reason for Mao wanting Tibet!' I replied.

'Exactly!' Richard concurred.

'Doesn't the Indus River of Kashmir and Pakistan also originate in the Himalayas?' I asked.

'Yes they do.'

After breakfast, we continued our journey. Only this time we had two additional guests, an extra guide and a yak. It was my first experience with the mighty animal. My first impression, it somewhat resembled the ancient paintings of bison. It looked like one of the long lost ancestors. The high plateau was its home, its natural habitat. I have heard that there is a similar animal known as the dzo, in the lower regions. It is supposed to be a crossbreed between a yak and a cow. They are all strong enough to do heavy field tasks.

The guide saw me observing the yak. He said, "Yak give us milk, butter, meat, dung, and hair. Good friend to us.'

Apparently yaks in these high woodless regions are invaluable. The Tibetans still use their dungs not only as a heat source but also to build their houses.

The yak packed, and us being ready, we continued our journey. It took us through one of the most beautiful scenery I had ever seen. The whole plateau and the Himalayas are constantly subjected to massive move-ments of the Earth's crust, which have gradually given them their shape and form. One could witness this; the various crust layers are visible to the naked eye. The entire plateau, with its vast mountain ranges, has been pushed up as a result of the collision of India. The earth-quakes being a continuing process are still moving the mountains to further heights. We also crossed occasional outcrops of hot springs. The water boils just below the surface as it emerges through deep fissures and faults in the Earth's crust.

I recalled reading a report on Tibet. It can be roughly divided into two areas; one being the so-called "high" plateau of the Quidam Basin, with an average elevation of 3,000 meters. On the other hand the core area of Tibetan culture lies in the so-called "low" plateau between the Himalayas, which lies more to the south. The climate there is comparatively mild, and some cultivation is possible. This is the heart of the Tibetan population cluster. We found ourselves in high plateau, so to speak. Hardly met anyone, it was intentional as Richard later explained. 'We have to be careful, there might be Chinese tourists.'

Two days later, we reached Hanle. We stayed in another guesthouse; the next morning we were awake very early as it was still dark and cold outside. After a good breakfast we proceeded eastwards. From then on we traveled partly on foot and partly on horses. We had more company, an additional yak and two Sherpas joined us. Nevertheless walking was still difficult. It took us the whole day to arrive in Lunguk. The night was similar to the last ones; cold. We could find a room at a guest house; this was smaller, with similar facilities.

The next day we would be leaving Indian Territory and entering the unknown world of Keajara. The landscape remained unchanged, on route into the high mountain regions. The Kunlun and Altun ranges to the north, the Himalayas to the south, the Pakirs or Karakoram Ranges to the west, and the high mountains of Szechwan to the east isolating Tibet; making a natural geographical boundary on all sides.

Our journey was through rough country. The stony tracks made traveling only by foot, horse or yak possible.

The next nine days we were very careful to avoid any unnecessary contact. On the way we saw some monasteries in the distance. I asked Richard the reason for the precautions although we were in the regions of Keajara. 'We never know who is around. There might be Chinese hikers in this region,' he explained.

A few days later, we were in higher regions. At this altitude the temperature fluctuates between extremes. The climb proofed difficult for me, even Richard began to show signs of exhaustion. The nights we spent in small caves in thick sleeping bags, and sometimes in a tent. The food consisted mainly of dried fruits, bread and water; in the evening noodle soup and hot tea. I could neither breathe nor sleep well. It was as all air had been sucked away.

During the day one had to deal with the warmer and stuffy air. As soon as the sun appeared from behind the clouds, it became unbearable. Despite the wind, which continually blew, one wasn't able to escape the heat of the day. I wore sunshades and skin protection all the time to avoid the UV rays. Due to the high level of perspiration, the Sherpas saw to it that I drank enough water. It did help.

The climb was steep and lasted three days. We were in the highlands of Keajara at approximately 5,700 meters above sea level. At these altitudes the horses were not very effective for carrying provisions. They got tired very quickly and we had to make frequent stops. We had to transfer the supplies onto yaks. The yaks were magnificent animal. At this altitude they seem to be the only animals capable of overcoming the cold and the thin atmosphere effectively. They are seemed to be made for these regions.

I was told that later, on the way down to the valley, we would have to repack again onto the horses, since they moved very much quicker compared to the yaks.

The days and nights seemed to prolong, one wondered when the journey would come to an end. Just as I thought it couldn't become worst, Richard warned, 'We are about to enter the most difficult part of the journey.'

We were still going up. My body ached; my throat was dry and my lungs empty of air. All I could think of was, "When is this journey going to end!" Richard encouraged me to focus on something else; it would make the trip bearable.

With feeble effort I concentrated on my surroundings. Since we began our journey, I had been observing the various climatic zones. Surprisingly I found the flora and fauna at this height still to be dense. I was of the opinion the thin air and rough climate allowed only a few types of plants and animals to survive. At the same time I had witnessed subtropical weather in some places whereas in others sandy desert regions.

"How this?"

Richard remarked, 'Well the Himalayas are undergoing structural and compositional changes due to global warming too.'

'A sad truth,' I added.

Gazing at the beauty which lay before me, I forgot for a moment everything else; for a moment I was embraced by the wonder of nature.

Richard explained, 'This area is thinly populated. Those living here are very peaceful people, contended with what life offers them.'

I wondered if it had to do with surroundings or with Dharma. 'The term wealth seemed not to mean much here,' I stated. 'The people here work together and help each other. In this part of the world, mother nature shows her raw side, it requires great inner strength to live with her.'

Looking back I still remember many beautiful moments, I had never seen such wonderful colors, sunsets or sunrises. Colorful stones brought to life by sunlight; the clear blue sky or such clear rivers in turquoise, cliffs shimmering in red, green and blue shades. The stars were so close one could touch them. One was able to differentiate the distance between the stars. The universe appeared closer and, at the same time, one could perceive its depth. On one full-moon night, I witnessed the largest full moon in my entire lifetime.

On the way we discovered prayer flags and even a temple. The monks welcomed us and gave us food and shelter. One of the monks explained, 'This area stretches into infinity. Your group would need a whole week to cross it. When you look back after a day's journey, you will still see the same view which you saw before beginning the journey that early morning. This route has great importance for transporting goods.'

Our guide asked, 'It took us four days to reach your monastery, and on the whole way we saw hardly anyone.'

'Yes, that why it's safer to travel in caravans; the climate can suddenly change and if you're alone you will have problems. At the same time it is important not to draw attention. We have to keep very silent.'

I understood what the monk meant by being silent. We spent that night in a warm room and had the luxury of a cooked meal. It was my first time in a monastery, with the fragrance of joss sticks in the air; sacredness was present, time stood still, and silence ruled. The monks spoke only when necessary and acted when duty called; the inner journey was visible and the world was accepted and loved as she is.

With the blessing of the monks we continued our journey the following morning. We followed their advice and joined a small caravan crossing the plateau. On the way, one of the Sherpa, named Bhisnu, explained about yaks to me. 'The lead bull is very important. It follows all the instructions of the caravan leader. For instance, if there is a crossing, the lead bull will stop and wait for the caravan leader to give instructions. If the leader heaves his right arm, the bull will turn left, if the leader heaves this left arm, the bull will turn right. If the lead bull is well trained, it will also pay attention to the voice of the leader. If one speaks quickly, the bull will move quickly, and vice versa. If something happens, for instance if goods loosen and fall, the lead bull will stop and wait. The yaks are ideal for this type of work, especially on this high and difficult plateau.'

As we moved on, I noticed that the plateau was covered mostly by ice. "Instead of naming it the wide plateau of Keajara, one should have named it the wide iced plateau of Keajara," I thought. The path went through small lakes and ponds. We had to cross the frozen surface to reach the other side; '…going around them would take longer…,' said the guide. Even the yaks had difficulty keeping their balance. 'The yaks use a lot of energy,' he told me. 'We need to feed them often, we make stops where possible, and they can only walk about twelve kilometers a day.' "Thank goodness!" I thought.

I also noticed trading at stops was a normal practice, called "make trade by fire" whilst enjoying hot tea; with sampa bread and yak butter. The caravan leader was carrying a sort of drum and was hitting it every fifteen minutes. I asked Tubten what that meant. He said, 'If everything went well, he would sound the "gong" once every fifteen minutes, but if there are problems or dangers, he'll hit the "gong" quickly. He has to be very careful when passing very narrow paths, and keep watch for oncoming caravans. Here the chance of accidents happening is very big.'

We continued to cross this magical and mystical landscape, which had very real problems. Only the determination of the yaks made it possible.

After a week's tedious journey, we arrived at the spot taking us downhill. The Sherpas transferred the provisions back from the yaks to the horses. At this point we separated from the caravan and bid farewell. Leaving the great plateau and moving downwards, we were faced with new challenges. We arrived at a cliff, which was so steep that one could only move in serpentine fashion. It took us three times longer than it normally would have. The only consolation was that we were going downwards and I was beginning to breathe more comfortably.

As we approached a monastery it was already late evening and the sun had disappeared on the horizon. There we spent the night.

The next day, I heard voices outside. Curious, I followed it and discovered people praying in a large room, they looked like pilgrims. Bhisnu was among them.

He signaled me to join them, sitting down, he said, 'These are people on the way to the holy Mountain Kailash.'

Some of them were turning prayer wheels, clockwise, in the direction the prayers were written. I asked Bhisnu why this was done.

'The wheels are to send the mantras to the heavens and into the world, for the benefit of all sentient beings.'

'Is this an old monastery?'

'Yes, it is. In the past this monastery was very important for this region. There were around five hundred lamas and four Living Buddhas living here.'

Contrary to what I had expected, he said, 'The monks don't isolate themselves from the people. They live side by side with them and take part in their daily life. They also do trades, grow crops, cook, wash clothes, manage the monastery, and help the needy and sick.'

I was somewhat surprised. I learned it is important for them to know what is going on in the world, and not only to practice Dharma in silence, more importantly to live it.

Some of the pilgrims were making their offering by dancing. Bhisnu explained, 'These were dances from the old tradition, the Bon religion.' With colorful customs and masks of demons, and to the sound of drums, they performed acrobatic movements. Watching the old customs one is reminded of the influence of the Bon religion in Buddhism. He went on, 'The masks indicate hindrances in oneself, projected as demons causing inner barriers and hindering oneself from moving spiritually forward.'

'Are there similarities between the teaching of Bon and Dharma?'

Bhisnu just smiled and said, 'Everything is Dharma.'

What did he mean by it; unfortunately I couldn't ask for more. The moment passed and the chance for revelation slipped by. So silently I continued to watch the dances and listen to the mantra recitations. Dancing, as Bhisnu explained, was also a path, to achieve mental harmony, to overcome the negative influence of the world. The South Indian Bharata Natyam is a good example. Bhisnu explained, 'Some say, it is the mother of all other dancing forms. The dance of Lord Shiva is the ultimate spiritual dancing form. It elevates one from this world to the world of pure consciousness.'

Later I spoke to Richard about this.

'We are travelers looking for a way home. The paths are many; some are virtuous and others are not,' Richard explained. 'Only the virtuous paths lead us to eternal happiness. Therefore it is important to choose wisely, choose those which bring us home safely.'

'Are you saying dancing is not the correct path?' I asked.

'There is a story of a man who wanted to be a monk. Unfortunately he was not versed in the readings, nor was he capable to meditate. The high monk of the monastery nevertheless ordained him and gave him a task, the man was asked to clean the monastery with a smile. This he did, day in day out. It was this task which helped the monk to realize emptiness,' explained Richard.

'So what you are saying is; everything can help to realize eternal happiness, if it is used with virtuous motivations. Therefore it is important to choose wisely,' I asked.

Without saying anything, he just made one nod.

The dances came to an end, and the puja was completed, the pilgrims continued their journey after receiving their blessing. We moved on, towards Keajara City. I too felt like a traveler, on the roof of the world finding consolation in the wide landscape, in the cloudless sunny day. The prayer flags agitated by the wind reminded me, I'm not alone on this trip. I'm sharing this route with others.

The majestic scenery, the holy rivers and barren mountains reminded me of one's feebleness. No one was in a hurry, all things were in flowing; one turns inwards for strength. We finally reached the end of the plateau, where Richard said, 'Behind this mountain lays the valley of Keajara City.'

We finally arrived at a junction where a truck was waiting for us. Our guide walked over to the driver and spoke in Tibetan. He explained the situation to us, 'The truck has engine problem. Narendra waiting here for the mechanic.' I assumed Narendra to be the driver.

Richard frowned hearing this. He was apparently not amused. He went to the truck and climbed into the back, saying, 'Roger, come, we'll wait here. This will take some time and it's getting hot.'

He needn't say twice. I was immediately behind him getting into the truck. I took a look at my digital watch, it showed 40 degrees Celsius. We were now 4,000 meters above sea level. Tired, we spread our sleeping bags on the floor and laid us down. An hour later, we heard noise. We looked out, as out of the blue a man appeared in the dusty road. Richard seemed contended as he said, 'Finally, the mechanic!'

At least the nap did me good. We got out and saw him go under the hood. We were all waiting anxiously for a diagnosis.

'Can repair, take time,' the mechanic reported.

Richard nodded, signaling him to begin work. I was watching impatiently, thinking, "I need a shower and a comfortable bed." Unfortunately the workings of a diesel engine were unknown to me. And so I could do nothing but wait.

Just as I was thinking it couldn't get worse, a strong wind began to blow. It created quite a chaos, swirled sand and dust into the air, and made practically any repair impossible. We hurried into the back of the truck. The Sherpas secured the horses under canvas and tied

116

them to the rocks nearby. Tubten switched on the little gas oven and Narendra began to unpack his bag. Before I knew it, they were preparing a meal.

'Sandstorm take long time, sir. Meantime make food,' explained Tubten.

We had enough provisions in the truck. There was flour, bread, butter, spices, and different kind of vegetables. The chapatti and vegetable curry they conjured up was simply delicious.

Three hours later the sandstorm dissolved. The mechanic continued with his repairs. By the time it was finished, it was already getting dark, and we decided to spend the night there and continue the next morning.

After breakfast Narendra started the truck. It worked. We parted from our Sherpas and thanked them for their support and help. They would continue their journey on foot with their animals. Tubten, contented and happy that we could finally continue our journey, took a seat in the back. I joined Richard in the front beside the driver.

'This road is difficult to drive. She like moody woman, must be careful,' Narendra said with a wink.

He obviously knew his woman well. I wouldn't want to drive on these roads.

Around dusk, Narendra stopped and parked at the side of the road. Richard tiredly explained, 'We will be putting up for the night here.'

We joined Tubten at the back of the truck. He was already busy preparing our dinner. Hot noodle and vegetable soup was served. With a full stomach and tired I walked to my tent, but just before entering it, I turned to the skies for a moment taking in the wonder of creation. It was a clear sky and the cosmos was lying open to be explored.

Tubten still at the fire place noticed this, commented, 'No clouds, all is clear, like in life, no?'

I watched him questioningly as he answered, 'When no doubts path is clear.'

We continued our journey the day after. I heard Narendra saying to the mechanic, 'Now must take care, dangerous road.'

The truck went through the dusty, cold desert. It was no easy maneuvering. Nevertheless we were driving through majestic snow-peaked mountains.

Narendra was all out to drive through the pass today. 'Very dangerous, landslide, sir.' He was totally focused on his driving and hardly spoke. We even skipped stopping for lunch.

We arrived twelve hours later at an open space. There, under some large bushes, we parked our truck and feeling exhausted went to sleep.

The next day too was not short of adventure. We were driving along a deep canyon. There were moments when my heart was ready to leap out. There was hardly a foot between us and a fall into the depths. The smallest mistake and we would be down there somewhere. But Narendra tried to assure us, 'I driving here fifteen years and nothing happen until now.'

His attempt to console us was not very reassuring. I just nodded, not wanting to disturb his concentration. I hoped we didn't have to take the same way returning to Leh. To my relief, we managed to cross the pass that day. That evening as Tubten was preparing noodle soup and chai for dinner, I noticed the strained faces around me.

Tubten commented, 'Many cannot live here.' As if he heard me speak my thoughts out loud. 'Sometime the rain very strong, cannot see much, must stop driving.'

'What helps?' I asked.

He smiled and said, 'Patience!'

The first sunlight was warming up the cold air as Richard informed me, 'We are now very close, another 20 kilometers.'

As we approached Keajara City, the landscape began changing. There were snow-peaked mountains; there was also a forest, rivers and streams. The truck left us and we were again on foot, walking through sands roads. Around midday, we crossed a river. We stopped to wet our throats. I couldn't help dipping my hands in and letting them be cooled by fresh water. A few minutes later we were headed to the nearest village. Some of the villagers recognized Richard and came out to welcome him. They brought us to one of the houses and offered warm food. Hungrily I ate. After more than two weeks I finally had a bath and slept on a bed.

A few hours of sleep did wonders. I felt light and contented. At the same time, for some unknown reason I felt as if I was coming home.

'Is it this place, or is it the fact I had rested?' I asked Richard. 'I have a strange feeling around my heart, it feels warm.'

Richard replied, 'It has something to do with the positive energy which surrounds Keajara.'

I raised my eyebrows wanting to hear more, but Richard gave me one of his mysterious smiles. 'Another day, everything needs its time.'

It was the final day of our journey. We reached Keajara City without any problems that early afternoon. As we were approaching the city, a group of people came to welcome us. They obviously recognized Richard. One of them, a young man, showed me to a small cottage, which was to be my quarters during my stay. Richard accompanied me and ensured that everything was fine. He mentioned that a small welcoming celebration was planned for the evening.

With a deep breath, Richard said, 'I'm very glad we made it safely.' I could see the relief on his face. 'This is Indira's cottage. She wants you to put up here. I hope this arrangement is fine with you?' Richard asked.

'Sure!' I replied with a smile.

After I'd thanked him, he left promising to pick me later for the celebration. I couldn't stop my curiosity and began examining the cottage, the place Indira normally lives in; the house had a living room, a kitchen adjoining a small dining room, two bedrooms, a study, and a bathroom. It was furnished with modern sanitary systems. There was a mirror on the wall above a wash bowl, a shower, and a bath.

The house had two middle-sized bedrooms and, although it wasn't very large, it had all the comforts of a home. Looking around, I noticed the little things that made it hers. Somehow this made me feel comforted. I realized I missed her. From the corner of my eye I saw a telephone. I wanted to call them, but looking at my watch I noticed it was four p.m. here, and with a thirteen-hour time difference, it would be five a.m. in New York. I decided to take a shower first. After the shower, I returned to the kitchen in my pajamas. I was happy to see a small meal waiting on the table. Someone must have brought it in. Being famished I sank into a chair. It is very comforting to sit at a table, without any fear, not having to swallow down your food and continue ones journey in a hurry. Yes it was a relief, just to sit there and enjoy ones meal quietly. Afterwards, I felt very tired and went to bed.

I was awakened by loud noises outside. I noticed it was getting dark and from the sound of it, I would say the festivities were beginning. Changing into fresh clothes I called home. It must have been about seven a.m. The phone was ringing and someone picked it up.

'Good morning, who is that please? This is Martha speaking.'

'Hello mom, good morning.'

'Hello honey, it is so nice to hear from you. We were so worried about you. We haven't had any news from you since you left. How are you, are you well?'

'I'm sorry mom, I couldn't call you earlier.' I recalled how Richard warned me from being detected by the Chinese.

121

'Roger, Indira just came down. I'll put you on the speaker.'

'OK, hello darling.'

'Hello Roger, how are you, we were so worried. We miss you.'

'I miss you too. I'm fine. We arrived today afternoon, safe and sound.' I was thinking of the escapade in Leh.

'Honey, did you have problems with the high altitude?'

'It was a little difficult climbing and we had to travel a great distance on foot. I wouldn't ride again if I really didn't have to.' It was a strenuous adventure. 'The slow climb helps one to get acclimatized to the high altitude. All in all we managed to over live our journey.'

'Darling, are you sure you're fine?'

'I'm fine now. A good shower and sleep does wonders.'

'Honey, do take care of yourself.'

'I will, and I'll call you daily.'

'Love you darling.'

'I love you both, bye.'

'Bye.'

I hung up. Lost in thoughts I sat there for a moment. They were so far away and yet it felt so near, they were in my heart.

A few minutes later Richard showed up and we left for the festivities. It was a warm summer evening; I had a polo shirt on with jeans and sneakers. Richard too was dressed casual. Walking up the path we noticed lights and music in the distance. The festivities were in the center of the city. Approaching it I saw people dressed in beautiful and colorful traditional costumes, all surrounding a large fountain, in the town square. A spiritual dance was going on. Many came to celebrate our arrival. There was music, dances, colorful costumes and warm food. We joined and mingled in. Many knew Richard, I was introduced but I hardly remembered their names.

As we took places at a table, the introduction continued. Many more warm welcomes and it was apparent that Richard enjoyed respect. He introduced me to many persons of ranks, the mayor and ministers. The Prime Minister was unable to attend but he had extended well wishes.

It was obviously a time of celebration. Everyone was enjoying themselves. Many spoke of expected harvest, some spoke of their families, and others about Dharma. I heard Indira's name mentioned. Many asked me how she was and if she was well. I had never met so much warmth and friendliness at one time. Everyone showed concern for the welfare of their people. It was an evening which opened my eyes to what is important in life.

"Let the storm come..." I thought "...the people of Keajara shall set their sail and navigate into freedom."

7

What is life without its shadows

One early wet morning, a man in a dark raincoat was waiting in front of the PSB Headquarter in Lhasa. He was shown into Lt. Chan's office. He took a seat. He was offered some Chinese cakes and a cup of black coffee.

'What do you have for me?' asked Lt. Chan smugly.

'I believe people have been warned. We expected a guest, but he managed to get away. I believe we have a leak. Things have become very quiet. Even the rumors are dying off. Not even the Chinese tourists are speaking of it,' said the man.

'A leak, you say,' said the Lt. scratching his head.

'Yes,' said the man.

'Who could it be?' asked the Lt., without even considering that it might not be the case.

'They are your people. How can I say?' said the man a little irritated.

'Don't get jumpy on me. I'm not suspecting you,' answered the Lt., impatiently.

'That is good!' said the one known as the "Shadow".

'I wonder if it's the Tibetan clerk,' said the Lt., more to himself than to Tashi, the stranger. 'But how does he get the information? Only I know about the whole operation in this house.'

'Perhaps someone is watching your activities?' said the man with a shrug.

'You mean I'm being followed?' asked the Lt., a little alarmed.

'Everything is possible,' said the man in his broken Mandarin.

'Can it be possible? Might it be!' said the Lt. a little alarmed. 'Do you mean the Tibetans have an intelligence organization in Lhasa? And we don't even know about it!' There was fear and excitement in his voice.

'Stranger things have happened,' said Tashi with another shrug.

The Lt. was irritated by the Shadow's unaffected manner. 'I want you to watch the clerk, and I want someone watching me. Maybe, that way we will know who is following me.'

The stranger finished his cup of coffee and left the office. The Lt. wasn't very pleased about the notion that someone was watching him; no PSB officer would be. They are entrusted with highly confidential tasks. He sat there long and thought it all through.

His mind was searching intensely for answers. Uncertainty was not something he had patience for. His logic dictates a certain common sense, which doesn't have anything to do with common sense itself. The important thing about his logic is, things have to work out for him, even if they are based on false information.

He came finally to the conclusion "It had to be the clerk," so, poor Mr. Drogpa, who was unaware of the working of Lt. Chan's mind, was predestined to suffer under the paranoid actions of the Lt.

His mind did not stop there. "But again the clerk must be working with someone. He is not the type to organize such surveillance activities alone. He is incapable, that idiot!"

But at the same time, he could not think of anyone else. He gave in, "Anyway I have to begin somewhere!" and so was satisfied with poor Mr. Drogpa as being the culprit. "I must do everything possible to find out the truth. Should that not be the case, the alternative is unthinkable. Not only would that have an impact on me but also on the entire PSB establishment!"

8

One journey's end is another's beginning

Early next morning, I was awakened by laughter of children just outside my window. It was a dreamless and peaceful sleep. Feeling refreshed, I was ready for the day. In the kitchen breakfast was ready, toast, jam, butter and tea. "I could get used to this," I was thinking to myself. While enjoying my breakfast, I was enjoying the view out of the little window in the dining room. In the distance were the mountains, high and proud they stood, with a green plateau at their feet and a river running downhill. With the second cup of tea I walked into the garden, from there, I had a clear view of my neighborhood.

The cottages were built out of clay and brick, with a small garden. Roses, clementine, edelweiss, along with many other varieties of flowers could be seen, forming a colorful landscape. In the distance were large trees, they threw shadows over the fields, and crops gently swaying by the touch of the wind. Somehow this place was magical. It was not only the nature or the people, there was something else. I was searching my mind for the correct word, what was it … and it came to me, "Healthy!" It was as if the mountains surrounding it were protecting this city from harm. Even the air tasted clear and sweet, like honey. The environment seemed to radiate serenity. "What was it that made it so? Was it the love for nature, for the environment, or was it some source of energy surrounding this place?" I asked myself, not realizing then, it will be years before I will know the answer.

I was supposed to meet Richard later for lunch. I decided to explore the town on my own. I grabbed my thin windbreaker and my notebook. Richard had already indicated that the Keajarans did not like photographs to be taken, either of themselves or of their city. Understandable, and to be respected, they value their privacy.

I stepped out of the cottage and took the pathway to the left, heading towards the center of the town. I saw again the old and large monastery at the foot of an impressive mountain range. I had noticed it last night during the festival. I could make out from a distance that the whole complex looked similar to the Potala Palace in Lhasa.

The city looked similar to other Tibetan towns, but the difference became apparent when looking closely. It was well planned with wide streets, not densely built, and most of the houses seemed to be spacious enough for large families. Among the orderly row of buildings were public facilities, such as an enormous granary and an assembly hall. There seemed to be an administration building, which looked like the mayor's office with a guard sitting at the entrance. As I passed the building, he smiled and said in English, 'Good morning sir.'

I returned his wishes with a smile, saying, 'A good morning to you too.'

The people, the town, indicated a high level of social organization and design. But other than that the town was completely unlike the busy and bustling New York. Calmness and peacefulness were present. It was as if time was irrelevant, it is as if the environment rested within itself.

I left the pathway and walked up to the main thoroughfare running alongside a river. This area seemed to be the heart of the city. All side roads seemed to meet the main road in the middle of the city. A turquoise and clear river flowed through the town, from north to south, like a lifeline, giving a feeling of freshness and life force. In middle of this main road was a beautiful water fountain with a golden Buddha statue in the middle. The fountain was decorated with various deities and other ornaments. It was built in the middle of the river. Two arms were stretching out of the fountain to either side of the river, touching two smaller fountains where water gathered.

My first impression was it had a decorative purpose, but a closer look showed it served a religious purpose. The people going by made the traditional salutations with both hands clasped to the heart and a bow, after which they took a sip of the water before going on. Around the fountain were shops, grocery stores, cafes and restaurants. I remember Indira telling me that Keajara was an agricultural society; its prosperity came from the land and the people's capability to farm. As I walked by these shops, the people I met on the streets seemed to know who I was. I was curiously observed, and greeted with warm smiles. No one made me feel like a stranger, in fact I felt welcomed and in a strange way I felt to belong.

I don't remember how, but somehow my stroll ended at the doors of the main monastery. Unfortunately I have never been to Lhasa, or seen the Potala Palace. But from the pictures I have seen, I would say this was an exact duplicate. The daylight made the monastery look even more impressive than it was the previous evening. Turning southwards, I noticed that I had actually walked upwards and not just northwards. From there I had a very good view of the whole city. The whole area was visible. The entire valley was bathing in the warmth of the sun. A beautiful sight; at the same time I also realized it was getting warmer and that I was feeling a little tired. So I decided to make my way back to the cottage. At about twelve Richard knocked on the door. We had lunch together. I mentioned my astonishment at what I had seen and what I felt during the little exploration that morning.

Richard nodded. 'Ah yes, it was indeed an interesting development. It began so long ago that one begins to take it all for granted. The Prime Minister and I are old and close friends. His father was a man of great wisdom, and he had a vision. Initially he was a lama. Normally a lama forsakes the worldly life and retires to the spiritual path. Being a single child and out of love to his father he agreed to take over the leadership of his tribe. Then, his influence did not reach all of Keajara. And as a matter of fact no one fully realized the exact situation at that time.'

'You mean that China had not made any claim on this area?' I asked.

Richard nodded. 'The realization came only later. In the early seventies, a high lama who had escaped to India returned to Tibet in search of his master. He was lucky to find him, and on their way to India they rested here. During discussions with the High Lama of Keajara they realized that China had no knowledge of this small area. Their annexation of Tibet did not apply to the region we call Keajara today.'

'I can imagine the revelation must have been a great surprise and relief,' I said.

'I was told it was indescribable,' Richard concurred. 'Both the lama and his master decided to stay. In due course, people were sent out very quietly to find out if there were other regions "forgotten" by China. To their astonishment an area of about seven thousand square kilometers remained unenacted. The tribal chiefs from these parts were invited here to meet. It was at this gathering they agreed to name the region Keajara. The tribal chief of the largest tribe was elected as the head of all the tribes. That was the father of the present Prime Minister, Mr. Champa Norbu.'

'So you met there?' I asked.

'Yes. Norbu was sent to study in Cambridge. We were two young men trying to find our way in life. After completing his law school, Norbu began talks with the UN. The UN kept a low profile in it and helped Keajara with the developments which you see today. A provisional government was established. Schools were built, students sent out to acquire foreign education. It was also agreed to wait for a favorable time to apply for membership of the UN; that was 1976.'

'Why send young people to foreign countries? It would have increased the chances of being discovered, or not?' I asked reluctantly.

'His father realized they would have to learn more about the world. Selected candidates were sent out to learn and bring back the expertise. He hoped it would benefit the country because modern development was needed to ensure national security and political stability,' as if looking into the past he continued, 'There were naturally conditions attached. The candidates had to be novices of a monastery. They were to have a deep under-standing of Dharma. In Keajara spiritual education is a prerequisite before continuing a conventional education.' Richard smiled. Probably he was thinking about his time as a student as he said, 'Most young minds are easily distracted by worldly pleasures, especially when one is away in a foreign country and living in a foreign culture.'

'Die they return?' I asked a little reluctantly.

'Yes, all of them, amazing isn't it!' he commented. 'Well, they brought not only their knowledge but also their experiences to help in building the country. Over the years, changes did take place; a legal system came into place, the infrastructure and the living standards of the people were improved. The raw materials come from Keajara. All local products produced here with local manpower. Only the technical expertise is imported.' He sipped his tea before going on.

'Why was it so important to allow external influences to be integrated? Was it not enough that Dharma was taught and practiced?' I asked.

'Good question,' Richard admitted. 'Buddha did not ask us to close our eyes to the world. While concentrat-ing on inner development, one should not disregard ex-ternal influences. I know it sounds a little bit paradoxical,

132

but allow me to explain. Our body is matter. Even if one strives for liberation, one should not disregard the body. It has to be maintained until liberation is attained.'

I repeated the sentence, thinking about the correlationship between body and mind. 'Of course, without this body, liberation would not be possible for humans.'

Richard nodded, 'Our mental progress can only be tested by facing life. For instance, there is an old story about patience. Once there lived a yogi. He went to the caves to meditate on "patience". High in the mountains, in seclusion, he found a barren cave. He had spent weeks and months meditating; he was very contented with his progress. One day, a man was visiting his family in a nearby village. He lost his way and accidentally found the cave. Entering it, he saw the yogi in meditation. He wasn't sure what to do. At first he did not want to intrude but since he had to arrive at the village by nightfall, he interrupted the yogi in his meditation and asked him if he knew the way. The yogi wasn't very pleased about that. He restrained his irritation and explained the man the way. The man however couldn't find the way and returned to the cave for help. "I'm very sorry sir, but if you please could describe the way once more? I shall not trouble you again."

The yogi was again irritated but subdued his anger and described the way again. As this repeated for a third time, the yogi suddenly erupted by shouting, "Don't you see I am meditating on patience? Don't you see you're being a nuisance???!!!"

Upon which the man suddenly changed into the Enlightened Being, the Great Bodhisattva, the Great

Buddha, and said, "My friend, patience cannot be practiced by just meditating on it. It has to be also practiced in life."'

'No matter how one strives towards inner peace, one should not ignore the happenings externally,' I concluded.

'Exactly!' said Richard. He took a deep breath and gathered his thoughts before continuing, 'When Norbu took over as Prime Minister, he confided in me and asked me to assist him. At first it was only on a "on need basis". Later I was approached by the UN Secretary General, asking me if I would be willing to entirely commit my time for this project; after much thought I agreed.'

'That was when you left Harvard!'

'It has been a few years now. Well, when I first arrived, I had a lot to do. It began with me learning about Dharma.'

'Did Dharma help you personally?' I asked. I was eager to know.

A moment of silence followed before he answered 'At that time I had many unanswered questions. Not only of spiritual nature. I was at cross roads; mostly my confusion about the correlation between man, nature, science, the universe, time and space.' He paused and took another sip finishing his tea. Bending over, he poured filling our cups. 'I always wanted to know how it all fits together. Dharma helped me to understand. Over the years I became a believer. Today I see Keajara as my home.'

I looked at him as he was sitting there with a tea cup in the hand. He seemed to be contented, no restlessness of earlier days. I have heard of people leaving everything behind to start a new life somewhere. Would I be ready to do the same thing? Indira appeared on my mind. Maybe soon the time would come to decide. "It would mean me leaving mom, my home, my job, my career! For the moment, I was not sure." Richard excused himself and I was left with my thoughts. "It was too early to decide."

The clock struck eight the next morning as Richard knocked on my door. We left the cottage together. The Prime Minister was expecting us at nine. It was a clear warm day and we had enough time. So we decided to take a walk. The people we met on the streets greeted us very warmly. One had a feeling of being among friends. I did not notice any sign of haste or aggression. In fact I sensed no negative emotions; an aura of contentment filled the space. Calmness and peacefulness made time stand still. One could say I was in the midst of what could be called "perfect harmony". Children playing, green trees and flowers blossoming everywhere; people laughing whilst going on with their chores. Didn't see any sign of "poverty" or unhappiness. Neither was this thing about wanting to reach somewhere in a hurry, rather they seemed to take their time.

Productivity and efficiency seemed not to matter. Profit margins had no real meaning, and time wasn't a measuring instrument. No hustle and bustle, no traffic problems. I understood now why Indira was disturbed by the hectic life in New York. There were times when she sought sanctuary in quite places.

Richard must have noticed my fascinated expression. 'The truth is everywhere around us, in the stones, in the forest, in the rivers, in the seasons. Only the courageous ones discover it.'

I nodded even if I didn't understand what he really meant.

The Prime Minister's official residence was a two-storey building, with very colorful ornaments painted on the outer and inner walls. The wooden front gate was decorated with deities. The doors were each about two meters high and massive. One could imagine in the olden days them being a source of defense.

The gate was manned by a guard who greeted us cordially. A wooden baton was hanging down from his shoulders. Opening the doors for us, we stepped into the courtyard. The grounds within the walls were plastered with sandstone, material, I myself have seen hereabouts. The entire complex looked harmonious. I realized again, "One doesn't need to be extravagant to lead a peaceful life. In fact, the last two days I witness this fact every moment.

The courtyard had a small bamboo garden. Between the plants were paths, which lead to the entrance of the building. We walked up to the front entrance. The front doors were closed. The red, wooden inner doors were decorated with holy figures. They were quite heavy, but we managed to open them ourselves. Going in, we stood in a small room with one window to the east, where the morning sun shone in. The rays brought the ceramic tiles on the floor, and the red-brick walls, to life. The fiery colors ignited the whole room and brought warmth in.

It was obviously a kind of reception. The clerk at the front desk seemed to have expecting us. He rang a clarion bell and came forward from behind his desk to welcome us, his palms clasped to his heart. He then ushered us into a study, where I saw the Prime Minister working at his desk. He raised his head as we entered the room. Placing his pen on the table he walked over extending his hand to us. I took his very hearty handshake. Mr. Champa Norbu was a man of medium size, with a short haircut, and dressed in what looked like traditional Tibetan dress. I liked him immediately.

'Ah, Dr. Cane, it's a pleasure to have you here. I hope you enjoyed the festival yesterday!'

'Thank you, Mr. Prime Minister, for welcoming me. I enjoyed it very much.'

His smile reminded me of a wise man and not that of a politician. 'I'm very pleased to hear that. I hope you rested well and everything was to your expectations, indeed after the long and tiring trip.'

'Yes sir. I can't remember having such a good night's sleep. I'm very thankful for your hospitality. It is a pleasure and an honor to meet you.'

'I'm very eager to get to know you. Richard has spoken very highly of you, and I have high respect for Richard's advice. The more the reason I'm very happy you having accepted this assignment, despite the dangerous and difficult journey to Keajara.' He nodded again to emphasize his thankfulness. I was impressed by his honest appreciation.

'I hope you will learn more about our culture and our people during your stay. Ours is in some ways a different world and in some ways it is not. To understand our way of living one requires an open heart.'

There was silence after him saying this, as if wanting to emphasize on those last two words.

'Experience speaks a different language. Awareness is the beginning of understanding. I hope your journey to us is the answer for our striving to become an independent and free nation. We believe it is important to safeguard our culture. We hope, one day to live peacefully without fear.'

'I understand Mr. Prime Minister,' I said.

'And just maybe we can help the world one day.'

'I don't quite understand Sir?' I asked.

'Dharma offers answer for many of the problems we face in the world today. We as humans have many fears in life, the main reason for us to act aggressively. Dharma has helped us in Keajara.'

'But many in the world have their own religion. They would rather turn to their own,' I replied.

'Of course and that should be so. But just maybe we can help when asked.'

'You mean as an addition.'

'Yes of course. You see Dharma is not a religion. The many temples and pagodas give the impression that it is so. The existence of Holy Scriptures and prayer wheels gives the impression that we follow rules, duties and underlying sanctions. In truth this is not so. Dharma is about us taking our lives in our hands and finding our path in life to achieve happiness, without wanting to hurt others.'

'I think I understand. You speak of taking responsibility for one's actions. That we mold our destiny.'

The Prime Minister looked at Richard and said, 'I see now why Richard speaks highly of you!'

Richard added, 'Dharma is everywhere. It is like the air we breathe; only we have different names for it. Some of us call it religion; others call it science or nature. The truth is, it is this and much more.'

The Prime Minister 'Without Dharma, it would be like a river without water. We will dry up.' He paused, his expression changed, it became sad. 'This has happened in Tibet, and it is our hope that it does not repeat here.'

It was very clear to me that he and his people have invested trust in us to help them secure their freedom; to be recognized as a free nation, among all free nations, an independent country, to live according to their culture and their way of life.

'To help you to find your answers,' he continued, 'we have made some preparations. You shall be meeting some important persons. Through them, we hope you will be able to see the light above the clouds, and more importantly to allow it to guide you.'

'Sir, I'm very grateful for your assistance.'

Subsequently we spoke on various matters concerning the application process. I was able to give him a first-hand briefing on our talks with the UN Ambassadors. He listened very attentively. The meeting ended after us planning the next steps.

I noticed during our meeting that Richard had been silent, a little tense even. As we walked down the road his countenance began to relax. So I did not prod on the reason for the moment. He proposed us to have lunch at his cottage. I had been curious to see how and where he lived. After a short walk we arrived at his house. It had a small garden, and wasn't much bigger than Indira's. To be honest I was surprised to see his garden so well kept. I remember the plants in his office, his attempts to keep some sort of greenery in his surroundings always proofed futile. The problem was one plant after another faded away into dust. The solution was actually very simply. Water! Somehow this fact slipped him. The more the reason I had difficulty imagining him as a gardener. He must have noticed my astonishment. He almost laughed when he said, 'I have a gardener and housekeeper.'

Entering his cottage however I was reminded me of his office at Harvard, with books and papers lying everywhere. It was as if he had turned his office into his home. The only thing missing was the smell of cigar. Looking at the carefully built-up piles of books, I concluded that the housekeeper was doing her best to bring some kind order into chaos.

We found lunch waiting in the dining room. Richard introduced me to one of the traditional dishes of Keajara; Tibetan bread with random balep. We also found noodle soup and spiced potatoes, all very delicious. As we were enjoying lunch, we spoke of our meeting with the Prime Minister. It was then when Richard spoke of what was on his mind.

'I have to speak of something with you Roger.'

'Of course.'

'It is about our timeline. We have been having reports that the PSB is very close to finding out about our activities and about Keajara.'

'You wish me to expedite.'

He nodded.

'I understand. I will do my best.'

'Thank you.'

He went on to tell me of the programme planned during my stay.

'I know you've had some discussions with Indira about Dharma. She has excellent knowledge. We have also arranged a few meetings with the High Lama of Keajara, and with the "Librarian" for you to have a deeper understanding. They are Living Buddhas. It means they are Enlightened Beings. They abide in total equanimity at all times.'

I nodded, although not really knowing what it meant. But the words "Living Buddhas" made me feel nervous.

Richard noticed it. 'Don't be worried,' he said. 'They are beings of great compassion, all will be well. You'll do fine. The High Lama will be giving you an insight into Dharma. He helped me to understand when I first arrived here. Your first meeting is set for tomorrow.'

I seemed not to have a choice, and submitted to fate.

'After your meetings with him you will be traveling to Ngari to meet the "Librarian". It is a small village a few hours' drive from here. Ananda will be escorting you there. The Librarian will be taking you through the safely kept treasures of Keajara. These treasures include unique artifacts, many of which are not known to the world.

141

Apart from that you will learn their correlation to Dharma and their historical value. After this it is planned for you to return to Keajara City before returning to New York. We hope by then you will have an understanding of the importance of this heritage and why it has to be preserved. With that information you should be able to formulate Keajara's application accurately.'

I left Richard's cottage around three o'clock. As I walked back to my cottage, I was not immune to the fragrance of spring in the air. The gentle wind carrying the freshness of nature aroused in me the wish to experience more of it. I remember Richard telling me of a bus route between the villages. I decided to walk up to the market place and hoped to find a bus stop. I was lucky. A few minutes later a bus stopped and I got on.

The tour took me through various landscapes. Unlike my journey to Keajara, I was able to sit back and enjoy the beautiful scenery on the "roof top of the world; no strenuous walking". The mountains were ranging up almost into the skies, melting into the universe above, breathtaking, rocky and sandy landscape mixing together, with waterfalls and rivers surging and disappearing into forests. I began to make notes but it was difficult writing in a shaky bus on uneven roads.

"Many in New York see the Central Park as a natural habitat. What they would say to this scenery?" I wrote. "Untouched and pure, wisdom in every movement, dignity in stature!" I could not help thinking of how blind men are. Not seeing the obvious. Our existence we owe to this world. We show our thankfulness by destroying it!

These are moments when one reflects about one's life, about all the things going wrong, the unnecessary suffering on this world. I deal with it every day at work; the ignorance of men. What could one do, to alter this foolishness?

Maybe the answer is not so much thinking about what is going wrong, more so with what can be done to correct them. It is up to those of us; those who have realized this to show the way, just as it has been done all through time. Not so much to criticize but to appeal to common sense. Negative motivations have proofed futile, one needs to be a role model, a path finder.

Anyone can change. Change is the most natural process. We have all done some sort of mistakes; all of us have a burden we carry. We carry them from one lifetime to another. The understanding of one lifetime causes difficulties, ones motivation for change seems to be hopeless. On the other hand, infinite lifetimes bring about hope for self-improvement.

As the bus stopped at a village, I left it. It was a small with hardly anyone around. Encouraged by the silence and tranquility I decided to explore it. I walked up the main road, where I met some people. They greeted me with friendliness, even if they were surprised to meet me. Strolling, I heard prayer bells from an alley; being curious, I followed it. Its origin being a small monastery; coming closer I heard mantras being recited, monks singing prayers with deep voices.

It seemed to be an unassuming building. The doors were open. I entered and crossed over the threshold. Inside the courtyard I noticed novices, between five and

143

ten years old, looking at me with great interest. I made some hand signals, saying I wanted to listen to the prayers. One of them nodded, came over and led me in. Very quietly I stepped into the small hall. There were about twenty monks and some villagers. I removed my shoes, and joined in.

No one stopped me, no one asked any questions, and no one showed any discomfort. I learned later the reason for this. It is all karma. Not so much about doing good or bad; that things happen when the time has arrived, no sooner and no later and it is part of life, part of change, part of accepting the now.

The monks were holding a bell in their right hand and a figure, called the vajra, in their left hand. They were performing a variety of hand movements called the mudras. A mantra recitation was followed with a hit on a drum. I closed my eyes and allowed myself to be carried away by the harmonic rhythm. I began travel from where I was to the high mountains of the Himalayas; over the Atlantic; and finally arriving home. Where the two people I loved were, who meant everything to me in this world, and whose happiness was more important than anything else in my life. The sound of the drum filled my heart with love.

When the puja came to an end, I walked silently back to the main street, feeling rejuvenated and alive. Happiness and contentment filled my heart. How wonderful life seemed to be, how grateful I felt having able to experience this day. The villagers invited me to have dinner and I accepted. I wanted to remain in this state for as long as it takes, enjoying not only the warm weather, the wonderful company but being able to reach a state of inner peace I had not known before.

It was late when I left; it was the last bus for the day. I was the only passenger and I spent the time watching the stars. The endless of space making us look to small, so tiny. Making our problems look unimportant. For some reason I began to understand about what Einstein meant with relativity.

9

Chasing after a goose

The clerk was feeling uncomfortable these last few days. He was sure it was not paranoia. No, he was sure! Someone was watching him, someone was following him. He spoke to his friends down at the café, but no one believed him.

'You're not someone important, or a lama. You never get into any trouble. Why should anyone want to follow you?' They shrugged the idea off. They said it was only his imagination playing tricks.

Lt. Chan was also behaving very strangely to him these past few days. Somehow he couldn't lose the feeling that he was being suspected of something. The next day, he went directly to Col. Yang, upon which the Col. summoned Lt. Chan to his office.

'Well, Lt. Chan, if you don't mind, could you please explain why you're having Mr. Drogpa followed? Please spare me any denial. I might be old, but I'm certainly not blind.'

The Lt. wasn't very sure what to say first. But he knew it was no use denying it. 'Col., I have a suspicion. Information is leaking out of this office. I suspect Mr. Drogpa. Maybe he has something to with it; he being the only Tibetan in service and all.'

Col. Yang became alert. 'What information and to whom?' he asked very sternly.

The Lt. knew he had to be very careful now or he would find himself in "big trouble"; disobeying a direct order has grave consequences in the PSB. 'Well Sir, it has to do with the open question.'

'What open question?' asked the Col. a little irritated.

He answered very reluctantly, 'We still don't have any concrete evidence; it is my duty as a responsible PSB officer to eliminate any doubt about its existence.'

'Speak up man, what are you getting at?' commanded the Col. impatiently.

'Sir, I'm speaking of the "Land of Paradise"!' he said adamantly. 'About its possible existence. I know you refuse to believe it, but the Tibetans do. The more reason for us to look into it! We have to use our resources to confirm of its non-existence.'

To his astonishment the Col. smiled and said, 'Lt. Chan, you're obviously a very capable officer. I think it's only fair for me to allow you to investigate this matter. I myself have not been successful. Needless to say it would be a major career boost for you, eh Lt.?'

'Sir, ehm... I mean it is my duty,' he said in a milder tone and a little confused.

'Nevertheless I'm giving you the permission to enhance your efforts.'

Although surprised, the Lt. said nothing; whatever the reason might be, he was happy to have the official go from his superior officer. That was all he needed. 'Thank you, sir.'

He was about to leave the room, when the Col. said, 'Please leave poor Mr. Drogpa alone, would you, and brief me every day on your progress.'

On the way to his office he thought to himself, "He wishes to benefit from my hard work, perhaps an early retirement, a better post in Peking or even a promotion. The old scoundrel!"

After the Lt. left, the Col. said, 'Mr. Drogpa, please ask the Sgt. to come in.'

'Yes Sir.'

A few moments later the Sgt. entered the room.

'Sgt., our friend has to be watched carefully. Make sure he is put under observation and also make sure that the Shadow is not successful.'

'Yes Sir!'

The Col. grabbed to his unregistered hand phone and pressed the number "1".

A voice said 'Yes' at the other end.

The Col. replied, 'Stormy weather coming your way.'

The voice replied, 'I understand', and hung up.

The Col. leant back in his chair with a worried expression.

10

Allow light to enter

The following morning although eager I was a little nervous to meet the High Lama. To tell the truth, I wasn't really able to sleep that night. Punctually, at eight, a young man, hardly in his twenties, knocked on my door; tall and thin, dressed in the traditional clothing of a monk. With a smile and hands clasped to the heart, he said, 'Good morning, sir. If you're ready, may I bring you to the High Lama, the Venerable Geshe Shariputra?'

According to Richard, the High Lama is an Enlightened Being. I wasn't very certain what that meant and it didn't help reduce my nervousness. With quick steps we left towards the monastery. I am not sure what it was, my eagerness or my nervousness which made me walk quickly. But soon I was out of breath. I had obviously forgotten the high altitude. It made me to become breathless. But for some reason the closer we came to the monastery, the calmer I was. Entering the front gates we reached an open space, a very large and spacious garden. To my astonishment it seemed to be as large as the north end of Central Park. In the distance was a large Bodhi tree, somewhere in the center. It looked very old.

From the looks of it, we were on the way to its direction. I was wondering how a tree such as this could grow at such an altitude. On the way I discovered other sorts of trees and even roses. There were many varieties; red, white and light pink ones. "How is this possible?" still perplexed. The monk must have noticed my bewilderment; he just smiled, not offering an answer. As we walked further, we passed other sorts of trees and flowers. It was a pleasant, simply breathtaking!

We passed a large pond with a number of small and large streams running in various directions. It was beautiful sight; made me stop for a moment. A deep breath inhaling the magical surroundings of this place, speechless I stood there, enjoying the fresh uniqueness of this place. Since walking into the garden, I noticed how I had become more focused. Doubts seemed to disappear, and my heart became lighter.

"How so? What was it about this place which seems to transcend me into a harmonious state of mind?"

The young monk asked to wait there. Taking a seat at a nearby bench, I asked him how he is called. I learned that he was known was Ananda. He spoke very fluently in English. I asked him how this; he replied, 'The children learn it in school,' as if it was a normal thing.

A moment later, a chubby looking older monk appeared. He asked us in a gentle voice to follow him. He walked towards the center of the garden. It took us, all in all, about twenty minutes to reach the Bodhi tree. As we slowly approached the tree, I noticed a venerable-looking person under it sitting in the vajra posture, crossed legged on a bamboo mat on the ground. There was something about him, something holy. He raised his head as we approached him and smiled at us. He gestured to me to sit down on a chair nearby. I greeted him and thanked him by clasping my hands to my heart and bowing my head. Ananda and the older monk walked away silently.

The High Lama was a man of small stature. "Probably no taller than one and a half meters, and very thin," I thought. He seemed to be in his late eighties, but his eyes were sharp and awake. "I have not yet seen a person such as him in my life." Everything about him seemed to be out of this world, eternal. His posture, his smile, his gestures, seemed to be the personification of perfection, of truth, of wisdom, of compassion. His smile reminded me of a smile I had seen before, full of serenity; it was the smile of a Buddha. Suddenly it occurred to me that he was no normal human being! My heart took a leap.

'How are you today?' He spoke with a calm and soft voice.

'I'm doing very well, your holiness, thank you,' I answered as if it was the most normal thing to address him with "his holiness".

He tilted his head to one side and examined me. It made me a little nervous. 'I heard you've come here to help us?' he said without any doubts in his voice.

'I hope I may be of help. But I'm not alone,' I added quickly, a little unsure even. 'We are all committed to work for Keajara's independence. I for my part shall do my very best for us to succeed.'

'I am sure you will. Thank you,' he said. He gazed into the garden as if he was far away. I waited anxiously, wanting to ask him questions. 'You know, Dr. Cane,' he said, 'we humans are all children playing an adults' game.' He went on slowly, 'Only those who mature succeed, but many of us spend our lives just trying.'

'I'm not sure, your holiness, if I understand,' I said, not really sure what to say.

He smiled saying, 'To grow and mature one needs a safe and stable environment, one needs a sanctuary.'

To show that I understood, I nodded.

'So you see, we aren't asking for much, just a place where we can live peacefully without any disturbances and according to our beliefs and culture.' The lama took a deep breath and looked at me. It was a deep and exploring gaze, as if he was searching for something in me. I didn't know what I was supposed to do, so I stayed silent and waited. After a long pause he said, 'It is important for the world to know that we intend to achieve this peacefully. Ours is a forgiving and compassionate path.'

I thought this was my cue. 'The world is aware of the patience and wisdom the Tibetan people have shown in light of their plight. I'm sure the world doesn't assume otherwise. I am also certain the world knows the people of Keajara would not act immaturely. Your perseverance in preparing for the application as a member of the UN proves this.'

He was absorbed in his thoughts and I didn't know if he was listening to my words. He added in a very sad tone, 'There is so much suffering in this world. Violence leads to more violence. It is our responsibility to help and not to judge. Only compassion can lead us to salvation.'

I thought about what I should say. Hearing his words I felt the obligation to explain why people act as they do in the "conventional world", as Indira calls it. 'I believe

152

we are all on the path of learning. We continue learning until we reach a state of no more learning,' as Richard once said. I thought it was a suitable answer. 'And so we shall continue to make mistakes,' I added, 'and we shall continue to learn from them.'

'You're right, of course.'

Hearing this I assumed it to be the right moment for me to mention my purpose meeting him. 'Richard arranged for me to meet you. He believed through this meeting I could understand Dharma better. I've only had a brief encounter with it until now. What I have heard of it has inspired me. My visit today is not only a professional one; it also has a personal touch.'

The High Lama smiled again. In the distance Ananda asked with a hand signal if he could approach. The young man then served his master tea. He looked at me and asked if I would also like a cup. I nodded and he poured me a cup of delicious herbal tea, and left as quietly as he had come. The lama took a careful sip of the hot tea and I followed his example. It was a fruity mixture of various herbs and was surprisingly sweet. "Amazing," I thought, "how different tea can taste."

The High Lama looked up from his tea cup and proceeded thoughtfully, 'My experience has been that the heart plays an important part in our choices in life. Your personal interest is the key to the answers you seek in life. I hope I shall be of help in answering some of the questions you have.'

I wasn't yet ready to ask any specific questions. I waited for him to go on. He took another sip from his tea cup before continuing.

'Let me begin by pointing out the most important factors in Dharma which I believe we should speak about. They provide the foundation. They are karma, rebirth, masculine and feminine energy, the very subtle mind, matter, time, space, virtuous and non-virtuous actions, and emptiness.'

I nodded not really knowing what all these factors meant. "I somehow have gotten into this habit lately. I should stop nodding when I don't understand anything".

'Let's begin with karma. It's not only a natural law prevailing time and space, but also a phenomenon which embodies all the happenings around us. Karma is about actions and reactions. Every action has a reaction. When you roll a ball it inevitably causes some sort of reaction, it will either continue to roll until it comes into contact with an obstacle or lose momentum and stop. Is that not so?'

I nodded again.

'It's the same with our thoughts. As soon as we act, as soon as we think, we create room for a certain reaction. Through every single one of our actions we create karmic eventualities, which materialize as reactions when the time arrives.'

I offered, 'A reaction is something we experience when we act. It's also known as the law of causality. Causality is the relation between a first and second event, this being the cause and the effect. The second event is understood as a mental or physical consequence of the first event, is it not so?'

'Yes,' said the High Lama. 'All actions create eventualities in time and space. This is later experienced as reactions. But not only that, it's far more complex. Our actions are created in a certain dimension, which under-lies time, space, conventions, emotions, thoughts and so forth. The reactions will happen in a similar environment.'

As the High Lama was explaining, I remembered Richard telling me, '"Geshe" is a title given to a person who has achieved higher realizations. And they are respectfully addressed as "Geshe-La".'

So I asked him, 'Your holiness, may I address you as Geshe-La?'

'Of course you may.'

I picked up the conversation where Geshe-La left off by asking, 'Are these reactions saved somewhere?'

'They are, as you put it "saved" as what we call the "karmic seed". When a "karmic seed" ripens, an experi-ence is revealed! For someone to experience something one requires a body, the capability to comprehend, to feel, time and space. All these aspects are saved in the "karmic seed".'

I remembered reading about similar topics in a physics magazine, 'These seeds, are they what the physi-cists call a "quantum field"?' The moment I asked him this question it occurred to me that he might not know what I meant by a "quantum field".

But surprisingly he nodded and said, 'I see you're quick, Dr. Cane. Yes, you can compare it to a quantum field. Karma engulfs all facets of life. It's the one which ensures that all our actions, be they mental or physical, receive the appropriate reactions. It's that which acts as a mirror to our actions.'

I interrupted him politely by asking, 'Are you saying it's the instance which judges our actions?'

'No. It's not an "instance", just as the waves rushing to the shores are not. They are just waves which, when influenced, create a certain reaction.'

'So, karma is a natural law which sees to it that any action has an equal and opposite reaction.'

Geshe-La smiled. 'Yes, one could see it that way, but it's more. Karma is not only a law, which ensures that no action goes unanswered, but it holds the key to the creation of matter and with that, time and space. The collective "karmic seeds" of the infinite sentient beings holds enormous power.'

'It is then the most powerful phenomenon existing, and it possesses no consciousness?' I asked.

He did not directly answer me, but he said, 'No, it's not the concept of an almighty God. It can be described as a "keeper and executer".'

Not being certain if I had understood completely, but at the same time being contented for the moment of having an idea of what karma could be, I protruded no more. "Come time, come answer," I thought.

'Karma is change and change is inevitable. We are aware of it, but we fail to accept it. Most of our daily actions are based on assumptions and experiences we have learned during our childhood. We live in the past.' He smiled. 'So we continue to act like children. There is a very old saying in Tamil Nadu; "What you are at the age of five, you will be when you become fifty". Modern medicine has proven that the human brain grows only until the age of five. I only hope our mental development doesn't stop there.' He gave a little laugh. "A joke of wisdom, perhaps." Sipping from his tea, he gave me the opportunity to ask a question.

Reflecting on his words, a question arose in my mind. 'But we're able to change,' I stated. 'If not, it would not be possible for us to attain enlightenment. Correct? How could we develop without change in our lives?'

'Yes, we change when we allow change to happen. But most of the time we fear change due to the fear of the unknown. We therefore hold on to what we have. The more we hold on to things, the more mental barriers we build, the more fear we create in us. And before we know it, we are trapped within these barriers or walls.'

'But when we die, we do not have any other choice but to leave these things behind; things we so much treasure,' I noted.

'It is a point of time we leave everything behind.' He paused and took a deep breath before continuing, 'In the course of infinite time, there have been infinite barriers. We die and we are born again. We have taken infinite rebirths, and all those barriers of past lives are no more important.'

'Only through overcoming these barriers is one able to grow.'

'One has to learn to let go, to be free, and only by being free can one move forward. To be able to learn, one needs not only discipline, but also courage.'

'But our fear of losing is a hindrance. Is it created by a mind called the self-grasping mind? Is it the root cause of our fear of loss?' I said.

'Excellent!' he complimented. 'I see we will not need to spend much time together.'

'No, no, please! I still have much to learn.'

'Humbleness is the gateway to holiness.' The High Lama smiled and looked up in the sky. 'We know that there are things, which we are not able to see, but they exist. Oxygen and other gases, for example, were discovered by those who were willing to look beyond that which was apparent. Likewise there exist other phenomena, which have not yet been discovered, such as other earth-like planets. Likewise there are uncountable other worlds.'

Before I could say something, the older monk approached us, bent and whispered something to Geshe-La.

Geshe-La nodded and turned to me. 'I was informed we will be having lunch in an hour,' he said laughingly. 'Here too we are ruled by time!'

I couldn't help a smile.

There was a moment's silence before he proceeded. 'One of the phenomena our conventional senses don't perceive is the "very subtle mind". The very subtle mind, our real self, is as much dependent on karma as karma is dependent on the very subtle mind'. He remained silent before stressing, 'All that we see, touch or feel in the conventional world is in reality not enduring, it is perishable. Take this pebble, for example.' He picked up one of the light-colored stones from the ground before him. 'Today it's a pebble. In a few years it will turn into earth or into dust, or even into something we can breathe in. Why so?'

'Due to change, we live in a world which constantly changes.'

'Exactly!' said Geshe-La.

'But why does this not apply to the mind? Does it also not mean that in the end even the very subtle mind underlies this law?'

'A very good question! According to the teachings of historical Buddha Shakyamuni, it's written, "All Phenomena are empty of inherent existence". It means there are no exceptions. So to answer your question, yes, even the very subtle mind underlies this law.'

'Does that mean our "true self" does not exist, in the end?' I asked.

'No, it does not mean that. It means that all phenomena are subjected to change. Allow me to explain. Matter can be dismantled into the smallest elements it is made of. Karma dismantles it into its core and assembles everything again into something else. The law of karma dictates these happenings. Our actions are the cause to all reactions hence change is driven by karma. The mind though the master of all things, is also subjected to change. But at the same time it is the mind which is the source to all changes. The mind although being the source is also the one to experience changes. The only difference is that the mind cannot be dismantled into its core, because it is the core.'

'Interesting, so when you say the mind underlies the laws of change, you mean that it has the potential to learn and develop.'

'Yes,' he said with a wide grin on his face.

'But to learn and develop in the right direction the mind must see the correct path.'

'Correct again,' said Geshe-La.

'So all its actions, be it virtuous or non-virtuous serve in the end only one purpose, for the mind to understand what is happening and to liberate itself; is that so?' I asked a little uncertainly.

'Very well put!' said Geshe-La apparently happy at my summary.

In that moment it felt as if the twilight cleared, as if the shadow hovering over my mind was lifted and the stardust of yesteryears disappeared.

'Everything is subjected to change.' The lama raised his right arm and formed a circle with his thumb and forefinger, 'Modern physics has proven mathematically, that at the end of the chain called matter is nothing, zero.' He continued still holding the "zero". 'Living beings are known as sentient beings because they are conscious of their existence. Humans are only a small part of this family. As sentient beings we possess the capability to perceive directly the true nature of matter.'

'To perceive this state of "zero"?'

'Yes, but due to the barriers we build, we don't have access this capability. The barriers hinder us from perceiving things as they truly are, just as the clouds hinder us from seeing a clear sky.'

'You are saying matter does not really exist.'

Geshe-La's head was bent in a meditative state but he did not respond.

'Or do you mean that matter does not really have an existence, because it only appears to be solid although it oscillates, and because there is nothing inside when you dismantle it to the core?'

He tilted his head to the right and spoke. 'The world is controlled by vibrations. Everything is built on vibrations.'

'How do you mean, vibrations? Why "vibrations"?'

'It's only logical. Behind a thought is an emotion, also known as a motivation. Emotions create thoughts and thoughts create actions. At the same time, emotion is an energy form which creates vibrations. Every sentient being is a slave to its emotions. Even the ultimate aim, which is universal compassion, is an emotion.'

'How does that explain the fact that matter is unsubstantial at its core?' I asked.

Geshe-La stretched his arm to pick up a piece of stick, and began to sketch something on the ground.

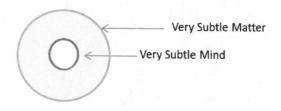

'Assume for example the circle in the middle being the very subtle mind; the circle surrounding would be very subtle matter. The very subtle matter has no substance, it is void like space, but it is not the space which we know. The surrounding space called matter is compressed by two forces. These forces are known as the masculine and feminine forces. Their nature is to create equilibrium. The moment the karmic seed reaches its "expiry date", this very subtle matter will also cease to exist.'

'And this very subtle matter is nothing else then vibrations caused by our emotions?'

'Yes.'

'And matter is nothing else but compressed vibrations!?' I asked, astonished by the revelation.

'Yes,' he said simply as if it was the most natural thing in the world.

'Geshe-La, your example speaks of an individual karma and not of the collective karma.'

'Yes, one needs only to multiply the effect,' he said as he began again to sketch something on the ground.

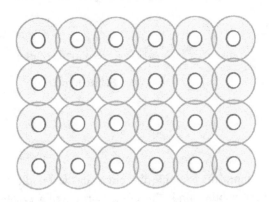

'It's important that you understand this simple example. The correlations are much more complex and multi-dimensional. Imagine this being the collection of all the existing very subtle minds and very subtle matter for a single town. It builds the collective potential of karmic events of the persons living in this small town. The persons living there will experience the karmic outcomes. As soon as the karmic seed ceases to exist, it will be replaced with a new one. The ripening continues without pause, which means that we continue to have new experiences.'

Looking at the sketch, it occurred to me, 'This is why everything is connected; everything exists in dependence with everything else. Nothing is really independent; we are all connected by a strange bond, throughout time and space.'

'That is correct. Our personal actions are always reciprocal to the thoughts of others. We act always in concurrence with the actions of others. Our thoughts and emotions are intertwined. We therefore don't experience events independent of others.'

'A change in one's life is therefore triggered by both the individual and collective karma, is that so?'

'Yes, that is so. There are times, for example, when two people live together for a long time and suddenly separate; there are those who meet only for a blink of a second. All this has to do with the collective and individual karma.'

'I understand.' After a pause, I added, 'It all makes sense.'

'All phenomena are subjected to change,' he said. 'Even if a phenomenon appears to look the same, it is actually not. We change every nanosecond, every nanosecond a seed ripens. Already in the next second you're not the same person any more. Your cells, your breath and blood, your thoughts and feelings have changed. Our body is not the solid and massive structure it appears to be.'

'Why then do we perceive matter as real?'

'When you grab your teacup, you would think it to be real. You even believe it to be inherent existence, meaning that the tea cup exists independent. Everyone stepping past would see it and call it a tea cup. But when I break it, you probably wouldn't call it a "tea cup" any more, right? Maybe you would think "broken teacup" instead.' He laughed so infectiously that I had to laugh too. 'But if strangers were to pass by, would they speak of a tea cup or rather of broken pieces?' He looked at me with a curious expression.

'Broken pieces!' I admitted.

'Hah, you see. Now, suddenly, the broken pieces seem to have an inherent existence, like the teacup did before.'

'The tea cup has disappeared, although the broken pieces are still lying on the floor in front of us,' I said.

'This over time will become something else, earth, dust, air, mud, water and other things. It simply ceases to exist.'

'And likewise, let's say a bird comes along, it wouldn't call it broken pieces. A bird would perceive it as a completely different object. So in short, it depends on the observer, it's a matter of opinion. That is what we call matter.'

I took a deep breath, thinking, "Wow! I hadn't seen it that way."

The Lama closed his eyes, probably to give me some time to reflect on what he had said.

When he opened his eyes again, he spoke with an almost affectionate smile, 'The core of what we are, our real home, the true creator of all that we perceive in our endless lives, is our very subtle mind; our true self!'

With a serene expression that stressed the importance of this revelation, he raised his left forefinger and carried on, 'But remember, nothing is free of change! Change is the only constant in life. This aspect of life is also known as "empty of inherent existence".'

The Venerable One paused and I took the opportunity to ask, 'Does that mean that only the very subtle mind really exists?'

'Everything exists, at the same time everything underlies the law of karma or change.'

"He is not really answering my question," I thought. Somehow he seemed to perceive my objection. '"Existence" is a conventional idea dependent on time and space,' he went on. 'The very subtle mind is far more than that. It has to do with "being" independent of time and space and not only "existing" within time and space.'

'If the very subtle mind is independent of conventionalities, how does it experience suffering?'

'Just as a parent would feel the pain of his child,' the High Lama replied.

'I'm not sure if I really understand the allegory,' I said, raising my eyebrow.

'The very gross mind is an extension of the very subtle mind. They are not separable. This mind is subjected to conventions hence it experiences Samsara. Thus every experience encountered by the very gross mind is also perceived by the very subtle mind. Likewise a child is an extension of his parents. The joys and sufferings of a child are also felt by the parent.'

'I see.'

'But the important thing about the very subtle mind is its capability to experience clarity, to experience the state of bliss. This capability allows it to understand and develop wisdom. Wisdom which is required to realize the futility of living in Samsara, where everything only keeps repeating, the cycle of suffering never ending.' There was sadness in his voice but there was also compassion. 'Is this what we want, to live in an endless and painful cycle?' he asked, looking up.

'It has more to do with not knowing or not wanting to know then it has to do with seeking for salvation.'

He added, 'Yes, and maybe a time will come, a realization that this life, this cycle is unnecessary; we will seek wisdom, we will look for salvation.'

'It is then we seek liberation, it is then we seek Buddhahood.'

'Through reaching out to the very subtle mind, it is transcendent and independent of conventions; to help us achieve liberation from Samsara.' He waited for me to finish taking my notes before carrying on, 'Impure thoughts; thoughts which have the purpose of selfishness create negative karma. Pure thoughts which encourage one to act for the benefit of others and create positive karma. We are mostly preoccupied with negative thoughts. When we analyze our thoughts during the day, we seldom have thoughts of compassion. They are

166

mainly thoughts of self-preservation, resulting then in actions which fulfill these thoughts. So the cycle keeps repeating day in day out, creating negative karma. Very few of us take the time to invest in spiritual reflection, which is the seed for pure thoughts. If only we would understand karma correctly, it would help us to evaluate our past actions. It allows us to create positive actions.'

'Are just positive actions sufficient to achieve liberation?' I asked.

'Positive actions are just the beginning. If not cultivated, it too perishes. It requires spiritual motivation and practice to achieve liberation!'

The realization came to me, 'So the only way to break free from the cycle of uncontrolled rebirth is to practice the correct spiritual path.'

Geshe-La nodded.

I felt how doubts in me melted away, and how things began to make sense, and why things happen the way they happen. At the same time, I was asking myself again and again, "How could I have missed this, how could people miss this?", but it is only natural. We are blinded by the curtain of illusion.

With an open heart, the curtain of egoism falls away and allows you to take a look at the mysteries of life. The answers are everywhere, in the cycle of the seasons, the ever-flowing river, in the whispers of the wind. But for one to understand one has to be ready for this knowledge. One needs the spiritual strength and the spiritual depth to understand this wisdom. Only an open heart can show one the way. For those who have left the road of "seeking" behind them and arrived at the destination of "inner peace", to them wisdom would be revealed.

The older monk approached us again. It was noon. The sun was shining with all its might, lighting the blue sky above us. "Yes," I thought, "wonder exists everywhere."

It was time for lunch. Geshe-La left with a calm and soft bow.

Ananda came forward and asked me to follow him. We walked side by side in silence. We entered a building which wasn't adjoined to the monastery; it stood alone in the midst of trees and greenery. Within I saw other lamas; all sitting crossed legged, on bamboo mat laid on the floor. In rows all waiting for lunch. I joined them. Soon afterwards lunch was served, eaten in silence. After which Ananda asked if I would like to take a walk. We had time. I enjoyed the walk. No one spoke. There seemed to be no need!

I'm not sure how long we were walking thus, enjoying the scenery and one's own thoughts, being in peace with oneself and with the world. All was as it should be.

We met Geshe-La later, at the same place. Seated, he said, 'Let's now turn our attention to the holy object, the very subtle mind. When one speaks of the mind in Buddhism or in Hinduism, one speaks of a holy object. In the West one calls it the soul. The mind, however, is much more complex. It is the core of intelligence.'

'You are saying that the brain is not it?' I asked.

'It is a complex machine, but no, only the mind possesses the capability to "think".'

'The western world would not agree.'

'Of course not, but it is not my problem.' He paused a moment, 'Where was I? Ah yes, the mind. It has various states of existence, beginning from the very subtle mind and ending at the very gross mind. The nature of the very subtle mind, as I have already mentioned, is clarity.'

'So one could say it has the ability to understand or to process information, and derive a conclusion based on the information provided?' I asked as he paused for a moment.

'Yes, Dr. Cane. But the very subtle mind, being a holy object, naturally has other capabilities. It has the ability to create matter, time and space. It has the capability to achieve the ultimate stage of balance called enlightenment, and the ability to identify the ultimate nature of all phenomena through the "direct realization of emptiness", also known as "the opening of the third eye".'

'The method for achieving this is through deep meditation, correct motivation, correct thinking and correct actions, I have been told.'

'Naturally. If we observe the universe carefully, we can conclude that there are two sides which always try to reach a balance. These two sides can be called "forces" or "polarities". They are responsible for creating a balance. They have many names, they are called positive/negative, the magnetic poles, good/bad, right/wrong, left/right, up/down, push/pull such as gravity, the binary one and zero, and so on.'

'Just as the continuous creation of cause and effect is due to imbalance and dualities,' I added.

'Very sharp!' he commented with great contentment. 'Only through reaching the final state of balance, which

169

is Buddhahood, will one be able to stop all dualities. Karma is a self-regulatory system and has one important function, to act as a mirror. To help us witness the effects of our actions, to understand the duality of things and to acknowledge that this is nothing else but a war, which is raging within us, a war between egoism and altruism.'

'You mentioned karma works within the framework of the two forces and emptiness. What are these two forces?' I asked.

'They are known as the masculine and feminine energy forces.' He then rose from his sitting position and walked up to a maple tree not far away. I followed him. 'The mind,' he continued, 'is timeless, existing from beginningless times. Sentient beings have created infinite number of karmic seeds. It can only be broken when one uses karma as a helping instrument to liberate oneself.'

'We believe in our existence in samsara,' I said, 'but the truth is that our true self, the very subtle mind, does not require time and space as it exists independent of these phenomena.'

Geshe-La nodded but remained quiet, whereupon I took the opportunity to ask him something I had wanted to know. 'Does the very subtle mind really travel from one life to another, or is it stationary, with life arising and vanishing around it?'

Geshe-La did not answer immediately. He remained silent for quite some time before saying, 'The mind is stationary. Nothing is really mobile, matter arises and perishes. One should not confuse both entities.'

'I'm not sure if I understand.'

'Matter has two important characteristics. It has a void core and it is interconnected with time and space. Both these aspects make matter formable and stretchable. The object that initiates such activities is the karmic seed. It triggers a process, just like a stone thrown into a pond which creates ripples in all directions. But they are no more than ripples caused by pressure. The pond is the source from which something seemingly solid arises.'

"A very good example!" I thought, asking, 'This pond you speak of, is this the "voidness"?'

He gave me an affirmative nod. 'So, when one speaks of moving, it has nothing to do with an object traveling from A to B, but rather with the formation of new "ripples" from one split second to another. The ripples will continue to form; as long as the karmic seeds are available. The process ends when no karmic seeds are available for a certain chain. A new process will then begin. So you see nothing really exists!'

Another thought came to my mind. 'What is the core of the very subtle mind?'

Geshe-La smiled, he gazed into the distance. He looked into the sky above him and after a few seconds he answered with a mysterious smile, 'Everything and nothing.' He said no more. But strangely, I understood!

We continued our walk towards the small pond a few meters away. 'All thoughts arise through the mind. All actions have their origin in a thought. The reactions are "saved" as karmic seeds. All worlds are a result of karmic effects and these effects have their origin in an action. It's safe to say that all phenomena have their origin in the very subtle mind. That includes time and space.'

Of course, the creator and his creation are interconnected! The infinite minds, all interconnected, giving birth to the unlimited potential of future actions. They not only build a combined force, but also a network through which communication is possible. Information is accessible to all those who have managed to achieve enlightenment. Making them all knowing!

Geshe-La continued, 'Like all things in nature, every phenomenon is subjected to change. We witness this everywhere. For instance, stars arise and collapse, and they turn into other phenomena such as black holes, which in turn deform matter into more subtle forms. Stars don't arise and collapse on their own, this happens in dependence of other forces. Take the weather as an example; it's a complicated cycle. It depends on so many factors such as air pressure, warmth, the time of the year, the vegetation, the activities of human beings, etc.'

'It's a good way to elaborate the correlations existing in the universe,' I said.

He explained further, 'It is an universal law. Nothing exists inherently; nothing exists on its own. Everything is interdependent. The sentient beings living in all six realms are the source of all that is happening. Matter exists due to their activities; without the infinite sentient beings, there would be nothing. Rebirth and death are like everything else, a logical chain of events, just like the birth and death of a sun. Even the very subtle mind is subjected to a similar process, with one difference; the substance of this holy object does not change. The very subtle mind, being the creator, does not cease to exist. It's everlasting, but it too underlies the laws of change.'

172

'Impure thoughts,' I said, 'are those that harm others, or harm oneself. Hate, greed and attachment; these are thoughts created by anger and fear, in short through ignorance.'

'Yes.'

'Do we always experience rebirth as humans?' I asked, somehow already knowing the answer.

'No. There are six realms of rebirth, called the three higher and the three lower realms.'

'Why is it better to be born in the higher realms compared to the lower ones?' I asked.

'The conditions in the higher realms are more favorable to achieve liberation from samsara. Such births are seldom and very valuable. They offer optimal conditions to understand Dharma.'

'Are births as gods not more valuable and more infrequent?' I asked.

'Of course, but birth as humans allows us to reflect on causes and effects. One has to know about happiness and suffering, to differentiate. The human form gives this opportunity. The gods exist most of the time in a state of bliss. Therefore suffering is not very apparent in these realms.' After taking a deep breath he continued, 'In our existence as humans, we encounter happiness and suffering every day. They are very present. The moments of happiness are only a handful compared to those of suffering. But we have got used to suffering so much so we take it as something normal, a part of life. At the same time we possess the mental capability to understand and differentiate, we create solutions for problems and we try to look for ways out of a crisis. This makes us perfect candidates to strive for liberation.'

We walked silently alongside one of the streams flowing out of the pond. 'You know, Dr. Cane, in Dharma there are no evaluations, no right or wrong. One man's view has just as much true as that of another. At the same time it creates differentiation and segregation. It causes impure thoughts and actions.'

'Yes sir, I have seen this only too often in my work. The "conflict of interest", we call it.' I was thinking about the hundreds of cases I encounter in my work. 'Our world today is changing more dramatically than it did a hundred years ago. People seem more interested in making differences than they are in looking for similarities. We should strive towards living together in harmony. But how can there be peace on this world when there is little peace within us?'

'Correct!' he said, and for some reason began to speak of the very subtle mind. 'The only way to increase our communication with our very subtle mind is to remain in a state of inner peace. This is possible through meditation and contemplation on pure objects, such as "compassion for all beings". Of course the physical environment also plays an important part in helping one to achieve inner peace.'

'You mean a quieter place is easier to meditate compared to a busy one?' I asked.

'Yes. This brings us back to the point "the realms of rebirth". There are the realms of the gods, the half-gods, man, animals, hungry ghosts and hell beings. The conditions in the higher realms are more favorable than in the lower realms for achieving inner peace.'

I interrupted politely here, asking, 'Geshe-La, what are realms? Are they dimensions?'

'We tend to use various terms for the same thing. The reason, we are bound by conventions. Call it realms, worlds, dimensions or even universes, we mean, without even realizing it, the same thing. It is no more than a particular space caught in time. It is no more than a dream, a state of the mind, which assumes a specific space in time to be reality. It being a state of mind, all these realms and dimensions are able to exist parallelly. Just as we all are able to have our individual dream and we are not able to look into the dream of another person. As normal beings, we are not able to perceive what is going on next door. One needs either the correct equipment or must develop capabilities which enable one to do so,' said Geshe-La.

'That would suggest the modern medicine is correct. It speaks of the use of our cerebral capacities. It says a normal individual is only capable of using about ten per cent of his brain capacity, and the rest is not accessible.'

'The ability to access the other regions of the brain has a direct relationship with our spiritual development. What is known as "cerebral capabilities" in the modern medicine is the ability to come into contact with a higher state of understanding. When one achieves this, barriers fall away and one is able to tap on infinite amount of information. We begin to learn more and to be clear about how the world around us really exists.'

'Why do we build barriers and hinder us from accessing this information?'

'Out of fear. We fear losing what we already possess,' he answered.

'These "firewalls" might secure the existing information, but they don't guarantee progress. With time this information becomes obsolete,' I said.

'We humans are busy about "having" than we are about "being". We forget about growing. And growth means to continually learn. It's not about learning to survive in Samsara, no. It's about becoming your higher self.'

'And these barriers protect the illusionary world we live in?' I asked.

'Yes, we stop spiritual development unintentionally. One needs a free mind to grow, to tap into the areas of our brains which lie unused.'

We came to a bench, where we both sat down. 'The brain is only a tool,' he said, 'It is matter. What's relevant are our spiritual capabilities, our understanding of the workings of our very subtle mind, our direct communication with it.'

'The door to one's heart is love,' I quoted.

'Yes, that's correct. The very subtle mind is situated in the heart chakra. We are somehow instinctively aware of this. It's the source of all emotions and cognitive processes!'

'Modern science imputes the brain to be the source for cognitive activities,' I said.

He answered with a wave of his hand, implying this was nonsense. 'The brain is only a tool, a computer chip,

176

matter, created by the mind. It's a powerful tool, but nevertheless only a tool. It is the very subtle mind which understands. It has the capability to comprehend everything.'

'What do you mean when you say "spiritual development"?'

'It is about understanding Dharma and it is about understanding the very subtle mind. The wisdom of it all is you can't separate the one from the other. We unintentionally begin to understand the nature of the one entity when we explore the nature of the other entity.'

'And there's something more isn't there? It's what we call our conscience!' I added.

'Yes, our "conscience" as you put is the "universal compassion" which mixes with our very subtle mind. Like water into water. One cannot be separated from the other. It is what which acts as a compass mirroring to us our virtuous and non-virtuous actions. It is also known as "the potential to achieve enlightenment".'

'Of course, that makes sense!' I exclaimed. 'Even as normal person, we feel it, it is an emotion that everyone carries within, only we know it as "love"!'

He smiled at my reaction and nodded. 'The very subtle mind also offers solutions to our dilemmas out of the "love" it feels for us. It tries to lead us away from ignorance, to pull down the barriers. Our barriers are our ego.' He continued after a moment of silence. 'Negative thoughts create blockages within our chakras; it's like living in a city of walls. Out of fear of the unexpected events in life, one secures himself within these walls and

177

tries to survive. Only by releasing these blockages will one be able to explore other possibilities.'

'Yes, sir, but dangers might wait at the other side.'

'Yes, but change is inevitable. Fear has brought no man happiness.'

'What does one do? Courage alone is not sufficient,' I added.

'No. One always needs an objective.' He looked at me and patted my shoulder before saying, 'It's not so much about overcoming the demon around you, as it is about overcoming the demon in you. It's called fear, ignorance, insecurity.'

'Therefore one needs an aim in life, a purpose!'

'A purpose with a compass, a destination, a map, without which one can become lost.'

'So one is willing to let go when one realizes that change is necessary and is convinced about the new course!'

A kingfisher landed suddenly some three meters away. Here?! A beautiful creature! It quenched its thirst and fly away. A moment later I turned to him and said, 'All this is irrelevant, isn't it? Time will pass and we too will cease to exist. It is sad.'

'I feel no sadness, I feel compassion. I have overcome my "self-grasping mind". I abide in bliss. I abide in one-ness. I'm here and I'm everywhere. Mine is the mind pervading time and space.' I saw the warmth in his smile as he spoke, the wisdom in his gaze. I knew then I was in the presence of a Living Buddha.

He continued, 'Achieving Buddhahood not only means using 100 per cent of your cerebral capabilities, it's more than that; it's about being transcendent, achieving a state of being all-knowing and all-experienced. It is about being liberated from time and space, being present and observant. It is about encountering the ultimate inner peace and having become one with the oneness. It is about being here and everywhere at the same time, about achieving all this to enable one to help other sentient beings to achieve the same state of enlightenment, through giving and not expecting anything in return, to love unconditionally.'

I remained silent and listened carefully until the end, allowed the words to flow into my deepest self. I somehow had the feeling that everything Geshe-La was saying made sense, that it was clear and generated a blissful emotion in me.

'Dr. Cane, enlightenment is not about seeking or learning, it's about being, it's about remembering. Only those who are willing to let the curtains of ignorance fall will allow the light to come in.'

He waited somehow for me to think it through before he returned to our earlier topic. 'The karmical seeds ripen when the conditions are right. This might take place immediately or in a distant future. A being who has achieved liberation has the capability to see beyond time and space, has arrived at the point of all beginning and of all end; which is the oneness.'

Geshe-La paused here again; his eyes were smiling, he was one with everything around him, one with the universe. He raised his head and nodded to the older monk. The older monk walked away and Geshe-La remained silent until the older monk returned. In his hands were thangkas. A thangka is a painting on a cotton or silk cloth. They looked very old. He handed them to Geshe-La, who accepted them, saying, 'These thangkas are about a few hundred years old.'

He opened one of them; a wonderful painting appeared; in the middle was a human form, seated in the vajra position. He opened a notebook lying beside him, looking for something, a page revealed a similar picture.

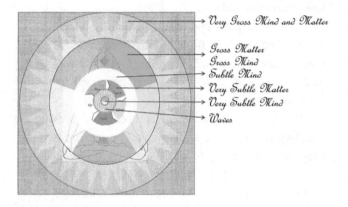

Very Gross Mind and Matter

Gross Matter
Gross Mind
Subtle Mind
Very Subtle Matter
Very Subtle Mind
Waves

'What you see here is a multidimensional view of how matter comes into being. The karmic seeds are located just above the very subtle mind. When a seed ripens it not only initiates a thought or an emotion, but also triggers the development of matter.'

With a smile he pointed to the image. 'Richard made the notes beside them.' Yes, it looked like Richard's handwriting.

'Just like a stone thrown into a pond which creates ripples,' I added.

'Exactly!' commented Geshe-La. 'The thoughts and emotions begin to expand outwards, at first very subtle, then becoming grosser. Parallel to this somewhere along the way very subtle matter begins to unfold, until it takes a form visible to our senses.'

'How can the karma of a single person create all the things around us?' I asked.

'That is not possible, Dr. Cane. But the collective karma of infinite beings is capable of doing this. For instance, you or I don't live everywhere, we are here and now. That is due to our karmic seeds. The cause for this meeting could have taken place a long time ago, or yesterday. We don't know.'

'Is this what people call "fate"?' I asked.

'I think people have many names for it, fate, destiny...' he answered. 'The world we see around us is created partly individually and partly collectively. The synchronization of karmic effects enables creation to happen as we see it.'

'That is because we are never alone when we act, are we? I mean, there are always others involved,' I asked.

He answered, 'We are always subjected to individual and collective karmic impacts. It's not only the physical action, but also the mental ones. The moment we think of a person, we have created a mental cause for which an effect is preprogrammed; a karmic seed is already generated during this process.'

It made sense!

'For something to be built one requires a foundation. As such for a reaction to materialize, it requires something equivalent, for instance a platform. The basis of this platform is time and space. The platform itself is Samsara.'

He paused before saying, 'Our uncountable lives have gathered uncountable potential experiences for the future. These experiences can be seen as seeds which will ripen when the conditions are right. The individual and collective karma ensures we experience events together, in most cases with the same sentient beings we have lived with in the past. This means the people we meet today, and we have met in past lives.'

He pointed to the middle of the thangka and said, 'When a seed ripens, the very subtle mind will expand into a grosser form known as the subtle mind. The expansion continues further until a state of mind known as the very gross mind is attained. Likewise matter begins to expand from a very subtle form towards a very gross form.'

'Matter is void at its core, something created by pressure.'

'Exactly! The masculine and feminine energies create the pressure.'

I looked at him questioningly, 'Feminine and masculine energies?'

'This I'll explain tomorrow,' he said and continued to speak on matter. 'Matter in its finest form is empty, non-existent. Through pressure it develops into vibrations. It then expands towards a grosser level. The vibrations "materialize" into waves, waves then materialize into very subtle matter and so on.'

'Supposing one analyzes backwards. Beginning from a very gross level, one would find nothing at the end of the material chain?' I asked.

'Yes. The material chain ends. This does not imply to the mind. The grosser level of the mind returns to a subtle form. Mind and matter never mix. They are two different entities. Matter emerges and perishes bound to the force of karma, leading to continual change in its form and thoroughly dependent on the actions of sentient beings. That is why matter is not permanent and will never be able to provide everlasting happiness.'

'And all the things we experience are only a perception, because nothing really exists. All phenomena are bound to time, they are perishable,' I concluded.

At this he spoke no more. As it was getting late he rose to his feet saying, 'Dr. Cane, let's pause here and continue tomorrow.'

'Geshe-La, you may call me Roger,' I said.

He smiled again, patted my shoulder, turned around and walked towards the doors of the monastery, without another word.

I had not noticed Ananda was waiting. He accompanied me to the monastery gates, where he politely bid me good evening. Alone, I walked back to my cottage and I realized I was tired. Entering my cottage, I was tired and also hungry. Food was waiting for me in the kitchen. After enjoying my small meal, I took a nap on the sofa. Sometime during the evening, I was awoken by a knock on the front door. Half awake and half asleep, I opened the door and found Richard standing on the front porch. He asked me if I would like to join him for dinner. Not really knowing what to say, I agreed. After a quick shower and change of clothes, we were walking along the pathway leading towards the open fields in the south.

'A friend of mine had invited us to visit him today for dinner,' he said quietly, before stopping and adding apologetically, 'Sorry for the short notice.'

I asked, 'Who is it?'

'He is Indira's father.' He looked at me as if waiting for me to respond. As I remained silent, he asked, 'He seemed eager to meet you, the reason for me to agree. I hope it is ok?'

What could I say; that I was a little nervous to meet my future father-in-law?' Having no reason to object I answered, 'Not at all Richard, I would be very happy to meet him.'

I noticed Richard had changed a lot; he was calmer, more at peace with the world, and most of all, with himself. We continued silently to walk along the open fields before turning right on to another path which took us to a small double-storey building. It looked a little different from the other buildings in Keajara. Richard noticed my curiosity and pointed out that this was a very old building, the home of Tendung Sherpa, Indira's father. It had been a family home for many generations, and the architecture previously was a little different. The building was surrounded by a two-meter-high wall, with only one opening, a heavy wooden front door.

'According to the old stories, the houses in olden times were built in such a way, to not only avoid natural calamities, such as sand or winter storms, and secondly to protect against dangers from animals but also dangers created by man.' Richard knocked at the door.

A friendly face peeped out and greeted us. The face, though older and attractive, seemed familiar. It was obvious that she was Indira's mother. Choden Tsering welcomed us into her home. We walked into a garden. It was twilight therefore I could not see much, only enough to notice a wonderfully kept garden. I could smell roses, and herbs. We were led to another door which opened into a smaller garden leading to the entrance of the house. The inner garden looked a little different, more like a Japanese garden.

Indira's father appeared at the front door. With a hearty smile and open arms he embraced Richard. Turning to me, he took my hand with both his hands and with a very warm smile. I noticed my nervousness slowly melting away, replaced by a feeling of being welcomed. It was in this moment I decided to enjoy the evening, the food and the company.

He was about five feet nine inches tall, robustly built with large, strong hands, hands which gave a person the feeling of security and stability. His face reflected an aura of friendliness and compassion.

We were showed into the living room. Tea and cakes were served, and from one moment to another, we some-how began to discuss about my work and my life in the UN, our mission and the future of Keajara.

Tendung Sherpa was a very pleasant and positive person. Calmly he spoke, and his smile was full of friendli-ness. The only other person I know with such composure was Geshe-La. He showed great compassion and hope for the world. I for my part was very happy to have made his acquaintance. Only many years later did Indira tell me what that evening meant. On this evening did Tendung Sherpa agree to accept me as his son-in-law.

The next morning Ananda was waiting for me at my front door. We walked towards the monastery in silence. I for my part was trying to 'become awake'. It was a late night. We met Geshe-La underneath the Bodhi tree. He was in deep meditation. We waited until he became aware of our presence.

As he raised his head and smiled at us we approached him. I took my seat as Ananda and the older monk walked away silently.

Geshe-La asked, 'I hope you've had a comfortable and sound sleep?'

I replied, 'I did Geshe-La, thank you.'

'So let us continue where we left off yesterday. The next topic is very profound. It concerns "the state of balance" or "the two forces". As we have discussed yesterday, the world around us is dynamic and is subjected to change; nothing remains as it is. Although change continues, there are moments of equilibrium.'

'Do universal compassion and wisdom have anything to do with the stability we experience in our lives?' I asked.

'Yes it does. Within a certain life many things can happen. But a lifetime is a period which remains stable until it ends. These moments of equilibrium are ensured by two forces. They are responsible for the duality of

186

views and for the elimination of it. Due to our misconceptions, also known as "ignorance", we are not capable of understanding the true nature of these two forces.'

'What is the true nature of these two forces?'

Geshe-La stood up without any effort, and with a wave of the hand signaled me to walk with him. I was wondering how old he might be. I had yet to see a person like him before. He walked with such calmness, as if every movement was filled with wisdom. 'Allow me to explain,' he began. 'It's those who have courage, who show compassion and those who are humble, who show the willingness to learn. Courage is a masculine attribute, and humbleness is a feminine attribute. One is not more or less important than the other. Both are important for reaching Nirvana. It has nothing to do with being a man or a woman, since both men and women have these attributes.'

'How do they create balance?' I asked.

'For instance, let's say there are two parties who have an argument. What would it take to resolve such an argument? Mutual understanding perhaps?' he asked, raising an eyebrow. Without waiting for an answer he continued, 'A compromise or an agreement perhaps?' He turned away and continued to walk again as I followed him. 'To come to an agreement, both parties not only have to possess wisdom, but also have the ability to show compassion. The combination of wisdom and compassion is what which leads to developing a compromise or an agreement. This rule applies to all facets of life, in fact in all realms or dimensions. They are holy objects, as their main objective is to help us to achieve enlightenment, and the freedom from samsara or uncontrolled rebirth. The masculine aspect in Buddhism is known as "Buddha Heruka", whereas in Hinduism it is known as "Lord Shiva" or "Lord Bhairava"; the feminine aspect is known as "Buddha Vajravarahi" in Buddhism, and as "Lady Shakti" or "Lady Kali" in Hinduism.'

'I saw a statue of Lord Shiva once. It was called the "Lingam",' I said.

'Yes, the Lingam represents the union of universal wisdom and universal compassion. We see other forms of these two forces here on earth. They are known as the positive and negative magnetic poles, push-and-pull phenomena such as gravity and magnetism, our tendency to segregate things into right and wrong, good and bad, mine and theirs, up and down, my side and your side, yin and yang, etc. – the list is endless.'

'Does that mean we tend to differentiate when we are not in a state of balance?' I asked.

'Here among the snow-covered mountains, I have become aware of the inner peace. Through it I was able to achieve a home for myself within me, a world which was unexplored and uncharted.' Geshe-La continued after making a short pause, 'Now let us speak about Emptiness. It is also known as the heart of wisdom. The Root Text is known as the "Essence of Wisdom Sutra" or as "Bhagavatiprajnaparamitahrdaya" in Sanskrit.'

I asked, 'Does Emptiness has anything to do with being empty?'

He smiled. 'When one speaks of Emptiness in Buddhism or in Hinduism, one does not speak of nothingness. In reality Emptiness has two characteristics.

The one is known as "inherent existence of all phenomena" which means that no phenomenon is actually
independent.'

'So we are never alone?' I asked.

'No, we are not. Even when we think we are alone,
we are not. We are always part of infinite thoughts,
memories which include infinite others, for now, and in
all times.'

'Everyone knows everyone?' I asked.

'One could say so,' he answered.

'The other characteristic you were going to mention
was…' I reminded him.

'Yes, the sutra speaks of the "non-existence of all
phenomena", meaning all phenomena are actually non-
existent.'

'Because everything perishes one day, is it not so?'

'Yes and that emptiness is empty of space and time.
It's a state where duality ceases to exist. If you observe
life, you will realize duality is everywhere.'

'How so?'

'We all seek some sense in our lives. We have many
names for it; we call it ambition, career, a family, home,
a purpose in life, a way of life, or even faith. We could
sum all this up in one word, "Happiness".'

I understood what he meant.

'But that is not enduring happiness. To achieve
enduring happiness one needs to stop the search, and
begin to remember.' He noticed my confusion
and paused. 'Don't be confused, I shall explain,' he assured me. 'All that we need we carry within us; the
source of all our sorrows is our ego or ignorance, and the

source of our happiness is our very subtle mind. Our ego is only interested in satisfying its wishes and pursuing an "outer", more material path.'

I added, 'The very subtle mind possesses the potential to achieve Buddhahood. Its nature is clarity. This enables the very subtle mind to overcome ignorance.'

He continued by saying, 'To find the path to true happiness has to do with being honest with oneself. To admit, that material gain does not lead to eternal happiness, to let go of the fear and hate we carry in ourselves, to embrace compassion. Doing this one tears down ones barriers hindering us from remembering the way to internal happiness, the way back home.'

If only it was that simple. How does one unknot the many conflicts one carries within oneself? The fear for the unknown, for the future, the hate making us to build great walls and yet the answer has always been love, has always been compassion.

'One more topic before we stop for today. It's about meditation. To understand meditation one needs to understand the idea of contemplation. Actually, we contemplate day in and day out. We are always looking for solutions. But if one wants to achieve inner peace, one needs to remain present, remain focused on one object. Changing one's thoughts each and every second leads to multiple generations of emotions, creating great confusion and uncertainty. Such a way of life leads to only more discomfort.'

After allowing a few minutes to digest this he added, 'One needs to remain focused on a single thought, more importantly it must be a peaceful one. Meditation is a form of contemplation; the only difference is, in meditation one strives to reduce the complication of issues to one single object, on one single peaceful thought.'

'It's only logical to rely on meditation to achieve the final state of oneness,' I added.

'It has been proved by modern medicine that the brain is capable of generating only one thought at a single moment. When we keep changing our thoughts, from one moment to another, the rate of distress increases. Over a lengthy period this would lead to chronic disease. Meditation not only has medical effects, but it helps one to travel deeper, to arrive at the moment where the red drop and white drop achieve union. The moment universal compassion and universal wisdom mixes.'

We stopped walking. I realized suddenly that Ananda and the older monk were standing in front of us, waiting.

'I hope I was able to give you a short insight into Dharma. Please feel free to come and see me, should you have any questions. I believe Ananda is waiting to bring you back to your cottage.'

I was awake early. Having dressed, I walked into the kitchen for breakfast; today, however, the dining room was empty. I heard someone in the garden and walked out to the porch. There I met Richard, sitting in a chair. He seemed to be waiting for me.

'Good morning,' Richard said. 'I had hoped to invite you for breakfast.'

'I would be happy to invite you, but Mrs. Choden left me none.'

'Ah, yes, that's the point we shall discuss on the way to my cottage,' he replied.

As we left my cottage and were walking towards his, he explained, 'Mrs. Choden has left us, and another person will take her place.'

'Left us?' I said questioningly, but Richard didn't want to go into it, and said simply, 'That is how it is here, people come and people go.'

I assumed it was a private matter, and therefore decided to leave it at that.

I had come to love these morning walks. All is quiet, a new day breaking, new hopes and dreams to be realized. We walked silently until we arrived at his cottage. I began to speak about my meetings with Geshe-La, asking him about Dharma.

Richard said, 'For me, it has become a belief. It's part of my life. During my younger days, it was just something which interested me. But now it's more. Dharma has given me what I needed in life. In it I found peace and purpose.'

'Please excuse me for saying this. I knew you as a sceptical scientist, someone who always needed empirical proof,' I replied.

He didn't answer immediately, 'There comes a time in life when one makes a leap in faith.'

'You mean to say you didn't need any convincing?' I asked.

'No, no, that wasn't the case. I needed time for convincing,' he answered with a laugh. 'Dharma was able to win me over. What I meant was, not everything needs to be proved. The logic in Dharma is unbeatable.'

I asked him, with a frown, 'How?'

'If you carefully observe nature, you would come to the conclusion that empirical proof of Dharma is everywhere around us. One just needs to ask the right questions. The problem with us humans is we need to see, to touch, to hear and feel everything with our senses.'

'There's nothing wrong in that, is there?' I said.

'It's not about wrong or right. We have forgotten we possess other capabilities.'

'You might be right,' I conceded.

'Yes, where was I, right, empirical evidence. Electricity existed even before we knew about it. All we had to do was to tap in. We needed the right tool. And so we learned how to develop a tool for it. We landed on the moon, something people living a thousand years ago would not have believed possible. The Indians knew that the earth wasn't flat, thousands of years before us Westerners, or Galileo.'

'How this?' I asked.

'Due to their knowledge of the cosmos, they were able to calculate the distance of the planets from each other, and the distance of each planet from the sun.'

'How was all this possible thousands of years ago?'

'Their astrology was based on scientific calculations, not some "humbug" magic, as we Westerners call it.'

I remembered his lectures; it was as if I was back in my old lecture hall at Harvard. He had not lost the talent to speak passionately about something he believed in.

'Any evidence about how the earlier Indians knew that the earth was not flat?' I asked.

193

'There is something called the "Nava Gragam", or the nine influencers. They are all visible physically as the planets Mars, Mercury, Jupiter, Venus, and Saturn, the Sun, the Moon. In addition, the final influencers are the intersections of the paths of the Sun and the Moon as they move on the celestial sphere, known as Rahu and Ketu respectively. The misconception is that people believe the Nava Gragam to be the nine planets, whereas it represents the nine influences on body, speech and mind. "Gragam" influences body, speech and mind negatively, whereas "Nava" influences them positively. The astrological treatise "Prasna Marga" speaks of infinite worlds created during the birth of the universe. Only a few, such as our solar system, create the conditions for life to evolve.'

He paused for a minute or two, as if he was collecting his thoughts. 'The yogis were able to look into the future and into the past. In deep meditation they were able to overcome time and space; they were in a position to gain new insights. Some of the yogis were mathematicians, who even discovered the value of Pi at 3.14, with which they calculated the size of the planets.'

He summed up, 'Their deep understanding of the mind was the key to the answers we seek in life. The problem we as sentient beings face is the inability to see things as they truly are.'

Richard paused to disappear briefly into his cottage. He came out with a photo album. I had not seen one of those for a long time. 'Over the past years, I have made photos of various documents and thangkas.'

'By the way, it was the Indians who first discovered the modern decimal system and not the Arabians. They also discovered the zero.' He took out an extract from the Encyclopedia Britannica.

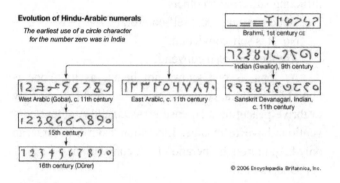

Evolution of Hindu-Arabic numerals

The earliest use of a circle character for the number zero was in India

Brahmi, 1st century CE

Indian (Gwalior), 9th century

West Arabic (Gobar), c. 11th century

East Arabic, c. 11th century

Sanskrit Devanagari, Indian, c. 11th century

15th century

16th century (Dürer)

© 2006 Encyclopædia Britannica, Inc.

'How that?'

'It is the idea that everything is a cycle.'

Of course, what else! 'We westerners believe in empirical evidences.'

'OK, where is the evidence of the existence of an Almighty God?' he asked.

I thought it through and said, 'It is contradictory I admit.'

'We believe in right and wrong, good and bad, but in reality values or judgments are all relative. They are not absolute. They depend on the "eye of the beholder" and as such it's only part true, part accepted, part practiced. To be able to experience the true nature of all phenomena one has to be free of all values, all opinions.'

'But what would we be if we didn't have values?' I interrupted. 'Anarchy would rule.'

'Of course, but not when we practice universal truth. Truth which lead to virtuous actions, such as not harming one another in any way; we would be free of suffering or inflicting suffering on others.'

'Which require great self-control.'

'No. It is self-conviction.'

'Are they not also conventions?'

'As long as one knows not better, as long one is bound in Samsara, conventions are required for a society to thrive peacefully. To ensure sustainability, these conventions have to change. Liberation from Samsara can only begin through liberation from conventions.'

'Understood!'

He continued, 'The conventions a society normally practices is based on local necessities, local needs.'

'That makes them relative, and not absolute.'

'Take for instance two colors, blue and red; you might like red and I blue. Does that make your liking "the better one" or mine "the worse one"? No! It's only a matter of "opinion" based on values which in themselves are not "absolute". The problem begins when opinions cause someone to suffer. A proof that a universal purpose is not served.'

'Wisdom is required,' I added.

'An Enlightened Being, a Buddha, is capable of perceiving a phenomenon without any prejudice; a Buddha is perfection. There are no judgments, there are no favors or friends or enemies.'

He paused asking, 'I believe the High Lama had explained about the dependencies between masculine and feminine poles?'

To this I nodded.

'Although the Indians were the first to discover the relationship between these two energy sources, over time other civilizations have also adapted this knowledge into their faith and culture. One example is yin and yang. I once took a few pictures of thangkas, please give me a moment.'

He began to turn the pages of his photo album, and stopped at a specific picture.

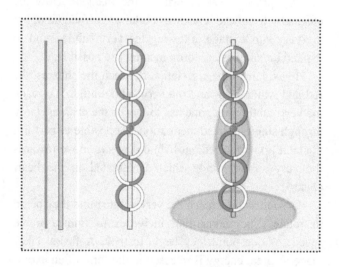

'This photo is something which I made on one of my visits to the main library. It shows the correlation between birth, karma and samsara. The moment a karmic seed ripens, it initiates a certain chain of events. For instance the beginning of a new life; the foundation consists of three channels; the central channel, which is transparent, the red channel and the white channel. The very subtle mind is situated in the central channel. The red and white channels tie six knots around the central channel, which build six chakras. The red and white channels are built by the red and white drops, representing the feminine and masculine aspects. The very subtle mind is situated about two fingers just behind the heart, which is the reason why the heart is the first organ which develops in a new life.'

This process was shown by the thangka. How the channels form the chakras, building a foundation at the very subtle stage, allowing the very subtle mind to expand into a physical form, making life possible.

He explained the correlation between the chakras, the red and white drops and the very subtle mind. 'To reach the very subtle mind, one has to loosen the chakras. Only through single-pointed meditation, is one able to perform this and allow the red and white drops to move towards the very subtle mind, which is situated in the heart chakra.

As soon as they reach the very subtle mind they begin to rotate. The momentum increases to immeasurable speed. At one point they begin to melt. A fusion takes place. A great energy is released in the form of an explosion, a great fire which completely destroys all negative impingements, which then leads to the Union of Bliss, also known as the Union of Universal Compassion and

Universal Wisdom. This is shown by the following thangka.' He then pointed to a photo on the next page.

'Amazing!' At the same time a thought crossed my mind. 'The red and white drops, are they the reason for the red and white cells in our blood?'

'Yes,' he answered.

'Why are the chakras so important?' I asked.

'The chakras are energy centers which act as our backbone, and they are important for our existence in a certain realm.'

'At the same time,' I added, 'they are also holding one in a certain life, or in samsara. And to be able to liberate oneself from samsara one has to learn to loosen the holds of the chakras.'

'By the way, this hold does loosen itself automatically at two points in time, one being during death and the other during sleep. The difference being, during death it loosens completely. This enables the very subtle mind to undertake a new birth in samsara.'

He then returned to the initial topic. 'So, coming back to my point earlier, to be able to loosen the chakras, one has to practice single-pointed meditation. As you can see here, on this photo.'

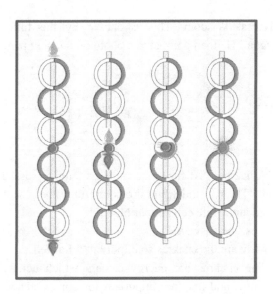

'When one reaches the stage of utmost single-pointedness, the chakras begin to loosen. The red and white drops begin to move towards the very subtle mind situated at the heart chakra. It's like two poles of a magnet; the positive and negative poles begin pulling each other. As soon as they reach the very subtle mind, they begin to rotate. A great fire ignites, eliminating all negative karmas.'

'What happens then?'

'One is free of uncontrolled rebirth, one is free of the dualities of Samsara, open to perceive all things in their true nature, not blinded by ignorance.'

"How else can one see the light if not free of the clouds surrounding, how else can one be free if not gaining sight?" I thought.

'The two triangles are actually the two drops, the white and red drop, which represent masculinity and feminity. When they unite, one experiences the Union of Bliss. This double triangle ✡ or hexagram can be seen used in other cultures.'

I scribbled the following picture in my note book, the red and white drop moving towards each other, mixing, as water into water and finally igniting the great fire of wisdom, extinguishing all personal negative Karma accumulated since beginningless of time.

'Upon accomplishing this state of Union one meditates further to realize Emptiness directly. This is known as the Union of Bliss and Emptiness.'

It was afternoon, and we decided to meet later for tea. As I walked back alone to my cottage I realized how much I still had to learn, how much I still had to be; I stopped on the way at a stall and ordered a bowl of noddle. The shop owner spoke English; I was surprised. He was in his late fifties, with dark black hair and of a medium build; a friendly man. We spoke of the weather and the crops. Calmly he spoke, and calmly he served other customers as they come into the shop. He seemed to be interested in the world I lived in, and asked many questions. He invited me to come to meet his family when I had the time. 'You're always welcome, sir.'

I finished my bowl and bid farewell.

"Interesting," I thought, "everyone is happy. Everyone is at peace."

Arriving at my cottage tired, I laid myself on the sofa, and with these thoughts I dozed off.

I was awakened by a strange movement. I opened my eyes. There was a cat sitting on the couch table, staring at me. Amused, I asked, 'Where did you come from, my friend?' It didn't answer. Instead it decided to join me on the sofa. 'That wouldn't do, my friend,' I said, lifting it up and setting it back on the table. 'I have an appointment. I have to go now.'

I jumped into the shower and put on some fresh clothes before making my way to Richard's place. It seemed to be "siesta time". All was quiet on the streets. Not even the children were playing.

Entering his cottage, Richard asked, 'Is that you Roger?'

'Yes.'

'Come to the terrace,' he called. 'Tea and cakes are ready.'

Pouring a cup for me he said, 'Help yourself, please.'

Then he continued speaking where he had left off. 'Emptiness has two facets. The first being; all that is matter evolves out of emptiness and dissolves into emptiness; the second facet being that no phenomenon exists on its own, but only in dependence with other phenomena. Let me begin with matter. It's been proven by physics, that at the end of the chain called matter, there is nothing. Two forces play an important role in the development of matter. These are the masculine and feminine forces. They push and pull, which helps matter to evolve from one form to another.'

He paused and sipped his tea before going on. Thoughtful he turned the photo album to another page and showed me a photo of a thangka, with handwritten notes. Looked like his.

'A few years ago, I came across this thangka. A picture speaks for itself and helps us to understand easier. I still use it to explain the relationship between mind and matter.'

Richard took the teapot and asked, 'More?'

I nodded, while I was studying that colorful picture.

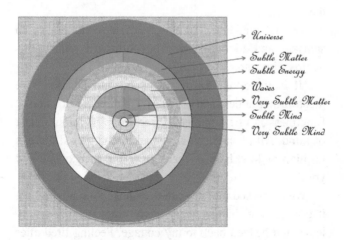

One sees the world with a different eye. We do get lost in our conventional mode of operation; we hardly have time to register what really is going on every second passing; how mind and matter continuously interact. According to Richard it requires more time to understand the sutras than the tantra scriptures. During his lifetime Buddha Shakyamuni had given 84,000 teachings. The tantra teachings have nothing to do with sexual intercourse. The sutra builds the base, and the tantra is a method to achieve enlightenment. Tantra is also known as "the method for a quick path to enlightenment".

'Everything in samsara is a matter of interpretation,' Richard explained. 'One might even call it half-truths. It is limited to "opinions". A non-spiritual path leads to egoism. We believe in good and bad, mine and theirs, right and wrong. All this leads to more degenerated beliefs and ideologies. We witness this on our planet today.'

To that I added, 'All this binds us continuously to samsara and to suffering. The ability to realize this begins with a spiritual path.'

'It is important for us to understand Dharma. We must further understand only through direct realization of Emptiness is one completely free from an impure state of mind. All phenomena are equal in emptiness; there is no high or low, here or there, now and then or me and you!'

We discussed into the late evenings, not realizing that it got late and hunger was slowly crept up. I took my leave and headed back to my cottage. Feeling tired after dinner, I went to bed early. It would be an early rise the next morning. Ananda was to escort me for a week to see the country and meet the Librarian. Knowing Ananda, he'd be punctual. More than a week had passed since I first arrived in Keajara. Still much to know!

And I was right. Ananda was waiting the next morning with a horse and cart at the doorstep, on time.

11

We are never alone

It was dark and the Lt. was on his way home. "There has not been any progress!" he thought. He had not been able to report anything new, and the Col. had this amused smug expression on his face. He hated that man.

At work the next morning, the Shadow was in the office.

'What are you doing here, so early in the morning? Someone would have noticed you,' said the Lt.

The Shadow shook his head, 'I've been here since last night.'

'Why that?' demanded the Lt.

'I'm in danger. My people are suspecting me,' said the Shadow.

'Goes with the job; anything new?' asked the Lt.

He thought, "You scoundrel!", but he didn't speak it out. He still needed the Lt.'s protection. 'Yes. We have someone who might have been there. A Chinese hiker.'

The Lt. was apparently tensed. 'What! And you don't inform me immediately!'

'It's not of much use; they've given him some sort of medicine to delete his memory. He only remembers bits and pieces. Not much of a help.'

'I'll decide that. Where is he now?' asked the Lt. impatiently.

'In Saga,' answered the Shadow.

'Place him under arrest and bring him here. I want him here tomorrow.' He walked over to his desk and prepared an arrest warrant. 'What's his name?'

'Mao Tse Tung,' said the Shadow.

The Lt. looked up and said, 'Are you joking?'

'No.' He handed the Lt. the man's ID.

Looking at it the Lt. said, 'Whatever. Here's the arrest warrant. Get him here, no excuses.'

The Shadow took the piece of paper and turned to leave the room. The Lt. seemed to be pleased with himself. "At last, a breakthrough." The Shadow walked out of the door.

Someone else walked into the Col.'s office. 'Sir, the Shadow has just left the Lt.'s office. He was in there all night,' reported Sgt. Choo.

'Anything new?'

'The Lt. has sent the man to bring the hiker to Lhasa, possibly for interrogation.'

'Do you think the hiker is going to cause a problem?'

'My contact in Saga says he hasn't been able to say anything. He doesn't remember.'

'As soon as the man is brought here, you should get involved.'

'Yes. Sir,' the Sgt. replied and left the room, leaving the Col. alone with his thoughts.

At five p.m. the Col. left the building. Strangely, the Col. lived nearby on Barhkhor Street, also known as the Tibetan Squatters. Although the Potala is an important monument for the Tibetans, this place is considered far more significant. It is the spiritual heart of the city which the Chinese tried so hard to destroy. The Barhkhor forms one of the holiest places in the whole country. The Jokhang Temple sitting in the middle of it acts as a focal point for the entire culture. The Col. usually takes a stroll after work, circling the Jokhang Temple. He has been doing this since he first came to Lhasa. He calls it "keeping the pulse to the ground". The soldiers guarding the area know him well. He usually ends his stroll by climbing on to the roof. Standing on the rooftop of one of the most religious buildings of the world, it becomes clear that Lhasa is indeed an occupied city.

12

The Librarian

It was a five-hour trip to Ngari, the next village, where I was to meet a lama known as the "Librarian" of Keajara. He was known to be a man of great knowledge. The journey took us through some of the most beautiful scenery I have ever seen. No borders, no buildings to block your view. The horizon in sight. We traveled through amazingly different landscapes, especially for this height. There were forests, green grass and huge trees, pines mostly with stems with two meters in diameter. Mesmerized by the scenery, I didn't notice approaching it. A large blue lake with seemingly no shores on the other side, glass clear water, as blue as the skies above. We stopped for a rest at its shores. Stepping into the cool fresh water bare feet was a blessing. The drops were crystal clear, pearl of diamonds, brought alive by the sun. And so I remained until it was time to leave, to leave my sanctuary.

On the way, Ananda assured me there were deer, bears, foxes, wolves and many other animals living here, all unharmed and harming no one. The journey was mostly a silent one. As Ananda was meditating I contemplated on my life. It had to do with the hustle and bustle of the modern world. Here on the other hand I was inhaling freshness and tranquility. Not like one of those trips to Colorado Springs. This had much more to it. I had not felt this way before. I had finally come alive. More than just seeing, hearing or touching, it had to do with becoming part of nature, unmistakably united. "A strange word," I thought, "*united*, as in the *Union of Bliss and Happiness*." I noticed Ananda watching me, as if he could follow my thoughts.

'Dr. Cane, there are things one does not see through the one's eyes. One needs the heart. Sight through the heart needs inner peace. It might be that you're beginning to experience this; meditation helps one to be aware of subtle phenomena. There is more to Mother Earth, or the universe for that matter, than what meets the eye.'

'I don't quite understand,' I replied.

Ananda explained, 'On the path to enlightenment there is no hurry, all will come in time as time is a great teacher.'

With those words, Ananda closed his eyes and continued his meditation. I wasn't sure if I understood him. But for some reason I chose not to ask. We crossed mixed terrain; the path was now large enough for two carts to travel side by side. Trees emerged suddenly on the horizon in the midst of sandy hills. Further away were the snow-topped mountains reaching the skies.

Sometime before midday we arrived in Ngari, a small village with a couple of hundred inhabitants. We were taken to a monastery. From outside it looked like a small and unassuming building, built into the foot of a mountain. The front door was large enough for only one person to enter at any one time. As we walked in I noticed that the inner part was much larger, a labyrinth of hallways paving its way into the mountain. We walked along one of these hallways and came to an opening leading towards a beautiful garden, green and tropical, the light floating in through an opening from the top of the mountain. We walked over fresh green earth, and passed by streams with fresh water. Standing there in the middle of this beautiful cocooned world, I was speechless. Looking at Ananda I asked, 'Is this real, or is this a dream?'

Ananda smiled as he said, 'A dream it is not. It's one of the wonders of this land.'

'How old is this garden?' I asked, still astonished.

'I'm not sure. It was here before the monastery. We have been very fortunate with this gift.'

Ananda continued towards the other end of the garden, where another opening could be seen. Unable to stop my fascination over this biotope, I reluctantly followed him. We approached another opening, a small door; going through it, we emerged into a hall where monks were having their lunch. The hall was lit by giant oil-lamp chandelier. One could see the entire cave, which was as large as the White House. Something else I noticed; the entire cave wall glowed, as if light was reflected from gold paint. We joined the monks at the table and silently food was served. During lunch I asked Ananda why the walls were painted gold.

He saw my uncertain look, and said, 'Dr. Cane it is not paint, it is real gold.

'What do you mean by that?'

'The entire mountain is made out of gold.'

I thought I had missed something and asked him, astonished, 'Are you saying the whole mountain is a gold reserve?'

His eyes showed no sign of greed when he said, 'It is all gold.'

A mountain made of gold, but... 'How?'

'I'm unable to answer that; a natural process lasting many million years, I believe. The Indian subcontinent crashed into Asia 25 million years ago and created the Himalayan mountain range. Over time a set of events must have led to this result.' As he spoke he pointed to the mountain.

"Amazing!" I thought. This land doesn't cease to astonish me!

After lunch we were led to a room, I must have dozed off. I had a dream. I was on top of a mountain. Looking around me I saw other snow-covered peaks, with blankets of cloud around them.

I seemed at first confused. But for some reason I had a feeling I knew this place. It was very familiar. How? Where was I? It suddenly dawned upon me, it was the holy Mount Kailash. At that moment I saw him, he appeared, covered with white powder, on a lion throne he sat, covered with tiger fur, lost in meditation. There he was, the great lord, the union of wisdom and compassion, the all-knowing one, Lord Shiva. I stood there awed. Strong emotions flowed through me, of inner peace, of oneness.

I heard a voice, at first in a distance and it came closer, I wanted not to leave him the Lord, there I wanted to remain but the voice reached out and brought me back to Samsara. As I awoke, baffled and confused, I wondered where I was or what had happened? I looked up and noticed Ananda standing over me, asking with concern in his voice, 'Are you well, Dr. Cane?'

I realized my shirt was wet. I must have been sweating. 'I'm not sure,' I said, a little uncertainly, 'I had a dream.'

'Would you like to talk about it?' he asked. I needed a few minutes to gather myself, and told him of my dream. He listened intently before saying emphatically, 'I believe, Dr. Cane, you had a vision. A strong one. That is good. Time will explain the meaning.'

As I began to slowly come to myself, I noticed cakes and hot tea on the table before me. Ananda poured me some to soothe my nerves. After tea and some delicious cakes, he escorted me to another section of the building. It was our sleeping quarters. Ananda showed me to a room with a bed, a small table, a chair and an adjoining bathroom. The room had a very friendly atmosphere, and was warm.

'Are all the rooms like this one?' I asked him.

'Yes, renovations in the monasteries began a few years ago,' he replied and quietly left the room.

After taking a warm shower and changing into something fresh, I tried to sort my thoughts. The experiences were many that day but strangely I was at ease. At the same time I wished Indira was there. To take my mind of her I began to explore the monastery. The hallways were endless. Not really knowing where I was going, I let myself taken by "destiny". I passed a monk or two who politely smiled. Coming to a wooden door, I entered into

213

a large and spacious hall. From the look of it, I would say it was a library. Monks were silently reciting Holy Scriptures. The wooden shelves reached to the ceiling, each stacked with uncountable books and rolls of scripture. They looked ancient. I had not seen anything like it before. The deeper I went I realized, it must be four or five times larger than the Congress Library.

I approached one of the shelves with a wooden shield on it. On it was written; "All life is about change. Do not build barriers rather tread the path of courage."

'How well said, but it is a long way from where I am standing,' I said aloud.

Ananda suddenly appeared. 'Dr. Cane, may I escort you to dinner.'

'I believe I'm a little lost,' I said apologetically, as I was sure he was looking for me.

He smiled saying, 'Not at all Sir. You are safe and well, that is what matters.' He paused a moment and said, 'We are in the main library of Keajara. There are smaller ones in this monastery but this is the largest and oldest.'

'The library stores millions of books and palm writings collected over the last two thousand years. We have other artifacts such as statues, thangkas and paintings, all stored in save keeping. If you wish we can explore the library again another time, but now it is time for dinner.'

I nodded as we began to walk towards the exit and towards the dining hall. After a few minutes of maneuvering ourselves out of the labyrinth, we arrived at a great hall where monks were having their dinner. We joined them and being hungry I practically swallowed the naan bread, vegetarian curry with potatoes and tea. After dinner as it was late, I went directly to bed.

The next morning there was a knock on the door. I slowly opened it, a young monk stood there with breakfast. I thanked him and took the try and enjoyed the sweet smell of hot tea in the freshness of a new day. I walked over to the window and opened the curtains and to my astonishment I realized my room was facing the inner garden. I moved my chair nearer to the window and enjoyed my breakfast. An hour later Ananda escorted me to our meeting with the Geshe, the Librarian.

I remember Richard saying that this monastery used to be the world's largest at one time. It used to house up to 10,000 monks, on a landmass of 200,000 square meters. There is still a large population of monks residing here, numbering up to several hundreds.

After passing various hallways we finally arrived at a large wooden door. On it were Tibetan writings. I asked Ananda what they meant. He translated 'We may wear different clothes, or come from different parts of the world but we all become one through love.'

He opened the door and we went in. In a large room, an old man was seated on a meditation pillow. He rose, walked towards me with extended hands. He took both my hands into his and said, 'Dear Dr. Cane, I'm very grateful to meet you.'

"An unusual but at the same time a very warm greeting," I thought.

'The pleasure is mine Geshe-La,' I replied. A tall man, thin with sharp eyes.

'We are all very happy that you've come to visit us.'

'The pleasure is all mine,' I repeated.

'Please have a seat.' He had a friendly face, a face one trusts.

'Thank you,' I replied.

'I had suggested to the Prime Minister that you visit our humble library.' Looking around I noticed the room was filled with books, some old but some seemed new.

'Thank you very much for your invitation.'

'I hope everything was to your satisfaction?'

'Yes Sir. Thank you,' I confirmed.

He nodded and paused before saying, 'This monastery is at the same time our largest and oldest library. Many of Buddha's teachings are kept here. Apart from them the library also houses writings of Thirukural authored by Thiruvalluvar, Silappatikaram, Manimēkalai, writings of Pathmasambhava, Atisha, Je Tsongkhapa and of other Enlightened Beings.'

'How old is this library?' I asked more of curiosity.

'It's about two thousand years old,' he said. 'At the beginning ours was only a small collection. With the annexation of Tibet many artifacts were brought here for safekeeping. We have managed to keep this Library a secret since then.' There was sadness in his eyes, 'Many have lost their lives in doing so.' He turned his eyes to the ground for a moment before saying. 'Our jewels and treasure which we have safeguarded until now are the Teachings, Dharma. It's our most precious jewel. Some of the scriptures date back to over 5,000 years. Some are written in Pali, Sanskrit, Old Tamil and writings from Indus Valley.'

'I'm beginning to understand why you're anxious to keep this heritage in safe hands.' I said.

He nodded, 'We have also put great effort in understanding the old scriptures, in fact we have managed to decode some of the writings from the Indus Valley and have come to very interesting information, which naturally doesn't have direct influence to your visit here, but which I'm willing to explain should you be interested.'

'I'm very interested. I'm fascinated by everything I see and learn here.'

'I'm glad to hear this. I'll do my best to quench your thirst.'

'I'll be grateful for your help,' I replied.

'Very well, let's begin with the Indus Civilization. I'm certain you've heard of it.' As I nodded, he continued, 'We have been able to decode many of the texts from this period. According to what we have come to understand, there are no differences between Buddhism and ancient Hinduism, in fact they are brothers. Both Buddhism and Hinduism speak of Dharma. The Hinduism practiced today is much influenced by the caste system. It has been diverted away from the early teachings. The caste system is not part of Hinduism. The writings further point out that...' stopping here, he bent and picked up a parchment and read out of it, '"...a new folk called the Arians have introduced the cast system into Dharma some three thousand years ago. They were of fair skin and very poor people coming from a land very far in the north where water was firm..." I believe the texts speak of snow. This document is about five thousand years old. If our interpretation was correct, the jour-

217

ney of "Arians" began in the northern Hemisphere and ended in the north of present India. Along their journey, they learned to fight for their existence. The legend says the Arians came to India hearing of the rich land in the south. India with its natural resources, spices, gems, jewelry, craftsmanship, artistry, literature, architecture and civilization was well known around the world by travelers and merchants. In India, it was the "Golden Ages". Arriving in the Indus Valley the Arians learned about the "Dharma". They witnessed a flourishing and civilized society. Here they saw for themselves a great opportunity and settled down. They learned to influence the local Kings. They learned to control "Dharma" and establishing "priesthood", themselves at the top of the caste system, as Brahmins, as priest. It was the beginning of the caste system.'

'And the people just accepted it?'

'We are not sure, we don't have enough material on it to understand the whole story, just bits and pieces.'

'It's obvious that they concentrated their efforts on Dharma it was a central topic in the society. By controlling Dharma, they then could also control the people and the rulers,' I added.

'That is also our assumption. Today one would take control of finance system to control a society. They positioned themselves as Brahmins putting them at the highest level in the caste system. The Satria Caste or the royals were equal to them. Being in this position, they were able to control 'knowledge'. Henceforth only Brahmins were allowed to learn the Dharma. By and by the society became dependent on the institution of "priesthood". They became the center of "Learning", the ones between "me" and the "Gods".'

Geshe-La rose from his seat and walked over to the window. Looking into the garden he turned around and said, 'What I'm about to reveal now is not something which many would not like to hear, but it's something which we have been able to translate.' He paused a moment. 'The writings further reveal that between ancient Hinduism and Buddhism there are no contradictions. The Teachings at the Indus valley, originated from South India, we assume it came from the vicinity of Tamil Nadu and Kerala. We found also drawings of Holy beings. These are found both in Buddhism and Hinduism.'

'Are you saying that ancient Hinduism is Buddhism?'

'I would not go that far. But the cores of both lineages are the same. For instance Lord Shiva and Lady Shakti are Buddha Heruka and Buddha Vajravarahi.'

I was about to raise a question when Geshe-La said, 'I shall explain the reason very shortly.' After a moment he said, 'Initially known only as Dharma, the teachings were also practiced then in the Indus region. The Indus Valley was known so due to the Indus River flowing through it. The Arians arrived here first. At the same time Dharma was known as "the teachings of the People of the Indus" hence to be known as Induism, later spoken as Hinduism. At the same time the area was then known as Industan or "Land of the Indus". In short, Dharma which initially had no name later became known as Indu or Hindu.

'I see, but why was it called Hindustan?' I asked.

'In Sanskrit "stan" means "the land of", you see even today many countries have such endings, Pakistan, Afghanistan, Uzbekistan, Kyrgyzstan, Turkmenistan, Turkestan and so on.'

'That is very interesting.'

'The region known as the Arabian world for instance was once known as "Arravastan". It's Sanskrit for the "land of horses". Once this whole region knew and practiced Dharma. Also to the east and south did one breathe and live according to Dharma. Malaysia for instance was then known as Malay Nadu, it is Tamil for the "Land of Mountains", or Singapore then known as "Singa Puram", which is also Tamil for the "Isle of Lions". In short Dharma or ancient Hinduism was spread not only in the Subcontinent but throughout the Middle East, North Africa, South Europe, the Americas and Asia.'

'That would explain the fact why the great Temples such as Ayutthaya, Borobudur, Angkor Wat are of Indian origins,' I added.

'Yes, that is true. Even the great Temples of the Mayas and Inkas have the same Architectural designs used by the Temples in South India,' he commented.

'But there is no concrete evidence found by the modern science for any connection between these two cultures,' I said.

'You would agree when I say that science is not perfect!'

'Yes, of course you are right. But the scientific methodology, "to proof based on empirical data and research work", has its strength and validity,' I objected kindly.

He went on to say, 'That might be so, but even then, many scientific findings have been proven wrong. I do concur that the scientific methodology used, is feasible. But two things stand in the way to the ultimate truth. Firstly, the empirical data science uses to evaluate and to conclude is not absolute, and secondly, there is always a certain amount of prejudice in the persons doing this evaluations.'

'You're speaking of being biased,' I asked.

'Naturally, the ego plays an important part. It's impossible for a being who has not realized oneness to be neutral. Many findings which have been claimed as new discoveries were findings which others have discovered before them. For instance, the Indians knew of the nine planets even before Galileo discovered them.'

'I see what you mean, scientist see themselves as absolute. In a certain way they too have developed a form of religion. But a scientist would say that it's important to proof before believing. That makes them different from those who are ready to follow with faith.'

'What is faith or proof or even belief. They are only words, opinions or viewpoints. Such thoughts only separate and not unite. To achieve the oneness one needs to reach the source of clarity and understanding deep within us. Everything else is only matter, duality, and conventions.'

'But proof is important to believe and one's belief becomes one's faith,' I ascertained.

'Of course! One needs these to begin the path. One needs to question one's purpose in life. As Buddha Shakyamuni said, "Doubt me and the Teachings". It's his way to point out the importance of believing with clarity and wisdom.' Geshe-La walked towards me and sat on the chair opposite to me, with a gentle smile he took my hands and said, 'Yes. We humans have much in common, more than what we are willing to admit. We are all but children playing an adults game.' He nodded and continued, 'The writings from the Indus Valley are about eight thousand years old, and they managed to pour light into many questions as to where the "Cradle of Civilization" could be found. Our research points to South India.'

He then rose and walked towards a Thangka hanging on one of the walls. 'I would like to speak a little about what I call the "Primal Dharma", although Dharma is primal. I'm sure you've heard of the three main Gods in Hinduism; Brahma, Vishnu and Shiva. According to the "Primal Dharma", the three Great Lords represent "a single consciousness". It says this single consciousness is the concentrated Compassion of all very subtle minds.'

'I'm not sure if I understand,' I said. My heart felt deeply touched by this description.

'According to the ancient texts, the Great One is thus described "The Great Consciousness everlasting now and then; the Presence before and after Time, before and after Space, of being and not being, the beginning, the birth, the Creator". He was there before the universe awakened, will continue after the universe returns to its state of slumber, ever conscientious of the present, ever being of the now and yet also being the future, the universe being the Great One and the Great One being more.'

'The Great Consciousness is the Subtle Mind?' I asked.

'The Great Consciousness is the sum of all Subtle Minds, the Auspicious One, the Great Compassion. He is known by many names, the Lord Shiva, Buddha Heruka, God Bhairava, worshiped as the Lingam, limitless, transcendent, unchanging and formless. He is the one who lives an ascetic life on Mount Kailash. He is the householder with wife Parvati respectively Buddha Vajravarahi. He is the union and the ultimate truth.'

Geshe-La then walked over to a cupboard and opened it. Retrieving a large box he returned to his chair and drew out two very ancient looking drawings. 'These drawings are documents we have managed to protect since a few hundred years.'

Laying them side by side on the table he explained, 'The left one portrays the Hindu Goddess Kali and God Bhairava in Union and the right one portrays Buddha Heruka also known as Buddha Chakrasamvara and Buddha Vajravarahi in Union.'

'Geshe-La, I admit, I'm a little confused. I thought Lord Shiva is also known as Buddha Heruka and Lady Parvati also known as Buddha Vajravarahi, both being identical Holy Beings representing the masculine and feminine powers. The represent compassion and wisdom and secure the balance in the universe. How can they also be the Great Consciousness?'

'That is the problem with Samsara; we tend to lose ourselves in the chaos of conceptions. There is none other than the mind and the Great Consciousness is none other than union of all minds.'

'Are you saying that even the masculine and feminine powers are extension the sum of all very subtle minds?'

'Of course, how else can the union of bliss come into being? Water can only mix with water.'

"Of course!" I thought. "How else!"

Another question pooped up as I asked, 'A question I have on Emptiness. It is known as the "the source of all things" out of which all matter arises and returns in accordance to the law of karma. Why is this so?'

For a moment he looked at me. 'We are all but dreams, all illusions subjected to our state of consciousness, all Maya, subjected to the impermanence of time and space.' He paused again. 'Many scientific theories explore what they call the micro-cosmos, that microscopic world which is not visual to our common eye, the Quantum Theory or the String Theory, yet one won't be able to excess the final "frontier" of the micro-cosmos known as "Emptiness".'

'Why is this not possible?'

He answered, 'At least not through conventional methods. The conventional methods rely on two sources, the gross mind and matter. Matter is subjected to time and space, whereas "Emptiness" is a holy entity beyond time and space. To realize Emptiness directly one needs to access the very subtle mind. This is only possible through single pointed meditation. Only the very subtle mind is capable of identifying Emptiness.'

'Is that due to the nature of the very subtle mind, that being clarity?'

'You're right. There is also another reason, only the very subtle mind is subtler then Emptiness. The higher one climbs a mountain, the better and clearer is the view of the surrounding.'

I understood, but it was getting late. Ananda rose and approached Geshe-La silently.

Geshe-La nodded and with a gentle smile turned his gaze towards me.

'My young friend Ananda believes, we should continue tomorrow. I tend to agree with him. I wish you a good night.' Geshe-La then left the room without waiting for an answer.

Ananda turned to me. 'Dr. Cane, if you would follow me, I shall guide you to the dining room.'

Taking another entrance we walked out of the room. Opening the door we were standing in another hallway, it was about two meters wide. Turning to the right we walked a few meters before coming to another door. Opening it we entered the dining hall where monks were being served with meals. I and the young monk walked over to a table and took our seats. We didn't have to wait long before dinner was served. The dining hall was spacious with colorful drawings on the walls and on the ceilings. There were monks who served the food and others who assisted them. Every monk had a small wooden bowl. There was chapatti and hot vegetable curry served and butter tee. Everyone was busy enjoying their meals silently.

After dinner we were on the way to my room as we passed by a statue, similar to the figures on the drawing I had seen earlier. I stopped and asked Ananda what it meant.

He saw my confusion and said, 'Appearance can be deceptive.'

I waited for him to go on.

'What you see is the union of the feminine and masculine aspects in all of us.'

'I have seen statues of Gods and Goddesses, feminine and masculine Holy Beings, but none such as this,' I said.

'They not only represent the balance in us but that of the universe.'

'They also carry weapons.'

'These weapons have no conventional meaning. They serve a more ultimate purpose. They possess a symbolic character representing concrete actions in overcoming ignorance. They also represent an ultimate truth, but for the moment I think it's enough to say that these weapons have a symbolic character showing us ways to cure ourselves of ignorance. They represent no physical action.'

'I assume this is one of many aspects of Dharma which is misinterpreted and misused on our world,' I said.

He nodded. 'Dharma does not encourage non-virtuous actions, be it mental or of physical nature.'

We walked further until I came to my room. I bid good night and we parted.

13

Misguided views

These rooms were hardly used. Left overs of the "purging period" in Lhasa, but there are times such as today when a PSB officer takes it in custody. Mao Tse Tung was brought in; weak, overweight, almost bald and in his mid-thirties. He seemed to be on drugs, he could hardly stand. The two soldiers placed him on the table and tied his hands and legs.

The Shadow looked a little nervous. He remembered his days in this room. He could smell the burning flesh und feel the pain. The Lt. saw him. He knew what went through the man's head.

'Don't worry your painful days are over. So don't make it come back,' he said mockingly. 'Anyway we have other methods today, no more electricity cables or broken bones.' He took an injection needle, in it a transparent liquid substance. 'This is a powerful truth serum'.

The Lt. injected the man and waited. Ten minutes later, the man began to speak, about nothing, about everything.

'Hold him!' said the Lt.

'Have you heard of the Land of Paradise?' the Lt. asked the man in a harsh voice.

'Ahhhhhh.......?'

'Do you know the whereabouts of the Land of Paradise?'

The man stopped mumbling. He looked at the Lt. 'The laand of Paaraadiiseee...' he called out in pain, 'Beeeautifull, haapppppyyyy.'

'Where is it, you idiot, tell me the exact location!' shouted Lt. Chan.

'Ooooh.' Mao Tse Tung became calmer but then suddenly he cried out, 'Doon't hiit mee...'

'I'll if you don't answer!' shouted the Lt. Chan once more.

A few minutes passed and the man began to understand the Lt.'s question. He gazed at the ceiling above.

'It is there in the skies, out of reach, out of reach...' and then murmuring '...peaceeee...' Then he closed his eyes, becoming silent.

'What happened?' demanded the Lt.; the Sgt. nearby walked over and felt the pulse. He shook his head and said, 'He is dead, Sir.' Adding, 'Maybe of overdose.'

The Lt. grabbed the Sgt. and threatened him, 'Are you trying to be funny, are you blaming me for this. Get the doctor, now!'

A few minutes later came a physician. He was asked to confirm the death, which he did, and asked to perform an autopsy. 'But Sir, I don't have the equipment.'

'Check if he died of overdose, will you?' said the Lt. impatiently. 'And get the man buried.' With a finger on his lips he said 'Silently!' and then looking at the doctor, 'Officially he died in the Himalayas, it was an accident. No bodies were found, understood!'

Everyone understood. Two days later, the medical report confirming the death was on the Lt.'s table.

"Overdose of Truth serum! What a disappointment. I was so close," thought the Lt.

Meantime at the other end of the building, there was a knock on the door. The Col. said, 'Come in.'

Sgt. Choo entered. 'The man is dead, Sir. The Lt. Chan made a mistake. He saved us the trouble.'

Col. Yang nodded. After a short pause he answered, 'Thank you, Sgt. Keep an eye on that man. We are too close. We can't afford any fallbacks.'

'Yes Sir,' said the Sgt. leaving the Col. with a troubled look.

The next morning on his way to work the Col. noticed a figure. The figure looked like a Chinese man, maybe PSB. The Col. paused to look through a shop window with electronic articles, remaining so he sent an SMS to Sgt. Choo, 'being followed, usual route.' He then continued his journey. A few minutes later he arrived at a traffic light, the lights were red, he waited for them to turn green. Suddenly he heard noises behind him; he turned and saw Sgt. Choo with two other soldiers in uniform disarming a man. The Col. hurried to the spot and ordered his men to arrest the 'figure'. They got into a van and sped away in the direction of the PSB headquarters.

In his office the stranger handcupped sat in a chair.

'Why were you following the Col.?' asked the Sgt.

The stranger remained silent. The Sgt. emptied the man's jacket pocket and retrieved a brown leather wallet.

Opening it, he took out a military identity card; Sgt. Yuan Ting Zhe of the sixth regiment, Special Forces.

'Now Sgt. either you cooperate and tell us the whole story or we will ensure you never see the lights of the day!' Sgt. Choo spoke in a calm threatening voice.

'Sir, I would ask you to speak with my CO, Capt. Lee Kuan Jee. His coordinates are in my wallet,' Sgt. Yuan responded.

Sgt. Choo inspected the wallet again and retrieved a business card with the information of the Capt. Lee. He walked over and dialed a number in Peking.

'Am I speaking with Capt. Lee? One moment Sir.' Pausing the Sgt. handed the phone over to the Col.

'This is Col. Yang speaking. I'm the CO of the PSB in Lhasa.'

'Good Morning Sir,' said a somewhat nervous voice.

'I'm not sure if this is a good morning Capt. I have an issue which we have to speak of.'

'An Issue, Sir?' asked the Capt. obviously still nervous.

'Yes Capt., obviously a man of yours, Sgt. Yuan Ting Zhe, has been ordered to follow me. May I know why I'm put under surveillance and furthermore authorized by whom?' The speaker at the other end of the line was reluctant to answer.

'Well Capt., I'm waiting!' said the Col. impatiently.

'Sir, I received the order directly from General Lee. He requested me to put you and Lt. Chan under surveil-lance. No details were disclosed.'

The Col. replied in a calm but stern voice, 'Thank you for your cooperation. Good Bye.'

Turning towards Sgt. Choo he said, 'Sgt. let the man go and put me through to the office of the PSB Director in Peking.'

'Yes Sir.'

A few minutes later a call was put through to the Col.'s office. 'This is Col. Yang speaking.'

'Good Morning Col,' replied Brigadier General Lee Boh Seong, the Director of the PSB in Peking.

'Good Morning Sir.'

'I hear you would like to speak to me.'

'Yes sir…' And without any small talk the Col. went straight to the point. 'May I know Sir, as to why I'm put under surveillance?'

'Well as usual you get to the point.' Pausing a moment the General said, 'We have been receiving strange information for some time now. Actually very contradicting ones. Your official reports show no indication of the issue.'

'With all respect, Sir, it would make things easier if you would say what you want to say.'

The General did not answer immediately. 'We have been receiving information from our people in the US and in India about Tibetans activities. The reports, although vague, indicate that Tibetans are moving in and out of Tibet illegally. They seem to travel over India to the US. At the same time the Office of the UN Secretary General is speaking with Tibetans not known to us. The strange thing is these people seem not to have any connection with the Exile Government of Tibet. We find no indication of such activities in your reports.'

'Well sir, if we knew anything we would report it.'

'Well Col., knowing your track report, I'm surprised at your performance. There are however others who have a different opinion. But I do have a suspicion, a different motive perhaps.'

The Col. did not answer immediately. 'I Sir have dedicated my entire life to the great course of our Motherland. It is beneath my dignity to speak about any "suggestions or ulterior motives". If you feel I'm too old for the job, it lies in your hands to replace me.'

'No, no Col., we don't want to jump the gun here. I'm aware of your loyalty and dedication to our Motherland. Maybe it is time we speak with each other heart to heart. Let's meet in Peking.'

'Thank you for the invitation. I shall have my office make an appointment with your people.'

'That will be fine. Good Bye Col.'

'Good Bye Sir.'

Hanging up, the Col. spoke to the Sgt. 'Sgt. book me a flight to Peking today.'

'Yes sir.'

At the same time a note arrived in a sealed envelope for Lt. Chan. He observed the seal very carefully and was satisfied that it wasn't tempered with.

He then opened it and began to encrypt the information with a code only he and the Shadow knew.

"A visitor is expected in Leh soon, a date is not known. Destination: Paradise City. Have already alerted our people in Hotels and Airport. Will keep you informed."

"This is very good news!" thought the Lt.

The next day the Sgt. Choo walked into the Col.'s office. He handed over a piece of paper. The Col. picked it and saw the contents.

'It seems the Lt. has been very busy and he seems to be on the right track. I believe it is time to eliminate the activities of the "Shadow".' He paused.

'A second thing, alert our people and ensure a safe passage is worked out. A second person is expected to arrive in India soon.'

The Sgt. nodded and left the room.

"So close, we can't let it fail!" the Col. thought.

14

Follow your heart

Indira landed at the airport in Delhi, this time with an Indian Passport. She was informed of the Chinese surveillance. The PSB had a tip-off; a Tibetan woman in her mid-twenties was to arrive any time this week at the New Delhi International Airport. She was careful and kept a watchful eye for anything out of the ordinary.

Her meditation skills helped. On her flight back she made friends with a group of Indian tourists returning from the US. Her Hindi was good enough that she could blend into the group.

The out of boarding process went through without any problems and at the passport control the officer couldn't discover any flaws. It was an authentic document.

After being outside she separated herself from the group and as instructed she rushed into a brown four wheel waiting at the far end of the taxi stand. Having practically no luggage, she was light on foot.

The car sped through the streets of Delhi. The driver did his best considering the traffic. He was very skilled and concentrated and took precautions that no one was following them. The driver avoided the villages, instead took the jungle paths.

After a three hours' drive, Indira arrived at a remote area. They stopped at a small house.

The driver finally spoke. 'Here we stay for the night. Early morning we continue.'

He got out and walked to the house. After checking the inside, he returned to say 'No problem. No lights, you stay inside, I hide car. I sleep in car.'

Indira did as was told. There was a bed, some dry fruits and two bottles of water. She ate the fruits and drank the water before getting into bed. Despite being nervous she immediately fell into a dreamless sleep.

It was still early when the journey continued, this time it went through rough terrains. After a five hour drive, it came to a halt at a lonely and deserted area.

Hiding his four-wheel in a nearby cave they hurried on foot up a hill and disappeared into high grass. A hundred meters later they were in the middle of a small jungle. A man was waiting for them.

The driver turned to her and said, 'He take you to Leh.' He left them without saying another word.

Indira asked the stranger, 'How?'

'We fly,' he said.

She has learned to ask no names. Another hundred meters, they came to something which was hidden under bushes. Looking closer she identified it to be a double passenger helicopter.

Indira helped the pilot to clear the bushes and both boarded before flying towards Leh, directly to the secret route to Keajara.

Flying low and avoiding Leh, they landed at a remote area where another vehicle was waiting for them. It was a seven hour flight. She got off and the pilot flew away without saying another word.

Another man approached her and said, 'You should be save now. The agents are expecting you at the hotel.' They then drove off in the direction of Keajara.

15

A life of sacrifice

The Col. landed in the Peking International Airport, he was picked up by an official limousine. The car drove off quickly north east towards Xinglong County. He was glad he didn't have to drive into Peking, never really liked the hustle and bustle. It was all a facade. Everything about it was dishonest, greed, hate ruled. After a three hour drive they finally reached the remote area of Xinglong County. Just before entering the town, the limousine turned off into a gravel road leading to nowhere. They arrived at a small lake, another limousine was parked there.

An older man in dark suit was sitting on a bench; standing near him was a tall, well trained looking person. "Special Forces, maybe!" thought Col. Yang. Obviously the body guard.

The Col. walked over to the gentleman, who arose and came towards the Col. and embraced him. They stood such for a few moments.

The Col. said, 'Thank you father for coming.'

'I'm very happy to see you. We hardly have a chance to meet nowadays,' said Yang Tsu Tse.

'I miss our talks,' said the Col. with a hint of sadness. 'I hope you're well?'

'A question an old man such as I can answer with a "yes". But this is China and anything can happen. How is your mother?'

'She has risen,' said the Col. carefully, knowing his father had a very difficult time letting his mother go. His father had loved his mother very dearly. In fact it is one of those love stories where a boy meets a girl very young and their love for each last not only a lifetime but is eternal.

Yang Tsu Tse with tears in his eyes nodded slowly. He did not want to leave yet, he could not. He had to make sure his son was safe. But his wife couldn't wait, she was ill and had very little time left on this world. It was time for her to "rise", to achieve Nirvana.

'I'm sorry for the show of emotion. I miss her.' He said while rubbing the tears away with a napkin.

'I miss her very much. My heart aches.' The Col. looked at his father with love and embraced him once more. He is not known to show his emotions. Even as a young child he was able to stay in tune with the oneness, attentive of his emotions. But there were moments such these where he allowed himself to be overcome by his love for those he cared for.

'Are you fine?' asked the father.

The Col. said, 'There are good days and there not so good days.' The father nodded understandingly.

'Don't worry I have taken care of the issue with the PSB General. He'll not be looking into your affairs at least for the moment. He has given you time. We need to bring the issue to an end.'

'I know, but timing is an important factor. We need to be very careful.'

'Yes, of course. Do you think we are on the right track?'

'Yes, I think we are.'

'My dear Son, I am worried about you.'

'Father, I too am worried about you and I believe it is time for you to leave.'

His father looked at his bodyguard 'Strangely Wang believes it too. He will be traveling with me.'

'I will make preparations for you to leave soon.'

'How much time do I have?' asked the father.

'Three weeks,' said the son.

'I will see you in ...' said the father leaving the sentence unfinished.

'Are you sure everything is fine? Do you need to leave earlier?' asked the son with concern in his voice.

'No. I'm fine with the plan.' With a short glance at his watch he said, 'I think it is time for us to return.'

'The call will be on short notice.'

'Yes, I have already finalized everything. We are set to go.'

Both men embraced each other once more before turning around and driving away.

The next day at PSB HQ in Lhasa another discussion took place.

'What do mean she wasn't there? Where was she?' Lt. Chan asked, while thinking, "If I wasn't so dependent on him, I would shoot him."

'I'm sorry to say, she did not appear at the hotel,' said the Shadow.

'Where was she then?' shouted the Lt.

'We don't know. We posted agents everywhere in Leh and also at the airport in Delhi. She did not show up.'

'She didn't turn into air!' exclaimed the Lt.

'No, Sir. Her name didn't show up in any passengers list. It can only mean two things. She cancelled her flight or she flew in with another name.'

'What are you saying, she had a false passport?'

'That is one possibility.'

'This is turning into a scandal…' said the Lt. slowly. Lt. Chan didn't like what he was hearing, 'We don't only have a leak in the PSB but we also have someone who is helping these people with legal documents.'

'That seems to be the case.'

'Wait here, I have to report this.' Lt. Chan walked directly to Col. Yang. The Col. was having his morning tea as the Lt. came in.

'Sir, we have a major problem,' he said a little exited.

'Major problem?' repeated the Col. 'How so?'

The Lt. reported the case.

'Lt. are you very sure of your accusation.'

'Yes sir, I'm very sure. You must report it to Peking.'

'You are aware, that if I report about this to Peking, there will be major consequences,' warned the Col.

'Yes, Sir.'

'There will be investigations and no turning back,' he repeated the warning.

The Lt. seemed to have finally understood what the Col. was trying to say; the investigation will not be limited only to this case. They might also find out what happened to Mao Tse Tung. A shiver went through his spine.

'What would be your recommendation?' the Lt. asked.

'I propose we begin our own investigation. You should lead it. Use all the resources you need.'

Somehow the Lt. liked the idea. He'll be in control and discovering the responsible person or persons would give him a boost in his career. 'Yes Sir. I think your proposal is the better solution.' He left the room.

The Col. took a piece of paper and jotted down, 'The snake is looking for food. It's only a matter of time,' folded it, inserted it into an envelope and sealed it.

He picked up his phone. 'Sgt., could you please come in.'

He handed the envelope to the Sgt. who left the office without any comment.

"Yes, it's only a matter of time!" thought the Col.

16

*The journey to enlightenment
begins with the first step*

The smell of incense awoke me the next morning. My watch showed five a.m. Curios I peeped out into the halfway. Monks were on their feet, busy walking up and down the hallway. I took a quick shower and left the room. In the hall I could hear chanting. I followed it. Coming to an intersection and taking a right I found myself in front of a large doorway leading into a great hall, a prayer hall. Monks sitting on the floor, in long rows reciting the holy verses from palm leaves. There were others spreading the incense in their hands throughout space. In the midst of chanting, stillness resided.

My gaze stopped on one sentence written on the wall. It was in Tibetan. In that moment I noticed Ananda beside me. I asked him what it meant.

He translated the sentence, "Whilst existing in time, timelessness was striven. All opinions are only half truths, bound by time and space, relative to our existence. I was lost in the midst of manyness. Choose wisely and one is rewarded by perfection. It exists in all of us, my heart reached out, looking for salvation, in the oneness."

"Yes," I thought. "All is one". Our blindness not wanting to accept this truth, our ignorance, our ego, buried under the weight of self-attachment and fear; creating pain and suffering; building barriers, limiting ourselves of our true capabilities, holding ourselves back from becoming free, liberated and enlightened.

Our ego stands in the way. We would rather live in pain than seek salvation. We continue to blame others for our perdition. It's always someone or something else, the enemy, the weather or nature. The ego is tricky, it blinds, it clouds the senses and so ignorance continues to dominate.

Our refusal to accept change makes us vulnerable. We believe in the illusion of security, we build walls to defend the 'status quo', calling those who are not within as aliens. We continue to live in an illusion and misconceptions, from one life to another.

As I was in this state of contemplation, Ananda gently touched my shoulder and lead me to the side. He informed that unfortunately Geshe-La had to postpone our meetings; he had to attend something important.

This gave me the opportunity to take part in the daily routines, at least for the next few days. Waking up early, doing morning meditation and helping out where one can. Ananda and I spent much time in discussions. Not so much about Dharma more so about how the people lived. We went out into the village and helped the farmers to plant the crops, to water the fields and to reap the grains. One need not ask or speak. It's about getting involved, about being one with the environment.

Snow covered mountains in the horizon, clear blues skies, sun shining with all her might and nature in its full blossom. Nature does not hesitate. Nature performs, nature acts with an open and full heart. There are no half ways or postponement. Everything exists in nowness. This one learns.

Every word, touch awoke a positive effect. How can it be anything else? With all the richness Dharma has to offer. Our existence is dependent on our environment and the basis of our environment is our planet, our solar system, our galaxy, our universe. This too is nature, nothing else but an evolvement of time, space and matter.

What is technology but an evolvement of our mental capability to use matter and the environment in more complex ways! That too is nature! Standing there, watching the clouds pass by and the wind stroking the leaves of the great trees, I saw oneness.

A gentle touch returned me back to the present. I turned and saw Indira. Thinking first her to be a mirage in a distance, I did not react. Only as she came into my arms did I comprehend her presence. We stood so for many minutes before I released her. Happiness flooded my heart; a part of me had returned, a friend, a companion.

'I'm very happy now that you're here.' We looked into each other's eyes. Her face, her mouth, how much I had missed her, 'I have missed you terribly.'

'Ditto,' she said smilingly, her eyes lighting up.

'Tell me my dear,' I continued, 'how is it you're here?'

'Oh, that is a long story, but for now let's just say, it was a question of priority,' she paused and added smilingly, 'you being the higher.' I didn't know I could love someone so much. 'Let's speak more, later. You shan't be late for your appointment with Geshe-La.' She then took me by my hand and led me to a nearby temple.

I was surprised, there was a meeting. 'A meeting, but Geshe-La is away,' I said.

'And he has returned. I met Ananda on the way here, he asked me to bring you back, my darling.'

Without another word and arm in arm we marched towards the monastery. As we passed a small outer temple I whispered, 'I don't want to be separated from you anymore.'

She stopped, looked at me and said earnestly, 'That will never happen!' and then gestured me to face the statue of Buddha Shakyamuni in the temple. I couldn't take my eyes of her as she whispered, 'Let us pray.'

My life until now, on the other side of the world occupied me. It was a time I had not known of this world. Not realizing there is more to this life then only following the clock. One needs courage to tear down these walls, and explore the other side. Liberation of the self through the act of courage and compassion! In the wisdom of salvation lies the secret of achieving the higher self, the state of true bliss.

Our continual reliance on matter, our fear for the unknown leads us away from the true purpose of our existence. These times, where faith continually degener-ates, we are faced with never ending suffering. We are drifting away from our inner self. One finds it difficult to believe or to reach out for that which is everlasting. One's submission for short lived "excitements" has grown and is ever increasing.

Keajara is a rare jewel, important to be preserved for those seeking liberation from Samsara. Contended was I, with this world, peaceful was the world surrounding me, deep was the happiness within me. Everything else is the wisdom of silence. We spent a few more minutes there before hurrying towards Geshe-La's study. We found no one there. We waited, but only for a moment as he entered the room and greeted us.

'I'm very sorry Dr. Cane for delaying our meeting. Something very urgent came up which needed my immediate attention.'

'I have enjoyed my stay here Geshe-La. It has given me the opportunity to learn more about Keajara. No harm done.'

Turning to Indira he said, 'Ah, Miss Indira, I heard you've returned, indeed I'm very pleased to see you. How are you and how are our things at the UN?'

'I'm very well Geshe-La and our efforts in the UN are progressing very well. So far we have been able to convince most of the parties to join our course.'

'Not to worry, all will be well!' he said. 'Let's now continue where we left off.' A short pause later, 'Where I was, ah yes, it was about time. We humans put too much importance on time. We measure almost everything with time. But when one contemplates on the phenomenon "time" one comes to the conclusion that time and not to forget, space, both exist in dependent of matter. One can say that both "time" and "space" are "by-products" of matter or that matter surfs on "time" and "space". '

'This is due to our conviction that the world exists as we perceive,' I added.

'Yes,' he answered. 'The proof is everywhere for the one to see. Let's take a river for an example. The flow of a river, one believes it begins in the mountains and ends in the seas or oceans. But that is not so. It is actually a cycle. Water evaporates into the skies and the returns to earth as rain or snow. It returns to the rivers. The cycle keeps repeating. So what does this example tell us?'

'That matter is ever changing.' It also dawned onto me, "It cannot be any other way; because of Karma! The karmical seeds keep ripening and as such new events arise, new experiences are made. In lies in the nature of things! To experience new things, one needs new events, new environments; matter reforms and with it time and space."

'One is subjected to a dynamic world, no event is the same, every experience is unique.'

'This also explains the cycle of birth and rebirth,' I added.

'What would happen if one increases the velocity? What would happen to the river?' he asked.

I replied a little hesitantly but at the same time think-ing the answer through, 'I believe the same thing which happens when one begins to increase the velocity of any object. I suppose at some point the river will cease to exist.'

'Exactly! And what does that tell us?'

'All things are perishable and transient?'

'Yes. But there is more to it. The river does not only cease to exist, it becomes one with the universe. It will return to its true existence. Every molecule will be dissected to its final core; the state of emptiness. It is the end of the chain called matter.'

'Where time and space do not exist, where only oneness is present and this oneness is the universal consciousness,' I added.

His eyes awake and alert, 'Yes. We speak much about time and space but there is still much to understand. For instance, imagine a world without linear time. No aging, nothing perishes; nothing becomes; in fact there is no movement. One could say there will be standstill.'

'But movement is important for interesting things to happen. It's important to overcome predicaments.'

'How can there be standstill, we are always making new decisions.'

'It is important for the process of learning. Experiences go hand in hand with development.'

'We are the sum of our decisions. With new decisions we become a different person, we continue to change.'

'In the course of time, mankind has gone through many changes. It has allowed men to access up to 10% of his cerebral capacity,' I said.

'Ah,' he said raising his finger in the air. 'It's not so much the brain which is in the center of our discussion.'

'No sir, it's the mind.'

'The mind is the software whereas the brain the hardware. You are right, when you say we are using less of the cerebral capability. The reason being we don't know how to access it. The human race has come to a point in which it needs a higher form of understanding. To access this higher form of understanding one needs to concentrate on inner challenges.'

'You mean we need an update, another version?' I asked.

'It's already there this software, only there are fire-walls blocking the access. One needs to overcome this firewall. The solution is to "live and become compassion".'

'How would one go about it?' I asked.

'We must learn to pull down the barriers, our fears, our pains, our conventions. They are our blockers or firewalls. Remember, we humans are more interested in having than are we about being.'

'The more we let go, the lesser the burden,' I said.

'When one is enlightened, one is free of all this.'

'What is this state of enlightenment?' I asked.

'It's a state of continual mindfulness, a state single pointedness, a state of oneness.'

'In this state of mind, time and space cease to exist?

'Yes.'

'In our present state of mind, it's difficult for us to comprehend such a state of consciousness.'

'We need to learn. The past memories we carry only in the state of very subtle mind. The gross mind forgets,' he said.

'Only by accessing our very subtle mind, do we remember.'

'Not only that, we would also be able to see our future lives.'

'So we reboot in every life.'

'One could say so.'

'It the days of Kali Yurga, which began some three thousand years ago, pure Dharma would be remembered

250

only by a few. The reliance on matter grows. One needs to see to believe. Very few understand something called higher state of mind,' said Indira.

'Science requires empirical proof, one which can be measured by scientific gadgets made out of matter. The problem is these gadgets are only capable to measure so far and not farther,' said Geshe-La touching his body. 'To go farther,' pointing to his heart, 'one has to explore one's mind.'

'And the only method to do so is through single pointed meditation?' I asked.

The answer was a simple 'Yes'. 'We are all trapped in Samsara not so much that providence has chosen this for us, no, it has more to do with our personal decisions,' explained Geshe-La. 'We have decided to lead a life which is full of suffering. A seemingly never ending process of actions and reactions, resulting in experiences, from one life to another. We have decided to follow our ignorance, our ego.'

'We ourselves are responsible for the calamities we face in life,' I ended his sentence.

At this moment Ananda walked in. Geshe-La smiled. 'I think we will continue tomorrow morning.' Saying this, he bid good evening and left the room.

After dinner we spent the remaining hours in the monastery garden.

'I missed you so much,' I said to Indira.

She had a pair of jeans and a white blouse on.

'I had not felt so before. It is as if a part of you is missing, one feels incomplete.'

251

'I know.' Somehow words couldn't describe what I felt. With her in my arms, finally together again, united was I feeling as a complete person again.

The next morning in Gesha-La's study he unveiled the mystery of time. He began by describing the cycle of existence. 'The "Primeval Dharma" speaks of the cycle of time as the continual repetition of "one Brahma day" and "one Brahma night".'

'A Brahma day and night?' I asked.

'It is written that one Brahma Day comprises of four time periods which builds a cycle called the "Yurga". At the same time one Brahma-Day equals to 4,320 million man-years. This table shows...' he opened a piece of cloth which lied folded on the table. In it was an old object, looked like bronze, a bronze plate. I jotted down the information in my notebook.

The Yurgas	Krta	Tretae	Draepara	Kali
The Strength of Dharma	1	0.75	0.5	0.25
The Concentration of Consciousness	Creation and Sustainment	Sustainment	Sustainment and Dissolution	Dissolution
Man Years	1,728,000	1,296,000	864,000	432,000
The Strength of Sutra/Tantra	Sutra	Sutra	Sutra	Tantra/Sutra

'This table shows the periodic system I speak of. It begins with the Krta Yurga which lasts approximately 1,728,000 million man years, ending when the second Yurga begins called the Tretae Yurga, followed by Draepara Yurga and ending with the Kali Yurga. Accord-

252

ing to this calendar, we find ourselves in the Kali Yurga. In the Krta Yurga Dharma is omnipresent. The beings in this period have a deep understanding of Dharma. In the Tretae Yurga and the following Yurgas the situation begins to change. The affinity to seek for Dharma deteriorates. Sentient beings are more interested to seek material and sensual gain. The beings living in the first three Yurgas are spiritually motivated then those living in the Kali Yurga. They have deep sense for that which is virtuous. During these periods, many sentient beings have been able to achieve enlightenment only by hearing the Sutras.'

'Were there fewer humans on this planet?' I asked.

'We don't know if they were humans or humanoid and no it was not on this "physical planet",' added Indira.

'What do you mean by "not on this physical planet"?'

Indira smiled and so did Geshe-La. 'It is a little more complicated than that. We speak of multi-dimensional universe. Take for instance our world. Alone on this world inhabits infinite variety of species. For an ant, for instance, a cup could be a secure place, an obstacle or something else. It would not identify it as a cup. Just so, right here only in a parallel time and space, worlds exist. There are infinite other space and times, homed by infinite other species. We are travelers.'

'So the Yurgas describe both an evolutionary process and a multi-dimensional inhabitance?' I asked.

'All worlds underlie this process,' answered Geshe-La.

'Not only those, the Sutra and Tantra teachings have different weight in all these periods. Whereas the Sutra is the explanation of the 'why', Tantra is of the 'how'. The beings living in the first three periods were less diverted by material or sensual pleasures, theirs were higher mental capability. The Sutras were sufficient to tread the path towards salvation. It is different for the beings existing in the Kali Yurga. They live in fear and doubt. They require more powerful teachings such as Tantra to lead them out of Samsara,' said Indira.

'Tantra offers many opportunities to achieve enlightenment quickly. Of course one needs to have knowledge of Sutra, without which Tantra could be misunderstood,' said Geshe-La.

"Degenerative thinking in our time makes it difficult for sentient beings to achieve liberation," I recollected Richard's words.

'Out of compassion, Buddha Shakyamuni took the form of Buddha Heruka and turned the Wheel of Tantra Dharma. What does this mean?' asked Geshe-La with a smile. 'There is a saying in your country "extreme situations require extreme measures" if I remember correctly?'

I nodded as Geshe-La continued, 'Emotions are very powerful, even more then thoughts. The ultimate of emotions is compassion. With compassion and the knowledge of Tantra one is capable of accessing the very subtle mind quickly.'

Geshe-La must have read the confusion on my face, adding, 'As you know, the great fire which destroys all negative karmical seeds is ignited by the red and white drops.' I nodded. 'Tantra helps one to take contact with the red and white drops quickly.'

I asked, 'The red and white drop; they are Buddha Heruka and Vajravarahi?'

'Yes.'

'And Buddha Heruka and the Lord Shiva; Buddha Vajravarahi and Lady Parvati, are they one and the same Person, known only differently?'

'Persons!' he said with a giggle. 'No they are not persons. They are forces created by the mind.' A minute later he explained, 'Buddha Shakyamuni was the fourth Buddha on this world to "turn the Wheel of Dharma". There have already been three other Buddhas before him. There will be a total of thousand Buddhas before this world ends. The third Buddha who turned the Wheel of Tantra, took the Form of Lord Shiva, so you see, it is not a coincidence that there are parallels between the teachings of Lord Shiva and that of Buddha Heruka.'

As Geshe-La paused, Indira continued, 'One sees similarities in both teachings. Take for instance the Union of Bliss also known as the Union of the masculine and feminine energies. In Hinduism it is Lord Shiva and Lady Parvati and in Buddhism it is Buddha Heruka and Buddha Vajravarahi. In both teachings the Holy Mt. Kailash is described as the center of the universe.'

I politely interrupted asking why the holy mountain is seen as the center of the universe.

'A good question!' he said. 'When you build a house, you need a foundation, without which it would difficult to erect a stable building. The same applies to everything else; everything needs a foundation to exist. The holy mountain serves as a strong foundation.'

He walked over to a cabinet in the room and opened a drawer and retrieving something which looked like a box, wrapped with a beautiful piece of silk cloth. With the box in the hand, he then returned to his seat and laid it on the wooden table before him. Unwrapping the silk cloth, a beautifully ornamented wooden box appeared. As I was observing the box, Geshe-La continued by saying, 'The artifact in this box is one of the oldest ever found. A detail description of its origin, with time and place, is noted down on it'.

He opened the box and withdrew a scroll. It was brown, looked like leather. On the one side, it had a rough surface, on the other side, the surface was smooth and clear. On it were drawings and writings. The scroll looked very well preserved.

'If you observe the writings at the bottom, it's written in a Tamil. The words say "In the last stage of the Tretae, in the holy city of Mahabalipuram, in the school of Dharma, by the hands of the holy sages, I was created". The Tretae Yurga began about 2.5 million years ago, and as the document clearly says, it was "created" at last stage of the Tretae Yurga. We are estimating the age of this document to be about 1.6 to 1.7 million years old, making it the oldest historical document existing.'

I raised my eyebrows and he nodded saying, 'Yes, this is one of the artifacts discovered in Indus Valley. It's one our most precious artifacts.'

He placed it immediately back into the box.

'We made hand copies.' He retrieved another piece of document, handing me an edited version of the original.

ஓம் நமோ சிவாய

பிரபஞ்சத்தின் மையம் கைலாஷ். ஒவ்வொரு பிரபஞ்சத்திற்கும் ஒரு பரிசுத்த பர்வதம் உள்ளது. இந்த பர்வதங்கள் உள்ளடக்கிய ஆண்பால் மற்றும் பெண்பால் சக்திகள் உயிர் தோன்றுவதற்கான சமநிலையை உருவாக்குகின்றன.

திரேதா யுகத்தின் இறுதி நிலையில் புனித ஞானிகளால் புனித நகரான மகாபாள்விபுரத்தின் தர்ம பாடசாலையில் தோன்றப்பட்டது.

He explained further, 'In general, to avoid any damage to the originals, we duplicate them. As you can see, the writings on the side begin with the words, "OM NAMO SHIVAYA", praising the Holy Lord Shiva. The writings further down say, Kailash is described as the center of this galaxy. According to this document, each galaxy possesses a holy mountain. These holy mountains are the embodiments of the masculine and feminine poles, such as the magnetic fields which create a balance to enable life to develop.'

'Meaning they possess extraordinary powers?'

'No more than the powers our backbone possess,' answered Indira. 'The important thing is the function it plays. Our spinal column as a whole is crucial for our

257

existence. As such the Kailash, the Himalayas and other mountain chains secure the stability of our planet. The Kailash being the center.'

Geshe-La continued by saying, 'The birth as humans is very rare. It can be compared to a "corn of sand on a beach of sand". The same logic applies to our planet. It is very difficult to find a world where humans exist.' Pointing to the document he said, 'Each galaxy possesses a center, a sustained balance, maintained by the masculine and feminine forces.' With a moment's pause he continued, 'One need not explore the space to understand the cosmos. One only has to begin with oneself.'

The correlations were apparent. There is no phenomenon in the universe independent of the two entities. Everything in life requires a balance to develop, to grow and to exist. Be it a partnership, nature, the climate, the rotation of the planet, the distance between the sun and the earth, the distance between other planets and even the very essence of being able to develop understanding. Without balance, nothing positive would develop or nourish.

The older monk approached Geshe-La, smiling he turned to us and said, 'I'm afraid we have to stop here, it seems it's time for lunch but let's meet again in the afternoon'. We agreed as he slowly left us.

We walked down the corridors silently and reached the large dining hall, where lunch was already being served. After lunch we met Ananda, who wanted to show us something. We followed him down a corridor, ending in a small hall. It was decorated with paintings of the historical Buddha Shakyamuni and of other sages. All colorful and well preserved. I turned to Ananda and asked him, how old they were.

'They go back to days of the Great Guru, Pathmasambhava, about 1,200 years ago.'

'They are very well preserved,' I commented.

'Yes, that is due to the wax we use to preserve the original painting.'

'Indeed, is it something you develop or find in the nature?'

Ananda did not answer immediately, 'It is something we develop.'

He seemed to hesitate. Due to my trust in him, I ignored to question further. There were two other corridors leading away from the hall, one on the left and one the right. Ananda took the left one. At the end was a heavy wooden door. We entered a large room with high ceilings. In the center were three huge stupa like constructions.

Ananda elaborated, 'What you see here is the Heruka Mandala, also known as the Land of Keajra.'

The Mandalas were about three meters in height. They had a rectangle foundation, measuring four square meters.

'The mandalas you see here depict the Pure Land of Keajra, the home of Buddha Heruka and Vajravarahi,' he said smilingly. 'I must confess, it took me many years to grasp their true meaning.'

We gazed the mandalas silently until Ananda continued his explanation. 'These mandalas are a three dimensional display of the Heruka Mandala. A Thangka on the other hand displays a two dimensional view. One can see many levels, chambers, Deities, Holy Beings, colors and structures in these mandalas.'

'You mentioned you were able to grasp their true meaning?' I asked.

'An inner journey, to the beginning of all things, the very subtle mind.' He took a deep breath before continuing, 'That all things evolve and dissolve; that our mental and physical actions are the reasons behind it; that our actions can be virtuous or non-virtuous; that our non-virtuous actions result from non-virtuous motivations. The self-grasping mind, also known as our ego is the reason for it. One could even say that non-virtuous thoughts are "unnatural". They don't serve eternal equilibrium. The problem is the paradox of thoughts. It's natural to want to be happy. But it is unnatural to think that happiness comes from self-centeredness.'

Saying this Ananda walked closer to the mandalas and began chanting mantras. I came to know later that it was the Essence Mantra of Buddha Heruka and Vajravarahi. As he recited, the room became brighter. I noticed the area around his chest began to glow. His face carried a smile of serenity. I had not witnessed such a thing before. He seemed to be in deep meditation.

An emotion of contentment overwhelmed me. Time stood still. All things in the universe were in one. I can't say how long I was in that room, I can't remember how I came to be in the vajra posture, but as I opened my eyes, I was in this state. Indira was still in the room and she was waiting patiently for me to open my eyes.

'Are you fine, is everything ok?' she asked.

I simply nodded, felling refreshed. She helped me to get on my feet.

The recitation came to an end, Ananda opened his eyes. As he did he said very softly, it was a silent whisper echoing into eternity, 'There is only one reason for our existence. It's to remember our way home.'

'That what you see on these mandalas are pathways, to help us to remember. We see it everywhere, these pathways,' added Indira. 'We only have to observe nature. In everything is Dharma imbedded. It shows us the way out of Samsara, reminding us of the logic of rebirth, of suffering, of the ever repeating process of leaving and returning, that this life lasts only a short period, in which we live and leave, only to return.'

'To break the chain, one needs to open the mind, to remember about finding the path of return, that which leads to oneness,' said Ananda. The words filled the room, they lifted my heart and enlightened me!

A few minutes passed, before we finally returned to Geshe-La's study to continue the teaching session.

'The workings of the Yurgas are much more complex than what is presented in this table,' he said, referring to the Yurga table.

The Yurgas	Krta	Tretae	Draepara	Kali
The Strength of Dharma	1	0.75	0.5	0.25
The Concentration of Consciousness	Creation and Sustainment	Sustainment	Sustainment and Dissolution	Dissolution
Man Years	1,728,000	1,296,000	864,000	432,000
The Strength of Sutra/Tantra	Sutra	Sutra	Sutra	Tantra/Sutra

'Words are inadequate to describe correlations between the realms, periods and consciousness. According to the Hindu cosmology, a universe lasts about 4,320,000,000 years or one day Brahma. A new cycle begins, known as the resting period, Brahma rests for one night, just as long as the day. This process also known as pralaya, a cataclysm, repeats for 100 Brahma years or 311 trillion and 40 billion human years which represents a Brahma's lifespan.'

'I remember reading about similarities between the latest scientific discoveries with the Hindu concept of a "day and night of Brahma" corresponding to our present scientific knowledge of the universe.'

Indira spoke, 'The days and nights of Brahma give a view of the universe that is divinely created, and is not strictly evolutionary, but an ongoing cycle of birth, death, and rebirth of the universe.'

I added, 'Dharma seems to be the only great faith dedicated to the idea that the cosmos itself undergoes an immense change. This change takes place in the form as infinite number of deaths and rebirths. This cycle corresponds to the time scale of modern scientific cosmology.'

Indira continued, 'A day and night of Brahma lasts 8.64 billion years. It is longer than the age of the Earth or the Sun and about half the time since the Big Bang.'

'This corresponds with the logic of birth and rebirth,' I said and Geshe-La nodded. For some unknown reason another thought came to my mind. 'Geshe-La, many speak of the possibility of traveling through time. Science is even researching on whether matter can be

262

sent backward or forward in time. Is this realistic, can this be done?' I asked.

He remained silent for a long moment before answering, 'An interesting question! Is that possible to transfer one's body to a certain time and space?' A pause. 'We know Buddha's are capable to transfer their minds to any time and space. They possess the capability to assume any form. One might say that this is a form of time travel, but it's not what you mean.' He paused as if thinking his answer carefully through. 'Let's think this through. The mind possesses the ability of projection. Only by thinking it's able to be anywhere, at any time without leaving its space. So for the mind, as you put it, to travel through time, would not be a problem. Our imaginations, visions, thoughts and dreams are examples of what I speak of. But what you ask of is whether we as individual, with our present body and consciousness, would be able to transfer ourselves into another time and space, another life.'

I nodded.

'A Buddha does not physically travel through time and space. A Buddha's mind is capable to appear in a certain time and space and take a physical form.'

'And Buddhas being pure mind assume a form when they arrive at a certain time and space?' I asked.

'We all do it. It is called birth. Only Buddhas are not trapped in the cycle of uncontrolled rebirth.'

'They are free,' Indira said.

'But Buddhas do not have the power to rectify Karma; their purpose is solely to reveal the spiritual path

263

leading to enlightenment, eliminating suffering through self-realization.'

'So one does not need to take one's body, since matter exist everywhere, and given the fact our karmical seeds follow us, we are able to create a body in another time and space,' I answered.

'Furthermore, traveling through time and space; it would prerequisite changes, intentionally or unintentionally; meaning one who travels into the past would change the course of events in the future, however small. If a person would do this, it would mean; affecting events such as resetting the state of enlightenment. Meaning those who have become Buddhas, would no more be Enlightened Beings and find themselves again in the chain of uncontrolled rebirth. That is not possible.' He smiled. 'The ways of Karma are complex but it would not allow one to physically travel through time, neither backwards nor forwards.'

'Of course Buddhas do not return into the cycle of Samsara. It undermines the logic of liberation from Samsara.' I agreed, but wasn't completely satisfied with the argument. 'But are there not scenarios where matter is transferable to other dimensions, and the past could also be a dimension,' I insisted.

'We never really transfer matter into another dimension. It is not necessary. Matter can be dissolved and evolved elsewhere.'

Indira interrupted, 'As you are aware of, based on the theory called entanglement in physics, it has been discovered; when two particles interact with one another, a special connection takes place, it's a unique relationship.

For instance, should one of these particles be affected in any way, say by observations, the other particle will reflect the exact same reaction instantaneously, irrelevant of their distance from each other, be it across the room or across the universe.'

'So these two objects act as one. They are interconnected despite the distance that lies between them,' I concluded.

'The interconnection allows copies of forms to be created. This is only one simple example; the interconnection of matter is far more complex, enabling infinite possibilities to take place.'

'We don't need to transfer matter, only the mind?'

'Actually no such thing as a transfer really takes place. What really happens is, mind retracts and expands. The retraction leads to awareness of subtle dimension, whereas the expansion leads to awareness of gross dimension. Through this process the mind appears in a certain world and disappears when the time has come,' Indira explained.

'We only have the possibility "to see or perceive" the past or the future,' said Geshe-La.

'You mean the capability to remember and to predict?' I asked.

'Yes. Through meditative practices one is able to remember ones past life and at the same time to predict ones future life.'

'Also those of others?'

'Yes, to a certain extent. Though, it requires great realization of Dharma.'

'How that?'

265

'Single pointed meditation allows us to travel into the realm of oneness. It's like going up a mountain, the higher one climbs the further you can see.'

'And as such one is capable of seeing the future and the past. But what does that have to do with Dharma?' I asked.

'Dharma is not mere teachings, it is more than that. Dharma is everything. It is questions not yet asked and answers not yet known. It is what you have and have not perceived. It is what humans and science have discovered and that yet to be discovered. What great physicist or mathematicians know and what they do not know. It comprises all universes and dimensions. That which are open and that which are lying dormant, be it the black hole, dark matter, worm holes or the endeavors by science to overcome the speed of light; all that and very much more!'

'The knowledge of the complete oneness,' I said with reverence.

'One could say that. Only, the state of enlightenment enables one "to see" and "to apprehend" all knowledge existing, the state where no barriers exists.'

'Meaning time travel is humbug,' I said, as if it was a realization.

'Another reason for time travel being impossible is Karma. We are all bound by individual and collective Karma. If one is able to travel through time and space, others too would have this capability, creating chaos!' said Geshe-La with a mischievous laughter.

'I believe it would be,' I commented thinking of the unfathomable turbulence such a thing would create.

'Karma is the sum of all potential reactions. It is the most powerful force existing.' After a short pause, he continued by saying, 'Although Karma dictates our lives; we do have the free will to change the course of our lives by practicing spiritual and mental discipline. We however don not have the power to change the individual Karma of others. Not even Buddhas are able to do this.'

Indira picked-up, 'Through our actions we influence the lives of others. One good example is the global warming. We see how this issue affects the world. The nations producing high levels of CO_2 gases could reduce the effects of global warming by changing their ways of life.'

'We should learn to live with one another and not against each other,' I said absently.

'It's an act of compassion.'

'That which one feels within, will be shown outwards.'

'Our actions speak the language of our heart.' Slowly rising from his seat he walked over to the window and looked into the garden. A few minutes passed before Geshe-La said, 'Where were we? Ah yes, time. The sentient beings living on this planet, share a similar karmical past, a past they don't recall.'

'Why do we not recall our past?' I asked.

He smiled. 'Due to Karma. We think everything happens in a sequence, one moment passes and another appears. Actually what really happens is, karmic seeds ripens one after another. The only mind which continuously exists is the very subtle mind. Whatever we experience in our lives, in Samsara happens with a gross mind.

This mind ceases to exist at the time of death, only to be replaced by a new gross mind in a new birth. Conventionally we see this as being forgetful. This happens even during a lifetime. We grow up and become older. Past is forgotten, it becomes a vague memory. Newer things occupy our mind and sometimes… we do not wish to remember.'

'Remembering a past lifetime could sometimes be painful.'

Geshe-La did not comment, instead he said, 'It is only natural for us to believe that we live in a linear time. At least on the surface it seems to be so.'

'The past is important for us to understand and learn from.'

'Yes it is. What other purpose would the past serve?' he asked.

'To move forward!' I answered.

'The past helps us to understand the causal effect, the futility of unvirtuous actions, of barriers we have built. To help us reveal the way home.' He paused a few minutes, allowing silence to abide. 'In the end we are all linked. None of us are alone. This connection creates or generates great amounts of energy, both in the subtle and gross dimensions. To build barriers is futile.'

'This subtle dimension you speak of, does it have anything to do with the quantum field?' I asked.

'Partly yes, but the quantum theory is mainly about matter. I speak of something beyond it.'

'You speak of the mind,' I concurred repeating his thoughts.

'At a very subtle level, matter is able to communicate with each other even apparently through great distance. But this is still the world of Maya or illusion. In truth there is no such thing as "distance". But to answer your question, the most subtle dimension is the subtle consciousness of the very subtle mind.'

'You speak of the very subtle mind as if it is the only thing which exists.'

He smiled as he said, 'There are no states independent of emptiness and as such there is no such thing as a final state. All things are bound by change.'

'So the concept of us being an independent individual is false.'

'Of course, just as matter, time, space, the universe, all things are subjected to change. Nothing exists independently. Nothing exists eternally, not even eternity.'

'While the eternity is a temporal concept.'

'Exactly!'

'So nothing exists. Our aim is to free ourselves of everything?'

'No, our aim is to achieve a state of OM, a state of non-conception, a state of non-duality, a state of oneness, the state of ultimate inner peace.'

'Wow!'

Geshe-La said with sadness in his voice, 'But humans go on hurting each other for things which do not exist.' The silence which followed made me contemplate on the foolishness of man.

Another question, 'Geshe-La I have learned that space and time is only important for the existence of matter. Is there some sort of space between the infinite minds?' I insisted.

'There is something like space which creates room between them. It's not the space we know.'

'So there is space,' I persisted.

'No it's not space, it's similar. One might call it "room uncontaminated from matter",' he said rising his finger to warn any misunderstanding. Not speaking anymore on the subject, he added politely with a smile, 'The very subtle mind is the beginning and the end of everything. It is the final frontier. In this very subtle state, all subtle minds are connected with each other, require neither time nor space to communicate with each other, there exists only clarity!'

'At this state we are all the same,' I stated.

With his calm voice he continued, 'The world is getting smaller, we are moving closer. Races, religions, and ideologies are colliding. The fear for the unknown would only lead to more unhappiness, suffering and downturn.'

'We live in a world of paradox. We are all alike but we prefer to see the difference and judge without any insight,' Indira added.

'Happiness and harmony begins within oneself, the path to liberation begins within oneself.'

'But, Geshe-La, what can we do to make this more apparent to the world?'

'The world surrounding us is there to help us understand this. It's there to encourage us to look for answers within and not to lead to more uncertainty. Our answers should lead us away from eternal suffering rather than keep us in an ever repeating and continual play of ignorance. We cannot force anyone to follow our ways. Each of us has the freewill to choose their individual path.' A pause, a moment to reflect. 'The universe, important as it is for the existence of life, is only another repetition of universes already existed since beginningless time. We can end this repetition of suffering, of Samsara. We are capable of making a decision to liberate ourselves from the fangs of egoism and ignorance...in this life or in another.'

As he was speaking, I remembered something, I had read once. I quoted this, 'Capra wrote in his book "The Tao of Physics": "This idea of a periodically expanding and contracting universe, which involves a scale of time and space of vast proportions, has arisen not only in modern cosmology, but also in ancient Indian mythology. Experiencing the universe as an organic and rhythmically moving cosmos, the Hindus were able to develop evolutionary cosmologies which come very close to our modern scientific models.".'

'Every new birth is a chance.'

I was impressed on how much effort he took to explain Dharma, the great compassion he exhibited. As it was getting late, Geshe-La wished us good night and left the room.

After dinner Indira and I went for a walk.

'I'm very glad you're here.'

Smiling enchantingly she replied, 'I'm glad to be here, with you. I just had to see you and so I decided to come.'

271

It was a clear night, the stars were shining. They seemed to be so close, one could have touched them. I was earnest. 'I had missed you terribly.'

Words were not necessary. Soulmates, she leant her head on my shoulders and watched silently into eternity. I don't know, but I think some things are meant to be. Every day I love her more, with all that I am. I couldn't imagine a life without her, nothing can change my love for her.

Early the next day in the meditation hall, Indira was waiting. We took our seats and joined the puja.

During breakfast I began, 'I must say, my experience here has been beyond my expectations. I have learned so much in such a short time. The most amazing thing is the logic behind Dharma. It's indisputable.'

Indira replied playfully, 'Strange things happen when one begins to follow his heart.'

I smiled. 'I agree.'

'I too made similar experiences. I too had to make my realizations. Only after hearing the teachings of the Heart Sutra, did I begin to understand. It was the point when my spiritual path began.'

Noises in the hallway caught our attention; we walked to the entrance and noticed monks moving towards a certain direction. We decided to follow. A few minutes later, we entered a large and spacious golden hall, there we spotted Ananda and walked towards him.

'Dr. Cane, Indira,' he said. 'Good morning. I had not expected to see you here.'

'I was curious and persuaded Indira to come,' I replied.

'We are preparing for a special prayer called the Tsog Offering. It's about bringing offering to the Buddhas and Holy Beings. Please do stay, it takes only an hour.'

'Thank you!' I said.

The monks recited prayers from a "Sadhana", a prayer booklet. On the altar, there were various offerings, beginning with fresh and dried fruits, sweets, chocolates, robes for monks, Buddha Statues, etc. I noticed that Indira knew the prayers by heart. I for my part meditated in silence. As the puja ended Indira explained we were waiting for Geshe-La to recite from the Holy Scriptures on the meaning of Universal Compassion.

As we were waiting I had the opportunity to inspect the prayer hall. Like most of the halls in this mountain, this too was very spacious. Decorated with very large Thangkas, depicting many Holy Beings, being curious I asked Ananda about them.

'During the annexation of Tibet, many brought these precious thangkas here for safeguard. The thangkas you see here depict Holy Beings. And this thangka here,' pointing to a specific large one hanging above the altar, 'represents both the Sutra and Tantra aspects of Dharma. Here are assembled all the thangkas of the seven hundred million Buddhas. Another important aspect about these thangkas; they are considered to be portals to another world, the holy world of the respective Buddhas. When a sentient being meditates on a certain Buddha single pointedly, he or she would be able to reach the respective Buddha's World at the time of death.'

273

'I'm not sure I understand, what you mean by a Buddha's World?' I asked.

'The description "world" is none other than a state of consciousness. A good example would be a dream. Worlds also evolve and dissolve. Out of compassion, the Buddhas offer sentient beings the possibility to enter their worlds, only these worlds are sustained. To gain entry, one has to secure contact with the respective Buddha. This is possible through spiritual practice and single pointed meditation.'

'It makes sense,' I said. Turning to him I asked another question, 'When did one begin using these caves as a temple and as a library?'

'We are not really very sure. The existence of these caves was kept secret for a very long time.'

'Yes of course, this being a gold mountain and all.'

He nodded as he continued, 'But it wasn't until the visit of the great Guru Pathmasambhava that people began to use it extensively. The caves offer natural illumination and conditions to store thousands of scriptures. Some of the works were written before the times of Buddha Shakyamuni. These thangkas for instance,' pointing to the thangkas hanging on the walls, 'are about a few hundred years old. Many monks have been able to leave their bodies and travel into these portals and return to report of their experiences, at the same time many did not. The reports speak of a world of pure consciousness; where neither matter nor time nor space are existent, where the state of utter bliss and single pointedness is omnipresent.'

"Wonderful!" I thought. As Ananda ended his sentence, Geshe-La walked into the great hall and took seat on the platform in the middle of the hall. The prayers began by us taking refuge to the three jewels, Buddha, Dharma and Sangha. The puja ended and Ananda offered to show us more of the monastery later. We accepted.

After lunch the tour began. We were exploring the inner part of the mountain this time. Even in this depth, it was as clear as daylight. The walls illuminated the butter lamps. The corridors seemed to be endless. The fragrance of sandal wood made its way up into my nostrils. In some parts the walls were very colorfully painted with images. I asked Ananda about them.

'They are historical documents. They are also sacred objects,' he explained.

'Sacred objects?' I asked.

'It not only a painting,' he said. 'They were painted by enlightened monks. That what you see here, are works of hundreds of years. It spreads miles into the earth and into the mountain top. Being an area free of natural disturbances such as earth quakes, we were able to conserve and protect holy artifacts.'

We made our way down. One specific room attracted me. I could smell exotic fragrance. I was curious and peeped in. Ananda noticed this and led us in. It wasn't a just room but a huge laboratory of some sort.

Ananda said, 'This is the main medical laboratory; here we train our future physicians in Tibetan, Ayurvedic and modern medicine.'

'You mean you teach modern surgery?'

'Yes, but it is used only as a last resort. The reason being, it is very important not to injure the body, it would damage the winds.'

'Which is to be avoided?'

'To ensure no blockades build.'

'Which leads to confusion?'

'And to ensure that single pointed meditation is possible.'

'I see.'

'Apart from that, we have possession of writings on Ayurveda medicine, dating back to the times of the Great Buddhist Master Lord Atisha. Along with him came other Indian yogis and physicians who shared with us their knowledge and experiences.'

As Ananda was explaining, Geshe-La entered the room.

I whispered, 'Good morning.'

As Geshe-La became aware of our presence he said, 'Perfect! I had wanted to speak to you about this...' his hands pointing to the room '...about Ayurveda and Tibetan Medicine.'

He then signaled us to a nearby table. 'Both Medicines...' he began '... the Tibetan and Ayurveda, approach the topic of healing from a "wholesome" view.'

'I assume the source for both medicines is Dharma.'

'Naturally, but it has more to do about healing the "body and mind" than it has with "repairing".'

'Therefore correct thinking, correct actions, single pointedness of meditation and oneness of the mind are sources which help to achieve a healthy body and mind,' added Indira.

Geshe-La explained, 'We have spoken of the central channel. It is located exactly in the middle of the right and left channel but more towards the back than the front of the body. It begins between the eyebrows and curves upwards towards the crown, from where it descends in a straight line to the tip of the sexual organ, as you can see in this Thangka.'

A monk brought an old painting to the table.

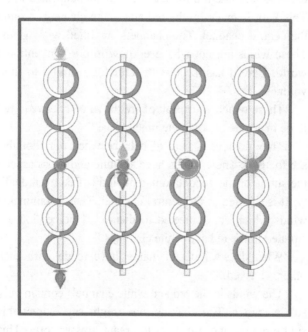

I had seen a copy of it once, but the original was very impressive, a whole new experience! I wondered about who had drawn it, the time and effort taken to create such a beautiful piece of art. One begins to wonder how it survived the influences of time and space, the journeys it had traveled and the places it had been to. If only it could speak, it would tell a tale of thousand years, of adventures, of great dangers and great feats. In my eyes it was not only a document of spiritual knowledge more so a time traveler, a vault full of secrets.

'What you see...' continued Geshe-La '....on the extreme left side are the chakras. Each chakra is a knot. This knot is made by the red and white channels around the central channel. The channels are filled with winds. These winds are not what we know in our conventional world. Here it has to do with something similar to fluid voidness.'

'These winds you speak of are the same ones required to be in a state of complete inner peace?'

'They achieve a state of balance when our thoughts are focused. These winds have a subtle and gross aspect, the subtle or the uncontaminated wind is free from duality. It is situated in the central channel. The contaminated winds which are subjected to duality of perception are situated in the red and white channels.'

'What does wind and matter have to do with each other?' I asked.

'The winds in the red and white channels contain very subtle matter. The chakras, one might say extract this subtle matter and use them to create grosser form. This expands as the state of mind changes. At the same time the masculine and feminine forces increase pressure, at some point matter begins to take visible form. An exam-

278

ple would be; how subtle channels become gross channels and go on to becoming nerves and blood vessels.'

'I understand,' I replied somehow trying to imagine the process.

'As you know blood comprises of red and white cells. Their roots begin at the red and white drops, just as all thoughts originate from the very subtle mind, causing certain reaction at a subtle level and influencing very subtle levels of wind, fire, water, earth and ether. Fear, anger, hate, all the negative emotions bring about unbalanced state of mind. These emotions when not dealt with; continue to grow. There comes a point they become chronic and lead to illness. Permanent cure is only possible by seeking the source of the imbalance.'

'The source of imbalances!' I repeated. 'Modern medicine is searching for similar answers, yet the findings are not really satisfactory.'

'The real source for illness lie not in matter or the body, it is about the vibrations our thoughts generate. Take for example tea, each tea type has a certain taste. In this case tea would be a thought and the vibrations would be the taste. Similarly each taste would have different reaction.'

'Thought not only influence matter, they can also cure?' I asked.

'They are more than that. They shape our destiny.'

'We are the sum of our decisions. Our destiny can be altered with a single thought,' I said.

'It depends on the destiny one chooses. The correct ones help us to unload and travel lighter. To release this burden we carry, this "ego".'

'Our ego does have a very important function. It protects us.'

'Of course, but it acts on false information, false assumptions and only on self-interest.'

'Meditation helps to reduce egoism?'

'Meditation helps. We practice attentiveness and observation. We need a holy object to be attentive and observe that our mind does not deter from this attentiveness during the meditation.'

'During meditation we experience incoming thoughts.'

'Thoughts which tend to distract us. Normally they are negative in nature, such as fear, anger, hate or regret, or all of them at once.'

'Can one really be rid of them?'

'One needs to accept these thoughts, forgive and let them go. Thereafter the process of accepting oneself will begin.'

'That would mean, during meditation we unintentionally diagnose our thoughts.'

'No, it has more to do with accepting my past failures and those of others, about forgiving oneself and others. It is the beginning of letting go, unloading the burden we carry; living compassion for oneself and others!'

'An act of love! The way a person thinks defines his way of life,' I said thinking of the correlation between mind and body.

'It is important to understand. It is our thoughts which make us happy or unhappy.'

'Only when we understand this, can we begin to make the necessary changes in our lives, and it's never too late to do so,' said Indira.

'Life is only a continuum. A struggle began so long ago and ending only when we achieve the direct realization of emptiness,' Geshe-La added.

Indira continued, 'There is also medical help. Ayurveda is an Indian healing science. In Sanskrit it means "The Science of Living". "Ayus" means life and "Veda" means knowledge. It takes all aspects in consideration in its diagnosis; the spiritual, emotional, physical and mental conditions. Ayurveda speaks of three life energies known as "Doshas". These life energies vary from person to person, meaning the individual faith of a person which guides him or her in life has much to do with the "Doshas" influencing this person. These three "Doshas" are known as "Vata", "Pitta" and "Kapha". "Vata" stands the principles of movement and represents the elements wind, air and ether, "Pitta" stands for the principle of fire referring to the principles of metabolism representing the elements fire and water and finally "Kapha" stands for the principles of structure representing earth and water.'

'So what you're saying is our faith or belief, which are a set of thoughts, influence the elements existing in our body. These elements when out of balance lead to physical and mental health problems.'

'Exactly!' exclaimed Indira by clapping her hands.

Geshe-La continued, 'Not to forget, the health of a person depends also on his astrology also known as the Prakriti-Analysis. Through understanding the karmical causes; one can address health diagnosis effectively. Our past actions are the main cause for the imbalances in our lives. Our Karma influences our way of thinking, our view of things. I cannot stress this point enough, that which creates unhappiness is our tendency to nurture, hate, anger and fear. Not removed these tendencies lead to chronic illness.'

After a short pause, Geshe-La went on, 'According to Ayurveda, everything in the universe is composed of nine substances. The first four are known as the "Panchamahabhutas". These being the mind known as "Manas", the soul known as "Atman", the space known as "Dik", and time known as "Kala". Followed by the five elements, water, earth, fire, air and ether, these exist as matter in different propositions. In short being healthy or having sickness has much to do with our way of thinking which controls all these nine substances.'

'What about external influences which interfere with our lives, such as climate catastrophe, wars, social problems. How do we deal with them? All these are also karmical influences. Is it possible to solve these problems through spiritual practice?' I asked thinking of my work, things I had to deal with every day.

'When an event had begun, when a seed has ripened, it is not possible to change the course of its influence. But spiritual purification helps in reducing the negative effects. For instance one can't do much if the earth or the ocean decides to move. But everyone can do everything to help those in need or affected by such events. Most of the things which you've mentioned, wars or social problems can be stopped immediately. For instance it is up to us to reduce the emission of CO_2.'

'Our thoughts are so powerful that it would bring the earth and ocean to move?' I asked again.

'Of course, thoughts trigger vibrations remember. Collective negative Karma effects genesis. Moving the earth is only a small issue,' said Geshe-La.

'We always have a choice to change the turn of events, we can change the course in life,' added Indira.

'Even in the most difficult of situations?' I insisted.

Geshe-La answered patiently with a smile, 'Yes, even in the most difficult of situations.'

'Even the living beings in the hell realm?' I repeated my question.

'Yes, even them. No matter how difficult this might seem!' He paused observing me. 'I understand your skepticism. I too would be if not for the things I have seen.' But he did not elaborate.

I walked to one of the shelves. There was a small Buddha statue, a golden one. I took it in my hands. 'How does purification really work?'

'It is all about the correlation between thoughts and emotions. It is the prerequisite to have clarity and clarity is the nature of the very subtle mind. For instance the act of regret is a great purifier. When one sincerely regrets on some past action, it helps to eliminate manifold of similar negative seeds. In this moment the past memories, the shame one feels, the humility one encounters, create a powerful emotion called regret,' answered Geshe-La.

'I still do not see it.'

'When someone sheds tears, he or she would feel lighter afterwards.'

I nodded.

'This act is a way for the body to react when it is under pressure.'

'You mean it is ventilation.'

'The pressure disappears.'

'So it is not only a spiritual act, it is also a physical one.'

He nodded. Time passed so quickly. It was afternoon. Geshe-La stood up and bid leave. We agreed to meet the next morning.

Ayurveda or Tibetan medicine was even more complex than I had imagined. It not only observes the current mental and physical health situation of a person, it also takes the past in consideration; the astrological calculations, the karmical seeds. The aim is to heal the mental ailment.

At lunch, naan bread and vegetable curry was served. It was simply delicious. Later we continued our exploration of the Monastery. I proposed this time to explore the upper part of the mountain. Ananda was reluctant at first, but agreed subsequently.

He led us through a labyrinth of hallways until we reached a staircase. Climbing it Ananda explained, 'The upper level is reserved for meditation. When someone has developed the capability to meditate single pointedly, they would come here. They would stay here for many weeks and even months in total isolation. They meditate long and deep as the deepest ocean.' We arrived at last at a door leading into a small hall. The staircase on the other hand continued further up into the mountain. Entering the hall I saw a large window at the furthest corner. Sunrays lighted the walls into a thousand suns.

Noticing my surprise Ananda explained, 'This is one of many halls with windows.'

The hall wasn't furnished. In the corners were meditation pillows. I approached the window, to be encountered with a breathtaking view of the Himalayan Plateau. We were about 5,000 meters above sea level. The Himalayas spread open as far as the eyes could see. The snow covered mountains silently greeting us. It was majestic scenery causing me to feel small but at the same time I felt as part of it. As if we are part of something greater.

Beneath us lay open green fields; monks working, harvesting crops and some collecting herbs at the hillsides. As I was witnessing this scenery I noticed some writings on the wall to my right. It was in Tibetan, I asked Indira what it meant. She read the following words:

'The past is no more than a memory,
the future but a dream uncertain.

Within these worlds we sway, calling it life,
calling it "truth".

Unsure is our path, heavy is our journey.

Uncertain are our choices.

All begins and ends with a thought,
nothingness surrounds us.

Ever searching for happiness, illusions we reap.

Simple is the answer to the question forgotten.
Lying dormant only to be found.

An open and free heart will discover.

Remembering the question of all questions.'

All it takes is to remember, to remember the journey back home. What is the purpose of life but to understand, to learn the skills of liberation. Instead we try to survive Samsara and allow to be confused by conventions.

I asked Ananda to guide me through a simple meditation technique. We sat down on a meditation pillow and began to observe our breathing. As I was doing this, I noticed that my thoughts began to wonder.

Ananda guided, 'Do not focus on the many thoughts arising, only on your breathing. Allow the thoughts to pass, as clouds do.'

Slowly I realized me becoming focused on my breathing, slowly I became single pointedly present. The world around me began to disappear and I became at ease. Warmth arose around my heart. Blissfulness surrounded my heart. As the moments passed my experiences became clearer.

It was dark outside as Ananda slowly guided us out of this meditation. Never I had felt such a state of contentment before, never had I gone through such an experience in my life. Only reluctantly I left this state of contemplation.

During dinner, I asked Ananda a little about himself.

'I'm an ordained monk but I do have a long way to go to.'

'To becoming enlightened?' I asked.

He smiled as he said, 'Yes, that too. No I meant to become a Geshe.'

'Do you still have contact with your family?' I hoped I didn't sound all that curious adding, 'You don't have to answer me if you don't wish to.'

'I don't mind it. Yes Sir, I have contact with my family. I visit them whenever time allows.'

'Are they living in Keajara City?'

'No they are living in a village nearby. I come from a family of four. My father and my mother have a small farm and I have an elder brother. It is tradition in Tibet that the eldest son joins a monastery; it was different in my case. From a very early age, I wanted to join the monkhood. I was fascinated by the color of the robes, the mantra recitations, the religious festivities, in short, everything about Dharma. When my brother was five, my parents wanted to send him to a nearby monastery, but he was reluctant. Although only three I volunteered, actually I was adamant to join. After many discussions between my parents and the Lamas, it was finally decided. So you see I was very young when I choose this path, and I'm very happy about my choice.'

'Could you imagine doing something else, or do you not miss the other pleasures of a normal life?' I asked.

'What is normal?' he asked with a shrug of his thin shoulders. 'Everything is relative.'

'I suppose you're right, beauty does lie in the eyes of the beholder?'

'But to answer your question, no I don't miss the "normal" pleasures of life.'

'What about a family and children or a career?' I prodded.

'I believe I do have a "career", one which is fulfilling. What I learn as a monk will help sentient beings to liberate oneself from the clutches of Samsara indefinitely, away from any impermanent moments of pleasures, away from suffering and towards everlasting bliss and happiness.'

I added, 'At the same time giving men a true purpose in life.'

'The aim is not only personal liberation,' he continued.

I said, 'I know, it is about the liberation of others too.'

'A Buddha will never rest until all sentient beings are freed from the chain of ignorance. I have a purpose in life. It is to liberate all families and all children from this world of impermanence.'

'Others would find it improper; they could think you forcing an ideology on them.'

He answered calmly, 'Ah, but that is the point. Dharma cannot be forced. It is given to only those who are seeking for it. Did not Jesus say "Knock and the door shall be opened"?'

'Yes,' I acknowledged.

We were now in the middle of the garden. Streams flowing from it towards the many corners of the garden. We were in a larger section; it was open, with hardly any plants or trees to be seen. It reminded me of a Japanese garden, with finely aligned granite stones and pebbles and a couple of large old trees. We sat underneath one of them on a bench.

I was reflecting on Ananda's words. How wonderful would the world be, when one could be free of the hustle and bustle of the industrial and monetary world? Not having the need to keep pace with the competition. To be away from attachments, of material things and all that is superficial, instead to live and let live, to live in search of inner peace and experience contentment; a quiet simple life.

What else can Samsara offer but the continuous struggle for material gain, an illusion of security and happiness, an endless struggle serving no higher purpose than satisfying one's ego.

The irony of it all, at the moment of death we leave all material behind. One is not even capable to transfer one's own body to the other world, something one had possessed one's entire lifetime, something one believes to be one's true self. What then is one's true self? Obviously not this body!

Be it a king, a president, a wealthy person, a beggar, a vagabond, it does not have any significance. This body will cease to exist. What then is the precious thing man is looking for if not for that inner self, that inner conscious-ness, that subtle mind!

I'm not sure how long we sat there. The silence, the quietness helped to ponder, to contemplate, to find. My attention was drawn to one of the small streams. The everlasting chain which creates water; streams running into rivers and rivers running into oceans, water evapo-rating becoming clouds and this again falling as rain, the rain dropping into this pond and the cycle repeats again. Birth, death and rebirth! What is the sense of this infinite births and rebirths if not to find the answer to salvation!

As it began to turn dark, we slowly walked towards the dining room and later retired for the day. For some reason, I wasn't able to sleep immediately. My thoughts kept me awake; above all, the thought about enlighten-ment. It was not an easy task. I was feeling very grateful to have encountered Dharma. It was not only hearing and understanding; it was also about the experience one has which brings clarity to oneself. Will I be able to achieve it? I don't know but I have to admit, I have become a believer.

I came here to observe and collect arguments for an independent Keajara. In the process it has become more. I did not see any problems with it. I was now more con-vinced of the preservation of this culture. The more I learned about it, the more I saw the importance of Dhar-ma for the world. To help them understand the true meaning of their existence. So logical, empirical, whole-some and universal were the arguments, how could I not but believe it!

Somehow I found it strange not having realized this sooner. One only needs to put one and one together. One only needs to listen, to understand and to comprehend the workings of every phenomenon around oneself. I under-stood now the correlation between the outer and inner world. I understood now the spiritual, that which is holy.

Deep in contemplation, deep in thoughts, did I fall into a dreamless sleep.

The next morning was my last day in Ngari, and there was this feeling of melancholy stirring in me. I had come to enjoy my stay very much. To have met someone like Geshe-La and experiences I had made there. Seeing and leaving the great library. Coming to know what sanctuary actually meant. Not wanting to lose all this made me feel the more fearful going back to New York. What was it that made this fear surge up in me, was it the hustle and bustle of a large city, the never ending manipulation of a modern society, the greed and personal motives leading, driving ones actions. Or was it the feeling I might get used to it again and forget all that I had learned the last few days. I'm not sure, but I believe it was then I decided to spend the rest of my life in Keajara.

'Good morning Dr. Cane, good morning Indira, I hope you had a good night?'

'Yes, Geshe-La, I slept very peacefully,' I answered.

'Thank you, Geshe-La, I slept well too,' countered Indira.

He smiled and offered us to take our seats. 'Dharma works wonders! I believe you're leaving us today, I do hope you will return soon to visit us again.'

'I shall make it a point. I have experienced inner peace here, I had not known before. It is difficult to leave.'

'All will come in time, and something tells me, our paths will cross again.' Allowing a moment to pass he said, 'Before you leave I would like to speak about one more point.'

'By all means,' I answered.

'There is a lot of mystery surrounding about the shape of the pyramid. We wonder why this form was chosen to build the temples and sacred buildings. We see this form not only in the Pyramids of Egypt, in the temples of the Inkas and in the temples of South India. According to the historical research we have done, we have concluded that this form first appeared in South India and this knowledge was then transported through various channels to other parts of the world.'

'Why South India?' I asked.

'To answer that question, I have to go back a little in history.'

He drew a deep breath before going on, 'I had explained the reason as to why the Holy Mountain Kailash is considered as the center of this galaxy. This world was instable before Kailash came into being, and this happened at the beginning of the Krta period. The Wheel of Dharma was turned for the first time on this world. This was about 3,891,000 million years ago.'

He paused again before saying, 'Dharma is ever present but unfortunately we don't understand it. To do this a mode of communication is needed.'

'Dharma is not perishable?' I asked.

'Of course not; all phenomena are bound to it.'

'So, it is in all of us, stored deep inside, like a treasure. We only need to remember, we need a map and a spiritual path is this map?'

Geshe-La did not answer but his smile answered my question. 'This world, as you already know, has gone through many change. There was a time when parts of this world went through the ice age, South India was spared this. It had a more favorable condition where life could develop and evolve. The cultural evolution remained sustained for many centuries. We know now that the civilization reaches back to a couple of million years. Even science has proven this through radiocarbon analysis of the underwater bridge between South India and Sri Lanka which dates back as far as a million years.'

'Are you saying that, in the earlier three periods, this being Krta, Tretae and Draepara, other Buddha's had already turned the Wheel of Dharma?'

He nodded saying, 'Buddha Shakyamuni was the fourth Buddha to turn the Wheel of Dharma in this world. Now returning to the pyramid form; there are two sources known to us as to how this form became into being, one being the form of the Holy Mountain of Kailash and the second being the form of the vajra position. This form, the vajra sitting position allows one to perfectly meditate. In this position, one is able to bring one's winds in perfect harmony and allow one's chakra to open leading to perfect concentration.'

He took a piece of paper and began to draw a human figure with the channels building the chakras.

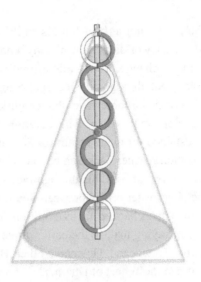

'In this position, all Chakras are in perfect alignment; this form is the basis to all higher attainments in the Universe. When the chakras are aligned, the winds within will begin to flow in harmony, one is able to achieve higher level of inner peace. At some point the red and white drops would begin to move towards the very subtle mind situated at the heart chakra. There they would rotate and begin to mix, as water with water, to become one entity, finally igniting the "fire of clarity" which eliminates all delusions and destroying all seeds of negative karma accumulated since beginningless time and finally achieve enlightenment and liberation from Samsara.' As he finished, silence filled the room.

I couldn't help saying, 'Is it not interesting that the pyramid has a widespread symbolic representation in societies and nature. You can see it anywhere. I sometimes can't shake off this feeling a natural power be behind it.'

Geshe-La said no more, instead slowly rose to his feet and walked towards me, he bent his head towards mine and both our foreheads touched. He said, 'I see a safe journey and a safe arrival.'

We parted in the traditional manner, Geshe-La hanging a piece of white shawl around our necks. As he reached the door, he turned around and smiled again before leaving the room. We stood still allowing the moment to pass.

I felt tears rising. Indira walked to my side and laid her hand around my back comforting me as I told her, 'I am honored to have met him, to have had the opportunity to talk to him, I could feel the love and compassion he spreads.'

A few moments passed before I could gather myself. 'You know, it is so important to preserve this heritage, not only for the people of Keajara but for the human race.'

I felt something in me waking. A strong conviction, a determination I had not known before.

'I'm convinced now! The role Keajara has to play! I have witnessed something unique here. I have seen the atrocities man do in the world, in the name of religion, ideologies, personal greed and egoism. This world is suffering from one sided views and ever conflicting actions. It needs guidance; it needs wisdom to overcome this dark period we are facing. There seem to be so little hope and clarity left in this world. We need to preserve every little hope of peace, harmony and humanity on it.

Keajara has a solution to questions man have been asking. It offers answer for the problems the world faces today. This needs not only to be preserved but also further nurtured and carried out to the rest of the world.'

17

The Lieutenant in a predicament

The phone rang, disturbing the Lt.'s thoughts. He picked up the receiver and hung up a minute later without saying anything.

A few minutes later the Shadow walked into the office. Without any greetings, the Lt. said irritated, 'I need results!'

'We are trying our best,' said the Shadow calmly.

'Your best is not good enough!' he shouted angrily.

'You've a mole in this office, it would be difficult to keep a secret!' answered the Shadow.

'Maybe you're the mole, maybe you're playing a double game,' said the Lt. suspiciously.

The Shadow raised his eyebrow and said, 'You know that is absurd.'

"He is right," thought the Lt., "he wouldn't dare."

'Do you've anything new?' he asked.

'Yes Sir, but I prefer to keep it for myself. There might be people hearing,' said the Shadow.

'What do you mean? Are you saying my room is bugged?' asked the Lt. becoming alarmed.

'Everything is possible,' the Shadow pointed out.

'I don't like what you're saying,' stated the Lt.

'If I was you, I would have your room checked out.' Saying this, the Shadow rose from his chair. As he was leaving the room he added, 'I'll keep you informed.'

The Lt. picked up his phone and dialed a number. Within minutes a team of technicians were searching his office for bugs. To his surprise they found one. Chinese made, standard product of the PSB.

The Lt. showed all symptoms of paranoia – "Who is listening? Am I being suspected about something? Am I in trouble?" – and decided to report it to his superior. He walked to Col. Yang's office and barged in without any notice.

The Col. was having his lunch. He looked up and asked, 'Anything urgent Lt.?'

'Yes Sir.' Opening his palm he showed the device to the Col. 'We found this in my office. Someone is listening on me. It's not the Tibetan, this is internal. This device belongs to the PSB.'

The Col. retrieved the device and inspected it closely. 'Lt., I think it's time to call in Peking. Your investigations have produced no results until now. This is even more serious. I believe someone in Peking is watching us or you very closely. Do you've anything to say before I report this to Peking?' he asked.

The Lt. with a very nervous voice said, 'No, Sir.'

The Col. walked over to his table and called in Sgt. Choo. 'Sgt., we have a situation,' said the Col.

He explained the situation and asked the Sgt. to make an official report to Peking, after which the Lt. left the Sgt. and the Col. alone.

A few moments passed before the Col. spoke. 'Make arrangements for the departure. We have no more time. And inform our friends that we will go missing.'

The Sgt. nodded and left the room.

The Col. thought, "Finally the time has come, I'll be going home."

18

The Journey back to New York

Ananda punctual to the minute walked in and signaled it was time to leave. We began our journey back to
Keajara City. We arrived around evening. Being tired,
we retired to our cottage.

The next couple of days I was busy briefing the
Prime Minister and Richard about my visit. They were
very glad to hear about what I had to say. At one point,
when I was alone with Richard I asked him why he had
chosen me.

'I had always felt deep inside you were searching for
something, a home, inner peace.'

'Did you face the same thing?' I asked.

'I wasn't sure what it was until I discovered Dharma,'
he said very quietly.

I couldn't argue with that. The last few days have
proven him right. I was very much certain I had found
my place in life. It's here and it's with Indira, there were
no more doubts about it.

Before we left, Richard visited us once more. 'Well,
we seem to have a problem. The Chinese have become
very suspicious and they are taking precautionary
measures. We have planned a different route to Leh.

Nevertheless we have to be very cautious. We shall be freezing all travels out of Keajara until further notice. Let's hope, yours would be the last inofficial journey.'

It was very early the next morning, still dark outside; our guide met us at our cottage. We were asked to carry one backpack each. The group consisted of me, Indira, the guide and a yak, to carry our provisions. As the journey back to New York drew closer, an uncomfortable feeling grew in me; so much so, I was at the edge of breaking up the trip. On the other side, I was also aware that we had to do everything in our power to preserve this heritage.

We had good weather, no rain and clear skies. Unlike my trip to Keajara, we had to travel on foot and through mountain regions. Being September, we were lucky not to have any snow. During the day, the temperature rose up to 35 degrees and during the night it dropped to about 5 degrees. The journey lasted 15 days and 14 nights. Although the days were long and exhausting, the nights were beautiful.

I had read once that the part of the Universe that we can see which is also known as visible universe is about 28 billion parsecs or 91 billion light-years away. The actual size of the whole universe is not known and some say is infinite. Even the universe underlies the laws of evolution, or change, it too evolves and has been ruled by the same physical laws and constants throughout its existence. In the ever repeating cycle of creation, neither is there a beginning nor an end. Like the birth and death of a human being, the cosmos too shall have its final moment only to return another time, another space.

On the 16th day we arrived in Leh. This time we stayed at a "friends" place not wanting to attract any attention. We were told all hotels and guest houses were under surveillance. After staying a couple of days we were taken to a remote area, a drive of three hours, south east of Leh. The area was desolate, within a rain forest. Our guide parked the jeep and asked us to follow him. The path took us to an open area where we saw an object covered by green canvas. Helping him to unveil the canvas, a chopper appeared.

The guide, it seemed, was also the pilot. It was the first time for me to fly in a helicopter. At first I wasn't feeling all too comfortable floating up in the air like that. By and by I got used to it. We reached Delhi safely. We were taken to a hotel. Tired we went to sleep. We slept the whole day and night. The next day we were picked up by our guide and brought to the airport. We were very thankful to him.

19

The Shadow disappears

Somehow the Shadow knew his time was almost up.
He knew they were after him. If he fails this time, he
would have to disappear before they get to him. The
counterintelligence spoke of three persons.

"They would want to leave the country," he thought.
"The next biggest airport would be the international airport in Delhi." This time he wasn't going to wait for
them in Leh. He would wait for them there, in Delhi. As
for Leh, he would leave it to the Chinese.

He waited, many days and hours, but nothing happened until suddenly one night he noticed three people. It
was very late. Only two more international flights left for
the evening; one to New York and the other to Australia.
He followed his intuition and waited at the check in
counter for Flight 627 to New York.

Three people approached the counter, an American,
from the sound of his accent, and a Tibetan man and a
Tibetan woman. The American and the Tibetan woman
both checked in and left for passport control. They
passed the gates and went out of sight.

As for the Tibetan man, yes, he was their guide. What
was a Tibetan guide doing in the middle of Delhi? The

303

Shadow followed the man, but the Tibetan was quick on feet. He wasn't able to keep pace. As he walked out of the airport, he saw the Tibetan man smoking a cigarette nearby a four wheel drive. The Shadow had his hand on his revolver. There were military personnel everywhere with automatic rifles hung over their shoulders. He had to be careful.

He approached the man unnoticed. As he came up he drew his revolver and stuck it into the man's back saying in Tibetan, 'Keep quiet and don't make a move or it will be your last one.'

The man obviously understood because he nodded.

'Is this your car?'

The man nodded again.

'Where are the keys?'

The man pointed to his left pocket.

'Take them out carefully and open the car.'

The man did as asked.

'Get in.'

As both of them got in, there was a sudden thud. The Shadow fell backwards on the passenger seat unconscious.

Another man in the car said, 'You were right. He is the one they call the Shadow.'

Without any further moment to waste, the four wheel drive with tinted glass drove away into the darkness.

20

Back in New York

What began as an assignment, turned into an inner journey. Dharma awoke something in me. Overwhelming tides of long forgotten emotions began to find its way to the surface. Burdens I carried so far. I also realized I was not alone. We all have it, this confusing and distracting waves of thoughts creating hate, fear and anger in us. Are they not the sorrow of the past we nature within us, unable to release. Not knowing how, unable to forgive. Letting them decide our future.

Perhaps one day, when the time is right we shall be free of these burdens and walk the path of a free man. Walk again with heads held high. But self-reflection is a difficult thing. It begins to penetrate into the deepest part of oneself awakening inner secrets and dormant memories. It is not so much the pleasant one, but the unpleasant ones which halts one in captive, the ones which cause pain and suffocation, not knowing how to forgive, how to let go. The cause for sleepless nights and questions one the very reason for your existence continued to haunt me. One is drawn into unfathomable depths, unleashing great waves of tears unable to console the soul suffering of actions past.

I found myself in this state of mind, unable to seek refuge as these emotions engulfed me. I had carried them for so long, they had become part of me, getting used to them. No, it's more than that. I had come to see them as my companions in arms, who had been faithful to me. They were my conscience, friends who reminded me of my past mistakes, at the same time foes who had led me astray. It is a world of contradictions, full of doubts and uncertainty. How does one free oneself from this chaos, from these ups and downs, from sanity and madness?

Maybe it begins with the acknowledgement that the past cannot be changed. The past is nothing more than memories. No I cannot undo the pain I had affected others. But I have to go forward. I have to learn not to repeat the mistakes. I have to learn to obey my conscience. Only then was I able to put aside this burden. Only then would I be able to forgive myself and to forgive others. Aye, only then was I be able to forgive and to say adieu.

It felt strange being back. Arriving home, embracing my mom. I had missed her. Heavy was my heart, torn between two worlds. A duality of perception, everything seemed familiar, everything seemed alien. As if I was a different person entering a strange world, at the same time I was the old. Although little time had passed I had changed but not so much that the old was completely gone.

Inner peace I had found; the tranquility of an environment which was so mysterious, but at the same time so clear. Dharma, Indira, Keajara, have become important to me. In the midst of that confusing state I remembered Geshe-La's words, 'All will come in time.' Yes, I shall wait.

We left the next morning for work; we decided to take the Subway. I remembered my early morning walks and how I used to enjoy them. Somehow it was different today; somehow things around me have become less significant.

On our way, Indira asked me to speak about Brooklyn. I found the question a little strange coming from her, until I realized, she must have noticed my change of mood. Maybe it was her way to distract me from whatever which was occupying my mind.

'Well…,' thinking of how to begin, 'Brooklyn is the most populous part of New York City. With about 2.6 million people, it's not very small. At the east you've Queens…,' pointing in the direction of Queens, '…and to the west you've Long Island. From 1896 until 1898 Brooklyn and Kings County had the same boundaries. After which through the new Municipal Charter, Brooklyn was consolidated with the other counties to form New York City. It was a long way getting here; the history of European settlement in Brooklyn began some 350 years ago.'

Indira smiled. 'So like all things in life, this land had to make its way. Changing to become what it's today. It changed with the people. The people make decisions which mold their way of living.' After a short pause she said, 'We are the sum of our decisions.'

'We are what we think and do.'

'And it doesn't stop here. Brooklyn will go through infinite more changes.'

We arrived at our station. I took a moment looking at the city I grew up in, thinking, 'Yes, she was right. My home will change and one day all that which was or is my home will be no more.'

We left the subway and walked towards the UN Building.

Indira commented, 'It is a beautiful day. A shame we have to spend it within.'

I smiled at her saying indulgently, 'We have work to do.'

We worked on the affidavit, editing, rewriting. We attended meetings, spent long hours at the office but the evenings we spent with mom. There were days we worked from home and in the evenings we ordered in. All through this stage Dharma was on my mind.

I still had to understand much. What for instance was meant by our "true" self or our "very subtle mind"; a state of the mind which was responsible to think clearly; it possesses the potential to experience emotions. That being the cause for it to experience "clear light of bliss"; a state of the mind which is not capable to create non-virtuous thoughts!

On one evening I spoke with Indira about my thoughts. Looking at her, I couldn't help thinking how beautiful she looked, her long dark hair lying open on her shoulders. When she spoke of Dharma, there was reverence in her tone.

'You know of the two sources of energies existing in the Universe!' she began. I nodded as she continued. 'The strength of feminine source arises through wisdom, whereas the strength of masculine source arises through compassion. The union of both sources; wisdom and compassion, leads to enlightenment.'

'My problem is I don't know what this actually means.'

'Everything we do in life is based on decisions. Decisions are made based upon the choices we have. We choose the best decision we believe would bring about benefit. This is a cognitive process.'

'Yes, we think and weigh the pros and cons and decide.'

'After being clear about the right choice.'

'Of course…., oh…., you mean clarity right?'

She nodded.

'So, if our decision is based on wisdom and compassion, we choose an enlightened choice!'

She nodded again. 'The very subtle mind requires these aspects to comprehend its purpose in life. Without this, its capabilities will only lie dormant.'

'Does that mean it too has to learn and understand?'

'No it needs to remember.'

'Why does it forget?'

'Well, it is like covering it with a blanket of ignorance, making the true nature difficult to show itself.'

'I see!'

'Does that mean we all the same deep inside, there are no individuality?'

'Yes, water into water, remember.'

'Creating one great consciousness,' I completed her sentence.

A few days later we spoke on clarity.

'Every form of clarity in the universe underlies the same process.'

'How is that?' I asked.

'If you observe nature, I mean all natural processes in this universe; they are continually in a process of finding a balance. Witness the polarities of these powers not only in us but also around us. We see it in the polarities of the magnetic fields maintaining equilibrium, the sides of two opinions only to be solved when a compromise is made, that the day and the night required for the correct balance of living, the two aspects of truth and untruth, that thoughts and actions be virtuous or non-virtuous, that distance is either far or near, that either we live or we die, that life begins or life ends. We see it everywhere and these aspects are inseparable from Wisdom and Compassion, one can't do without the other.' She was speaking without any pause. She stopped to take a deep breath. I smiled at how passionate she gets when it comes to Dharma. Noticing this she also smiled a little shyly.

'Yes, you're right, but between these two extremes, there is the grey area.'

'Samsara is grey, a realm where living beings experience great suffering.'

I said, 'Unfortunately, we learn to value light only when we are confronted with darkness.'

'You see, between these states of minds, the very subtle mind and the very gross mind, there are various levels of wisdom and compassion. Both a child and an adult have the same understanding of what wisdom or compassion is, but varies in its complexities. As we grow and mature we see the world differently. Things are no more as simple as they were.'

'One has to develop one's ability.'

'To understand life, to make the correct decisions, to choose the right path to liberation requires wisdom. But wisdom needs the clarity of the mind. The Four Noble Truths helps the mind to understand Samsara, to see it in its true nature, unmasked and transparent, free of conceptions, free of clouds giving the sight to perceive the finality of all things.'

Her words moved me. I needed a moment before asking her, 'What do they say?'

'They explain the nature of suffering or "Dukkha" as it's known in Pali. They serve not only as paths to liberation but most importantly to awaken our consciousness to the world around us, to our lives. To realize, that from the time of birth to the time of death, our lives are mostly filled with anxiety and suffering. They open to the path of complete liberation, to the attainment of ultimate happiness. They explain the truth of dukkha, the origin of dukkha, the cessation of dukkha and finally the path leading to the cessation of dukkha. They speak of the ever repeating aspects of life and the mental and physical pain surrounding them; birth, aging, illness and death.'

'Tell me more!' I asked eagerly.

She smiled patiently and took a sip out from her cup. 'The first noble truth speaks on how to develop the awareness on suffering. One has to be honest with one-self; to see things as they are and to accept things as they; without pessimism or resignation. To pursue inner change with great belief in Dharma. Suffering is every-where. One who lives in the west might believe that suf-fering can only be found in Africa. One forgets however that all of us underlie the law of Karma. All of us go through some sort of individual or collective pain. Through collective Karma we are all bound together. Our actions not only influence ourselves but also others and the environment we live in. Dharma by no means sees life as something negative, but more so as a chance for one to achieve lasting and eternal happiness. It is said that 90% of our life is predetermined by Karma, but we do possess a small but significant level of freedom in making and realizing our choices in life which will de-termine our future. For example…' Indira began to draw on a piece of paper '…the grey curve stands for example for one's destiny or fate. If one should act virtuously, then a new course could develop bringing about more positive developments, shown here with the green curve. Likewise, should one act non-virtuously; another direc-tion is preprogrammed, shown by the red curve. It is of utmost importance to have a positive mind and to be optimistic in life, in order to achieve liberation from Samsara.'

Karma

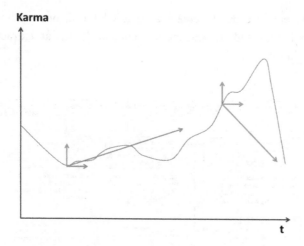

It was autumn and it was raining outside. I listened to the rain drops. I remembered the song "Rhythm of the Falling Rain". I liked that song; I used to hum it to myself on the way back from school, especially when it was raining. I watched the rain drops gently falling on the window remembering my time back in school, those happy and uncomplicated days. When did it all become difficult, why does it have to become difficult.

As Indira continued I was drawn back to the present moment 'As sentient beings, we depend very much on our senses. At the same time we are bound to various values which helps interpret all that we encounter in life. Apart from those universal values which we seem to know instinctively, we also create new ones. These we learn through our socialization process. These allow us to differentiate all that we see, hear, touch, smell, taste and feel. These values are rules which we have learned to accept in order to create a society.' Indira opened her notebook and showed me a document. It was an extract of a PhD Thesis.

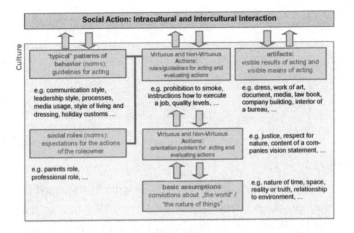

'I discovered this sometime ago. It showed me how flexible conventional values really are. They change according to geographical situations and conditions. The table shows that values differ from one place to another. They vary based on the climatical conditions, historical developments, technological changes and so on.'

'So conventions are all one sided?' I asked.

She nodded. 'It is in Samsara. The ultimate truth has to do with oneness; the realization that matter is perishable and that Samsara does not hold ultimate happiness. All things fade away; our body, everything that surrounds us, is perishable.'

'We disregard the notion we shall perish from this life one day. We believe in living eternally in a finite world,' I added thoughtfully.

'We will lose our beauty, our intelligence, our motoric functions, our friends and loved ones. But we prefer to remain blind and continue our best to ignore the obvious, the inevitable.' After a short pause, she looked into my eyes and said slowly, 'The ultimate truth speaks about virtuous and non-virtuous actions, and not about "good" and "bad", because there is no such thing as "good" and "bad".'

'Because all is one sided, half-truths.'

'Which leads us to being judgmental, which leads to more pain and suffering.'

'Because so-called "good" and "bad" is confined to time and space,' I said.

'Everything we perceive with our senses is not the ultimate state of things. In Samsara everything is relative, everything is only half true. The opinion of one person is just as true as the opinion of another person. Everything in Samsara is but a state of consciousness, a state of the mind.'

I looked at my watch. It was very late.

'Let's continue the discussion tomorrow darling,' Indira said tiredly.

The next morning, as mom was making breakfast, Indira walked into the kitchen with her bathrobe.

'Good morning,' she said looking fresh and beautiful.

'Good morning, darling. Slept well?' my mother asked.

'Yes, very well thank you. Smells good!'

'Almost done…' pressing out the oranges '…here we go!'

'Ihmmm, simply delicious,' complimented Indira taking a bite on the toast with butter and jam.

'Thank you!' said mom who had joined us at the table, sipping her coffee.

I on the other hand was not able to sleep the last night. Our discussion the night before was bothering me. 'Darling, you spoke of four noble truths, what are the other three?' I asked.

'Roger, you could at least wait until she finishes breakfast,' objected my mother.

'That is ok, Martha, I understand how he feels. Um, there are four,' she began. 'The second noble truth…' she went on '…speaks of the origin of suffering or dukkha. It's our craving or thirst predetermined by our ignorance. The third noble truth speaks of how suffering can be ended and the forth noble truth shows the way or the path towards cessation of suffering or Samsara.'

'I remember now, we have spoken of them before,' I replied thoughtfully.

We keep moving, doing, acting, not letting go. Repeating this cycle and not ending it. We do this, not so much for the sake of seeking answers. No! More so to keep ourselves busy, to keep going. Restless are we, self-centered and self-opinionated are we! We assume to be all knowing information but end up making decisions on incomplete knowledge. In the vast endlessness of Samsara, we continue to fool ourselves with half-truths. Only a handful has seen the correct path, only a few make the correct decisions; deaf and blind we travel Samsara, with the wisdom of a foolish one. We move from one life to another, not wanting to put an end on this theater called life.

It is said "to be egoless is to be timeless". This is true, but only when our true self rises and expands. Only then will one experience that which cannot be seen. From the depth, wisdom will arise, an experience of the final truth. I decided to let go, this bag of fears, complexes, worries, guilt, everything which stopped me from achieving ever-lasting happiness. I have carried it long enough. Since beginningless of time, a habit so hard to lose, but no more, I shall travel henceforth lighter.

We are born to comprehend the obvious. That which is simple, is uncomplicated. Comprehending is easier when one walks light. To let go, to move on, to learn to accept ourselves as we are, to learn, to grow, to begin the journey of learning to love oneself for who one is, to be able to tell that child within us that all will be well, that everything is fine, that it is finally going home.

That one source of peace we seek in life, that one truth, that one final frontier we wish to break through, is within us, deep within us, in the center of our heart, only waiting to surface, only waiting to be discovered. So near yet so far, is this truth, is this ocean of wisdom and com-passion, so near is this treasure, only waiting to be unlocked.

21

Lhasa Endgame

The Lt. sat there lamed, with a fax in his hand. It had the official insignia of the PSB on it. He read the document and leaned back in his chair, using his left hand to light a cigarette. As he inhaled the smoke, letting the sunlight shining through the window warm him. His eyes sharp and alert, but there was something disturbing about them.

From his chair he had a nice view of the snow-clad mountains. "Well, he has disappeared!" he thought. "The agents in Leh last saw him leaving to Delhi and since then no one has had any contact."

'All my endeavors have been futile,' he said out aloud.

A few moments later he walked into Col. Yang's office and briefed him of what had happened.

'Well Sir that is the situation. To summarize, the agents in Leh were not able to discover anything. My informant has disappeared. His personal things were found in his hotel room. As he failed to report in, a search team was sent out. We believe he has been abducted, probably even killed, but we don't have any evidence. The authorities in Leh are still investigating. They have classified the case as kidnapping, but they have little hope of finding anyone since no ransom has been asked. We believe the Tibetan Resistance is behind it, although they officially deny any involvement.'

The Col. listened as the Lt. spoke. He waited until the Lt. finished his briefing. The Col. remained quiet, allowing silence to fill the room. The Lt. straightened up, growing more and more uncomfortable as the moments passed.

'It is very unfortunate,' said the Col. 'Report it to Peking. We need to make it transparent before Peking arrives.'

The Col. rose from his chair and walked towards the door saying, 'Lt., let us go for a walk.'

The Lt. followed him a little nervously. They left the office and walked the corridor towards a flight of steps leading upstairs turned towards the side entrance. He typed in his security code onto the console and opened the door leading directly to the streets. It was a heavy armored door, strong enough to hold strong explosions. Very few had access to it. Stepping onto the pavement the Col. took a deep breath as he said, 'This is a nice day for a walk.'

It was summer in Lhasa; at 3,900 meters it could become pretty hot. The Col. began to walk towards the east as the Lt. followed him, a little nervously. There were eyes of anger watching them. About 300 meters down the road was a Tibetan restaurant, which serves a taste of Tibetan home-made recipes like yak meat in tomato sauce or droma desi, which is sweet rice with wild ginseng, raisins and yoghurt. The Chef and owner named Namdon wasn't particularly happy of these

319

frequent visits of a PSB Col. It could mean many things; his people taking him for a collaborator or worse still, a spy of the Chinese, or that his restaurant was under surveillance. Worse still today the Col. has another officer with him. This is bad for him and for business!

The nervous Namdon walked over to personally take the orders. Today the Col. preferred to have the authentic home-made momos or Tibetan dumplings and amdo-style noodles. The Lt. ordered some sizzlers and a yak burger.

'Sir I'm not sure, what are we doing here?' asked the Lt. having a watchful eye on everything moving.

'Having lunch, so stay at ease,' said the Col. with a tint of mockery in his voice.

The Lt. ignored it and continued their earlier discussion. 'Sir, do you know when Peking intends to visit us?'

'No. I'll inform you as soon as I hear anything. But you know how they work; such visits are mostly at short notice.'

After lunch the Col. called the office and ordered a car to pick them up. A few minutes later a dark four wheel drive made a halt in front of the restaurant. Entering the jeep, the Lt. noticed Sgt. Choo at the wheel. The jeep then sped away towards the highway into the south and out of the city. 'Where are we going?' asked the Lt.

The Col. answered calmly, 'To meet a friend.'

The wide highway merged into dust roads as the high new buildings became little more than glass cubes reflecting the sunlight. The Lt. noticed they were on their way to Tupphi Prison. On the way they had passed rows and rows of diggers and cranes. All around them, men and machines hammering away in construction sites with clouds of dust and clinging to the sides of iron rigs. New mobile phone towers were constantly shooting up around them, making the city look like any other Chinese metropolis.

After driving down a long sandy road, they halted in front of a complex, with iron gates and security personnel guarding it. The security personnel noticed the Col. and saluted him. He didn't need a pass to enter. A moment later there was a clunking sound as the old electric motors came alive and pulled the high rusted gates aside. Passing the long line of garrison quarters, his jeep came suddenly to halt at a specific building. The Lt. quickly jumped out of the car and opened the Col.'s door. The Col. stood for a moment in silence, surveying the environment. It was hopeless and desolate scenery. The Col. then began to walk towards the front door of the old building and the Lt. followed him a couple of strides behind.

As they crossed the remaining few yards to the main entrance, the Lt. averted his glance from the windows. This he knew was a hellish place. The sight above had very little to do with what laid beneath. Uncounted dark passages, all built in the 1950s, by none other than the prisoners themselves. There were hundreds of prison cells down there, with poor souls rotting in them. They will never see the light of day again. Electric lighting was only allowed in the interrogations rooms. It gave him the jitters just thinking about it. They entered the building and began walking down a dark staircase. As they were walking down the corridor, it wasn't so much the screams of the prisoners which got to him, it was the smell. He had never known anything like it. It was the smell of fear and total hopelessness.

The Col. showed no apparent signs of discomfort. As usual he was control in person. They came to a door; a pale looking guard was there to meet them. He had a flashlight in his hand and eyes which seemed to belong to a dead man. He gestured them to enter the room. A door buzzed opened and a procession security clearance began until they arrived at an interrogation room.

The Lt. felt it was getting to be a little cold. It was only a few meters, the heat and wind from outside had been replaced by chill, a shiver which bore into his bones. As the guard marched in front of them, flashing his flashlight to show the way in the darkness, the Lt. couldn't help thinking who this "friend" might be; or what a nice place to put a friend in. Every few steps they passed a cell door with an iron framed window. Through them wasn't much to be seen, only dark shadows, broken by the burden of the past.

As the guard turned around to check on them, the light fell on the Col.'s face. His features were white as cotton and he had his handkerchief bond over his nose and mouth. "The smell seemed to be getting him too," thought the Lt.; the smell of death and hopelessness. The guard made a sudden halt; he withdrew a batch of keys out of his pockets and unlocked the door. At first it was hard to recognize much. The guard switched the light on. Towards the back of the room were wooden buckets of water. In the middle of the room was a man in a monks robe tied up in a metal chair, screwed to the ground. The man was obviously unconscious.

A shadow appeared from the corner of the room. He was a small man, with absent eyes looking into the distance. The man was wearing a plastic apron and rubber gloves. He approached the Lt. and handed him a clipboard, walked pass the others and left the room disappearing into the darkness.

The Lt. read the name of the prisoner aloud, 'Tigme Chanpo, a monk from the Serpang Monastery.' The figure in the chair did not respond.

The Col. walked towards the man and lifted his head gently. He helped the man to sit upright again. This act of friendliness made the guard glance a little nervously. Everyone knew who the Col. was. He could make anyone appear and disappear, without having even the need to explain anything. The Lt. handed the clipboard over to the Col. The Col. scanned the pages. Notes had been made during the interrogation. It has been going on the last three days, with successively stronger tortures every hour passing. The Col. noticed the prisoner's eyes were dull and bloodshot from long hours of pain. During the entire interrogation he had only said these words, "Soon we will travel to Keajara, to the holy land of Heruka," and nothing more.

The Col. looked into the monk's face and said, 'You've done your duty and now you will be rewarded.' The monk stared blankly at him and looked confused. Tears swelled up in the corner of his eyes and he wept in relief.

The Col. looked at the guard. 'Clean him up. I shall take him with me immediately.'

The guard began to object, 'Sir I have special orders about him...' but he went no further as he noticed the determined look in the Col.'s eyes.

Within the next hour the monk was cleaned, bandaged and clothed. He was then escorted into the waiting jeep.

Arriving at the PSB office, the Col. and the Lt. alighted from the jeep. The Sgt. then drove off with the monk.

At the Col.'s door the Lt. finally asked, 'Sir, what is going to happen to the monk?'

'He'll receive his reward,' said the Col., and said no more.

Many years will pass, many a change would be necessary before the Lt. comes to understand the events of that day; a realization which will lead him to Keajara, where he will finally find peace.

22

All well ends well

The days passed and I began to acclimatize. Amazing how old habits return. Our work continued. One morning the office of the Secretary General called.

'Good Morning Dr. Cane,' said the young female voice at the other end.

'Good Morning.'

'The Secretary General asked if you could spare a few minutes.'

'You mean immediately?' I asked a little surprised at the short notice.

'Yes sir.'

I hesitated looking at Indira who was reading the affidavit. I agreed believing it must be important. 'Yes, we will come up.'

'Thank you, sir,' said the voice and hung up.

We entered his office; he was looking cheerful in his dark blue suit and grey tie, walked from behind his desk to greet us. 'Dr. Cane, Miss Indira, I glad to see both back, safe and sound. I hope that your journey proofed fruitful?'

'Yes sir. It was an enlightening journey. It gave me the opportunity to evaluate the situation.'

'Your resume?' he asked.

'I see now the importance of preserving this rare culture. It is a world heritage.'

'That is good news.'

'More importantly, the Keajarans are very capable people. They do not need China's "helping hand". They can look after themselves.'

'During my visit I too was able to witness the same thing,' said the Secretary General.

I interrupted by saying, 'I'm sorry sir but I didn't know you were in Keajara.'

'I'm sorry for not mentioning before,' he went on. 'It was a few years ago. I decided to see this world for myself. I learned of its importance, the reason to protect and safe Keajara from the influences surrounding it.'

'Of course!'

'A heritage which has to be preserved for future generations, and this can only be done through proclaiming Keajara as a sovereign nation.'

'I agree,' I said.

'If you could brief me on where we are.'

I began by saying, 'During my absence, Miss Yogini did well in addressing the issue with the Ambassadors. They have agreed to vote for the sovereignty of Keajara.'

'Will you now be speaking with the Chinese Ambassador?'

'A meeting is arranged for tomorrow. At the same time, irregard of the outcome of our meeting, I believe it is time to submit the affidavit to the UN General Assembly.'

'I agree. Please brief on your meeting with him,' said the Secretary General.

I handed over the affidavit. He seemed to be satisfied after briefly looking over it. He then asked me to officially submit our petition in accordance to article 135. "That was it, no more turning back," I thought. As the meeting adjourned we parted, there seemed to be so much hope in the air. But for some reason, deep inside, I knew all will be well.

That evening we called Keajara and briefed them.

'So it is finally done. We have crossed the bridge.'

'Yes Sir.'

'What will we see on the other side?' asked the Prime Minister.

'A new future.'

'I will also be hopeful Dr. Cane.'

The next day, I was a little nervous. So much was at stake. We waited until we were called in. Entering the office, I sensed uncomfortableness. I couldn't help thinking of how glad I was to be in the United States, to live in freedom and in safety. The Ambassador welcomed us and was a little surprised to see Indira. Not wanting to enlighten him, I introduced her as my assistant. I noticed how the Ambassador's expression changed as I began to explain the purpose of our visit and of what had taken place.

'Your whole enterprise has been, the least to say, dastardly,' he busted out outraged. 'Furthermore you have broken international law and all the rules your organization represents.'

'Sir, I can't say why that should be the case since, it is an independent nation.'

327

'I object to your insinuations. This piece of land is part of the People's Republic of China.'

'With all due respect Mr. Ambassador, I must object. Keajara does not lie in Chinese territory and therefore our work has not been unlawful.'

There was another man in the room. The Ambassador had introduced him as his assistant; Mr. Lee. It was a young man in his late twenties with a black suit, lean, average height with a clean haircut. He looked well trained. There was something about him, something menacing. Since entering this office, he made me feel uncomfortable. Suddenly it dawned onto me, "Yes, he is from PSB!" He seemed to be protocolling the meeting.

'That might be so Dr. Cane, but why were we not informed earlier about this?' asked the young man sternly.

'Excuse me Mr. Lee, we had no reason to believe you were not aware of this.'

'It is obvious you've done everything to keep this matter a secret. You've done so not wanting to alert us, knowing China would have acted accordingly.' He was obviously angry, and he made no attempts to hide his emotion.

'I'm a little confused here but do please enlighten me. What do you mean by "China would have acted accordingly"?' I asked a little sarcastically. I was not disturbed about it not being good diplomacy to irritate someone whose help I was here to seek. But I wasn't going to let in, I had to win this.

'Exactly what it means! It's obvious that we have been led into a cat and mouse game in this whole affair. The UN has assisted terrorists to separate the people of this small village from the People's Republic of China!' he accused me looking straight into my eyes.

'Firstly it is not a "village" and secondly your assumption is wrong. We have done no such thing,' I replied calmly. 'The people of Keajara have never been part of the Republic. They are an independent nation. It is our responsibility, in line of the Charter of the United Nations, to proof all applications for a membership into this organization. As such we have done nothing illegal.'

'This is a dangerous game you're playing and the People's Republic of China is not going to stand aside and let you win this game!' angrily he shot out.

I decided to not waste any more of my time with this man and turned to the Ambassador. 'Sir, it's about the freedom of a small nation. It's only about 7,000 square km, it has no natural resources or any strategical values to you. The people of Keajara are only interested to sustain their way of life and to live in peace and harmony.'

The Ambassador answered, 'Dr. Cane, the People's Republic of China cannot ignore the security problems. Approving such an endeavor could bring us in a very difficult situation.'

'Sir, the people of Keajara have never been subversive. Their wish is to live in peace and without any conflict with their neighbors. I can't see what danger this small country can bring to a powerful nation as yours.'

'Someone else could use this so-called "peace-loving nation" as basis to attack us,' said the man from the PSB.

Ignoring his statement, 'Again I'll ask; what danger could a small country such as this bring to a powerful nation such as China?'

There was a moment of silence. It was the first time Indira spoke. 'Mr. Ambassador, Mr. Lee, we do understand your concern. I have a suggestion.'

'How would this suggestion look like?' asked the Ambassador curiously.

'A non-interference agreement between the People's Republic of China and Keajara, in all matters of internal or foreign affairs, furthermore our assurance that we would not aid any parties who might have such intentions.'

The Ambassador was obviously not prepared for such an offer. I couldn't help noticing that he liked the idea. This was when I decided to lay the cards on the table.

'Sir, you must know that all other Ambassadors of the UN SC have given their blessings. They see the importance of the cultural heritage. They concur the need for this unique culture to be protected and the need for non-intervention.'

Indira instinctively understood what I was getting at. 'Mr. Ambassador the situation is somewhat different compared to 1959. Please do take that into consideration.'

'What do you mean by that?' asked Mr. Lee.

I interrupted saying, 'The world supports us in our endeavor. Some nations have even given us their assurance to send troops, to ensure that Keajara becomes a sovereign nation. How did the German Ambassador put it? "Not so much for the sake of the Keajarans but more so for the sake of humanity".'

Indira then said, 'Sir please bear in mind. It is about the independence of a small nation without any political significance or natural resources. It possesses no treat to anyone.'

There was another silent moment in the room. The emotions were high, but somehow better judgment prevailed.

The Ambassador then said, 'I'll have to speak with Peking.'

'I understand your situation, but Peking must also understand that the world will certainly not turn the other cheek this time. It is in your hands to come to a peaceful solution.'

He was silent. He walked the room up and down, before turning and saying.

'Dr. Cane, Miss Indira, thank you for your insight. I personally have no interest in an international crisis. I am considering how such a move would influence the Tibet-an separatist movement.'

'I know. But I could imagine, that a peaceful solution would help to ease the present situation with the exiled Tibetan government,' added Indira.

'I shall discuss this with the Party Leaders and give you an answer.'

After the meeting, we let ourselves out. We walked calmly towards the elevator. As the doors closed, I asked, 'What do you think?'

'I think it went better than what I had imagined,' she said calmly.

I answered with a smile of relief, 'Yes, I think so too.'

Entering my office, I immediately called the UN Secretary General and informed him of our meeting. He assured me, he too shall have a word with the Chinese Ambassador. We then informed Keajara.

We called it a day and left the building through the front entrance, taking a taxi to the 278 Street, a pizza house. During lunch we agreed to begin another row of meetings with the Ambassadors and inform them of our meeting with the Chinese Ambassador.

We had worked long days and the effort paid off. The Ambassadors reconfirmed their commitment. Meantime we still had no news from the Chinese. It was extremely quiet in that corner. I didn't know what it meant.

The Tibetans have shown great strength in their struggle for an independent nation. Through their peaceful way of life, their respect for human rights and Mother Nature, they have shown the world a "way to live" which is second to none. Considering the Chinese-Tibetan politics, the question would be if the Chinese could risk another international conflict.

The situation the world is in today, where wars predominate, where poverty rules and environmental problems only increase, Keajara offers a solution; to end suffering and turn towards a peaceful and sustainable way of life. It is the answer for the dynamic of today; lines becoming blurrier. Walls are just illusions, unsustainable and harm growth. Should we, can we stop change? On the other hand what is life if not change!

23

Life works in strange ways

As private Tan walked into Lt. Chan's office and saluted, the Lt. was on the phone. Closing the receiver he whispered, 'What is it?'

'Sir, you are asked to come into Col. Yang's office,' the private answered.

The Lt. nodded as the private left the room.

The Lt. asked, 'So, you're saying Sgt. Choo did not bring a monk to your facility! Are you very certain?'

The voice at the other hand answered, 'Yes Sir, we don't have any records of a prisoner being delivered to us last week.'

'Thank you. That would be all.' He hung up thought-fully.

He did not understand it. The whole thing seemed to be mystery. Where was this monk? Why was he asked to accompany the Col. to the prison? Confused he left his office.

Entering the Col.'s office he was surprised to see Brigadier General Lee Boh Seong waiting for him.

'Come in man and take a seat,' ordered the General. He obeyed. He was also surprised to see two gentlemen in dark suits seated at the other end of the office.

'Lt. Chan, how much do you know about "Keajara"?'

Rising his brow, he asked, '"Keajara" Sir?'

'Maybe you've heard of a place called the "Land of Paradise"?'

'Yes, Sir, we have. We have been investigating the issue. Col. Yang gave me his permission a month ago to officially investigate.'

'I see and what did you find out,' asked the General mockingly.

The Lt. didn't know what it meant but decided to ignore it. 'Initially as I approached the Col. on the matter, he seemed to be reluctant. He was of the opinion, it was only a legend.'

'And you left it at that?'

'No Sir. I began my own investigations. A matter of fact I had sent a report to Peking on the whole issue last week.'

The General looked at his adjutant a little irritated. The adjutant shrugged his shoulders. Obviously this report did not find its way out of the bureaucratically labyrinth to his table.

The General continued by saying, 'Well, if it was only a legend, the United Nations would not be discussing about it at this moment, would it?' The Director of the PSB shouted.

'I don't understand Sir, why would the UN be discussing about a legend?' asked Lt. Chan even more confused.

One of the gentlemen in the dark suits began to speak. 'It is obvious General that the Lt. has no knowledge of this.' He turned to the Lt. saying, 'Lt. Chan, there has been an incident.'

The Lt. looked at him bewildered.

'A week ago, the representatives of a Land named "Keajara", submitted a petition to the United Nations Secretary General. The petition under article 135 of the UN Charta is about the official recognition of a nation. The problem is following. This piece of land lies within the Tibetan territory. Unfortunately, this piece of land lies not within China's sovereignty.'

'How did this happen?' asked the Lt. shocked.

'Due to a "mistake" during China's claim of Tibet.'

'A mistake Sir?'

'Yes Lt., a blunder made by an idiot from carto-graphical division. This piece of land remained un-claimed, a "no man's land" if you wish.'

'Amazing!' said the Lt. in disbelief.

The gentleman in the dark suit ignored the comment and continued. 'We have also found out, that Col. Yang, Sgt. Choo, Mr. Drogpa and their families have left the country. This happened a few days ago. We don't know where they are.'

'Do you know anything about this?' It was more of a command than a question from the General.

The Lt. looking very perplexed and confused said, 'General I assure you Sir, I have no idea about where they are,' at the same time thinking of those underground dark and ill smelling interrogation rooms in Tupphi Prison. 'The Col. did have plans to go on a holiday, something about going home. The Sgt. would be accom-panying him.'

'And that was all!?' asked the General loudly.

'Yes Sir,' said the Lt. a little timidly. 'He placed me in charge.'

'And what about this Mr. Drogpa?'

'Well, the Col. mentioned something about him having acute bronchitis and being admitted in the hospital. He would need some time to recover. That is all I know.'

'Tell me Lt. didn't you find the whole thing a little suspicious?' asked the other man in the dark suit.

'No Sir, not really. The Col. is a highly decorated officer and he has not given me any reason to suspect him.'

'Even when he asked you not to investigate about Keajara?'

'Well Sir I didn't see any reason to doubt his reluctance. He had spent tremendous resources in investigating about it but discovered nothing.'

'Why did he agree later on?' asked the man.

'He said it was due to my persistence,' answered Lt. Chan.

The interrogation went on for another couple of hours. Lt. Chan gave a detail description of his investigations, his contact man and his disappearance. Only after his interrogators were satisfied did they allow him to leave.

He was put in charge until a replacement would be found. The General and his men left the very evening to Peking.

As they were speeding away towards the airport the General asked, 'What do you think?'

One of his men replied, 'It is obvious that the Col. had something to do with the whole thing. The question is how long was he involved and why?'

'Well, apparently his parents have also left the country. I just received a call. They took a flight yesterday morning to Hong Kong. Their traces disappear there. We have people looking for them.'

'How about the Col.? He is obviously our most important target.'

'I know,' said the General angrily. He knew the party will look for someone to blame. "It's not going to be me!" he thought.

'Why did we not see this coming? How could we have been so blind?' asked the other man.

'It is obvious, he had help!' said the first man.

'Whatever help he might have had; it didn't come from me. I became PSB Director only two years ago.' With a pause he said irritated, 'Why did this have to happen during my watch!'

'This thing is going to occupy us the coming months. We are just scratching the surface. We still don't know how deep this whole thing goes!'

'Any news about how the Party is going to decide? Are they going recognize Keajara as an independence state?' asked the General.

'There are very mixed sentiments. There are those who are not willing and there are those who do not want to jeopardize international business or relationship due to a small piece of land. Apart from these two main groups, we have another small group who plead for Keajara's independence to improve China's image on the Tibetan affair.'

'How soon do you expect a decision?'

'Well the UN has set a dateline. Two weeks.'

As the jeep, escorted by MPs, sped through the roads of Lhasa, the General said, 'Well gentlemen I believe we have not much of a choice. There is too much at stake both ways.'

'Are you saying that China will have to speed up its democratic process?' asked one of the men in the dark suit.

The General answered, 'I'm not quite sure what you mean by speeding it up. But I do believe China has a lot of potential to play an important role being a role model.'

'How do you mean that?' asked the man back.

'We still have a lot of work to do, should we want to fulfill this vision. I sense a new time breaking. I have lived long enough to know that we are moving into a new era, the only question would be how we are going to deal with it.'

24

The Decision

It was a Saturday morning. I was helping my mother in the garden as Indira came out to join us. She handed me the phone saying, 'Mr. Stevens!'

I rubbed of the dirt from my hands before taking the receiver. 'Good Morning, Roger Cane here.'

'Dr. Cane, good morning. It's John Stevens speaking. I hope I have not disturbed your weekend?'

'Not really Mr. Stevens. I was doing some gardening. It must be important for you to call me on a Saturday.'

'It is. I received a call from the Chinese Ambassador a few minutes ago. They have not made any decision as yet. They wish to have a meeting on Monday with the Secretary General.'

'I see,' I said a little nervously.

'The Secretary General wishes you and Miss Yogini to be present.'

'Of course. Is a time already fixed?'

'Yes, at 10 a.m.,' he answered.

'We will be there.'

'Is there anything we should be prepared for?' he asked.

'No, not that I know of,' I answered.

'Good!' said John Stevens.

'Did the Ambassador say why?' I asked.

'No. I too am a little unsure as to the purpose.'

'We have a weekly call with the Keajara, nothing out of the ordinary.'

'The usual political game I suppose.'

'You may be right,' I said.

'Please don't hesitate to call me should you have any new information.'

'I shall.'

'My apologies for the intrusion.'

'Not at all and I wish a nice weekend.' I hung up thoughtfully. I saw Indira's questioning eye.

'The Chinese would like another meeting.'

'With us?' she asked.

'With the Secretary General but he wishes us to be present.'

'When?'

'On Monday morning.'

'Any specific reason?'

'He didn't say.'

From her expression I could see she was a little perplexed, instead she said, 'Well maybe we have been a little naïve thinking it would be easier. Their politics on Tibet has always been a sensitive one. This only shows they are doing all they can to stop us. The only question is if they have found any reason to legitimate their actions.'

I nodded and looked a little astonished on how quick and clear her thoughts were. Of course she was right. 'Do you've any suggestions?'

'I think we should call the Prime Minister. If anyone he could help us.'

We went back into the house as mom walked into the kitchen.

'Good Afternoon. This is the Prime Minister's Office,' said a voice on the end.

'Good Afternoon Chugda. This is Indira and Dr. Cane on the speaker. Could we please speak with the Prime Minister? It is very urgent.'

'Good Morning, one minute please.' He put us on hold. A few seconds later he was back. 'The Prime Minister will speak with you. Please hold.' He put us through.

'Good Morning, it is morning there, isn't it?' asked the Prime Minister.

'Yes Sir,' we answered simultaneously.

'I understood it is urgent?' he asked.

We explained the situation and wanted to know if he had any information which might be of help. There was a pause before the Prime Minister spoke. 'Well, I might know the reason.' There was another pause, as if he needed time to formulate his answer. 'But I believe it be wiser if you were not informed.'

'Why the secrecy?' I asked.

'Dr. Cane it's not about keeping a secret.' He spoke calmly. 'It has to do with your credibility. Should China believe you being involved in any foul play, it would question the credibility of the UN. It is very important for you to be objective in this affair.'

"Yes, he was right!" I thought. I answered, 'I understand.'

'Please be assured that you're both doing an excellent job. Do not doubt on your motivation. Please continue your work and all will be well.'

Seeing he wanted to say no more, I thought it wise to end the call. 'Thank you for your word of confidence. We will call you after the meeting with the Chinese Ambassador.'

I hung up. Unsure of what to do I turned to Indira. She seemed to have read my mind, and suggested we walk the thing through. 'The Prime Minister intends us not to be involved, allowing us to be surprised if the Chinese should accuse us of anything, at the same time we are to leave no doubt about our intention.'

'I believe we should keep it simple, the complicated the strategy the more the room for mistakes.'

She bent her head to the right as the late summer sun fell gently on her hair. She looked at me saying, 'So that's it.' She clasped her hands and stood up. 'Now, let's make dinner.' She noticed my frown, knowing how much I hate cooking, and said with a pinch of amusement, 'OK...! I'll make dinner but you're going to help me.'

For which I replied, 'Gone are the sweet old days, when meals appeared on the dining table without me having to do much about it.'

'Well, you're still welcome to return to those sweet old days,' looking a little offended.

I took her into my arms and looked into those large light brown eyes. 'Not for the world.' We kissed each other, a long and passionate kiss.

A couple of days later at the office of the Secretary General, we met the Chinese Ambassador; two other Chinese gentlemen were present, John Stevens and the Secretary General.

'Good morning gentlemen and lady, thank you very much for being able to attend this meeting at such a short notice,' began the Secretary General. 'His Excellency wished to meet before the People's Republic of China votes on this subject.'

The Chinese Ambassador nodded with a smile. 'Thank you.' There was something in his voice, I believe it was nervousness.

'Not at all, we are only too happy to be of service,' answered John Stevens with his usual correct and businesslike voice.

The Secretary General continued, 'Mr. Ambassador I shall leave the floor to you.'

'Thank you.' His voice suddenly changed, from friendly to accusing. 'Gentlemen and my dear lady, the reason for us to meet today is due to some incidents we have been having in Lhasa and in Peking.'

'Incidents?' asked John Stevens raising his brow.

The Ambassador nodded and said, 'Yes, it has to do with the fact that the Commanding Officer of the PSB of Lhasa is missing from duty. Furthermore his family members have disappeared. We are still investigating the incident.'

'Disappeared? As of you are losing your people,' said John Steven a little mockingly.

'We are not LOSING people,' replied the Ambassador a little offended.

343

John ignored the answer and asked him, 'But what does that have to do with our enterprise?'

'Are you saying you don't know anything about it!' shot out the shorter of the two gentlemen in dark suits.

I was very impressed on how John Stevens kept his cool and said, 'May I ask who you are?'

The Ambassador cut in before the man could say anything. 'I apologize, Mr. Stevens. I'm sure Mr. Loo did not intend any disrespect.'

To which John Steven replied, 'Mr. Ambassador, this is not a Chinese prison where prisoners have no rights. I hope this meeting wasn't meant to be a form of interrogation by any PSB Officers. I too meant no disrespect.'

'We were only interested to know if you or your team has any knowledge of the incidents which had taken place.'

To which I replied, 'Mr. Ambassador, we don't have any knowledge nor do we have anything to do with these incidents.'

'I understand. I take it, you wouldn't mind officially answering our query?' asked the Ambassador.

'Sir, should you officially request for an answer, we shall officially reply your query,' I replied with a very serious tone.

'Thank you.'

John Stevens then asked, 'Sir, has the Chinese Government come to a decision in regard to "Keajara"?

'Mr. Stevens we shall soon make a decision on the issue. I believe an answer can be expected in a week or two.'

The meeting was adjourned. John Stevens then rose from his chair, we followed him.

We took leave together and left the Secretary General's office. As we walked into the elevator, John Stevens vented out, 'Talk about the audacity of the man.' He did not raise his voice, but we knew he was angry.

He turned to us and said, 'They are fishing for reasons to say no. We shall not allow it.' As the elevator reached his floor, he repeated, 'No, we shall not allow it.'

We reached my office; Amanda looked up and smiled at us. 'Amanda could you please get me the Prime Minister of Keajara on the phone.'

She nodded and turned to dial the number. A few seconds later my phone rang. I picked up. 'The Prime Minister is on the line Roger.'

'Thank you.'

'Good Morning Dr. Cane.'

'Good Afternoon. We have you on the speaker.'

'Fine. Hello Indira.'

'Good Afternoon Sir,' she answered.

'Is the meeting over?' he asked.

'Yes Sir,' I said.

We spoke at length and also about the two suspicious characters in dark suits. He listened silently without saying anything. After the briefing ended he asked, 'Was that all?'

'Yes Sir, it was a pretty short meeting.'

'I'm very surprised. They still do not know of what actually took place.' A short thoughtful pause later, 'This is very good news.' He was clearing his throat before he spoke further. 'So they will be deciding in one or two

345

weeks.' Another short pause. 'Dr. Cane, Indira you've done a very good job. Now I have some things to do. Please excuse me. Thank you very much for the report.'

'Not at all Sir. Good bye.'

'Good Bye.'

He didn't say what he wanted to do. It all sounded mysterious. I assumed it to be something we shouldn't know. The phone made click and the line went dead. I switched the speaker off. We looked at each other as I said, 'Let's hope all turns out well.'

'Only time will tell,' answered Indira.

'We can only wait.'

She nodded as she gazed into the horizon.

The days passed and no news came. I was only nerves. On the other hand Indira was the "Patience in Person". I didn't know how she did it.

Unexpectedly my phone rang one morning. John Stevens was on the other end.

'Good Morning Dr. Cane.'

'Good Morning Mr. Stevens.'

'I wanted to inform you of the new status. The Chinese have made a decision. However we do not know what it is. The Ambassador will be informing the Security Council tomorrow. The Security Council will be informing us of the final result.'

'Any idea of how soon we would know the results.'

'We hope tomorrow. But I believe it would depend on how the Chinese have decided. A nay to our cause would probably lead to more discussions.'

'I understand.'

'However the Secretary General wants us to meet him the day after. Could you and Miss Yogini please join us at 10:00 a.m.?'

'We shall be there.'

'Allow me then to wish you a nice day.'

'Thank you.' Indira was standing beside me as I hung up. I did not notice how my hands were shaking.

She gentle rubbed my shoulders and asked, 'Is everything ok?'

'The Chinese have made a decision. They will be officially informing the Security Council tomorrow morning. We are requested to meet the Secretary General the day after at 10:00 a.m. at his office. More we don't know.'

Two days later, I hoped for the best as we entered the Secretary General's office. John Stevens was present. As usual Indira was calm, beautiful and serene. I, on the other hand, was a wreck, hardly slept the last two days.

I kept thinking about what Geshe-La once said, "...despite the expectations that we have in life, we should embrace the consequences of events gracefully and face the future with courage."

As we went in, the Secretary General greeted us. 'Dr. Cane, Miss Yogini, please do take seat. Before beginning, I would like firstly to thank you for dedication and zealousness. I know it has not been easy. Our partners in the Security Council have required great convincing. This being a precedential case, it was even more difficult to find the correct arguments. But thanks to your detailed and precise formulation of the affidavit, we were able to satisfy many of the questions and doubts.'

He looked at us and paused a moment. 'However, much discussions and reflections took place. The matter was highlighted from all. The most important one on the table was however the question "What message does the United Nation want to send the world?".' There followed a very strange silence. I felt something was amiss. Was I being paranoid?

'Before going any further, I would like to inform you of the result. It was a long and tiring day, but the Security Council did manage to come to an unanimous vote.' He paused a moment, I could hear the drums.

'There was final result?' I couldn't wait anymore.

'Yes, there was,' he said with a smile. He seemed relieved. 'I had not expected it. Not so soon. Personally, I was anticipating a postponement.' He paused and raised his head looking at me and Indira. 'Fortunately we were spared of this. Therefore I shall not keep you under further suspense. I am very happy to announce that the Security Council has approved the Sovereignty of Keajara and through this paved the way for the creation of an independent nation.'

I heard the words but it didn't seem real. How many times had I wished to hear those exact words, how many times did I look forward for this moment! As it came, it seemed surreal. It was a strange feeling. 'The General Assembly came to the same decision.' Needless to say tears of happiness were flowing down my face as Indira took my hand into hers and shared that meaningful moment. 'Everyone agreed that Keajara is a peace-loving state. They believe it is able and willing to carry out the obligations contained in the Charter of the United Nations. The decision was unanimous. Please allow me to congratulate you personally and thank you for your dedication and personal efforts on this endeavor.'

I felt relieved and tired at the same time. Surges of emotions shooting from my heart, all filled with joy and hope, all unstoppable. I saw the tears flowing down Indira's cheek. I knew we were finally going home. I know not how long we sat there, was it a moment or an eternity, in silence.

'I understand,' he said with a warm smile. 'It is not every day, that one hears such good news. I too was overwhelmed. Indeed the plights of the Tibetans have been great and this victory should be a recognition for their fortitude.'

By and by I pulled myself together. 'I would like to add sir. This is an historical moment. We have finally managed to put Keajara on the map, a hope for many Tibetans, to live their lives in peace and harmony, without danger of being suppressed in terms of their belief or their way of life. The people of Keajara can now live in dignity.'

'Yes Dr. Cane, it is indeed an historical moment.'

There was again silence, as if he too was trying to keep his composure. 'We shall now begin with the official communication, which means officially informing the Prime Minister, press conferences, etc. I shall trigger the necessary activities to begin with the naming process and I shall keep you informed and need your assistance in the proceeding processes.'

'Of course. You may rely on our assistance.'

We thanked him for his support and the tremendous efforts he put in convincing the Chinese. After the meeting we called the Prime Minister and informed him of the results. I hardly need to describe his happiness. An end of a struggle began so long ago, and a new beginning.

We left the building and took a taxi to central park. It seemed right, to go there where we first began discussing about Dharma. Indira said, 'Something extraordinary has happened today. The world has recognized the struggle of the Tibetan people.' I waited for her to go on. 'Why are the Chinese so afraid of Dharma? Why was Mao so afraid of it?'

'Even a mighty country such as China has its weaknesses.'

'For the teachings of a peaceful man?' she asked.

'I know what you mean. It has much to do with insecurity.' I affirmed.

'You are right. It is not only China.' She tilted her head to her right looking into the distance.

'You witness this behavior everywhere in the world.' I continued.

'Be it religion, ideologies, political systems, etc., they are all afraid of change.' I have not seen her so restless before. She began to walk up and down.

'Men have always been afraid of things which initiate change. Out of this fear they perform unvirtuous things,' I said, trying to sooth her.

'If a religion, a dogma or an ideology were really strong, it would not be afraid of change or criticism!'

350

I stood up and took her hands into mine, softly saying, 'It is alright dear, you can now let go.' The pressure during the past months must have been great.

'Change is the most natural of processes. From the moment of birth until the moment of death change is inevitable. Everything in life is about change; aging, growing, the seasons, the cycle of the weather, planets are born and planets cease to exist; universes are born and also cease to exist; dust becomes life and becomes again dust; energy turns into matter and later turns back into energy. In such a dynamic universe, how do we come to the idea that we can keep the status quo, and why are we so afraid of change?' she asked as she stopped to see a sparrow sitting on a branch.

I added, 'I believe fear confuses us. It conjoins us to hold on to things.' "Moreover," I thought, "we are cynical of those who mean to help others, we imprison Green Peace activist for trying to save the environment."

'If a religion, ideology or system is truly strong, it need not fear for openness, for fairness, for CHANGE. Only those who are weak and lack self-confidence fear vicissitude!' Yes, the ventil was open, letting the pressure out.

'Sustainability has more to do with the capability of adaptation to changes and not about holding on to status quo.'

'Unfortunately the majority of us are misled,' she said, beginning to become calm.

'We are ready to sacrifice our morals and indulge us in the most ghastly of criminal actions.'

351

'Men's spiritual capabilities have become weak.' Suddenly she was passionate again, as if speaking out of past memories. 'The answers lie not in killing, torturing, imprisonment or suppressions. No, the answers are to be sought in compassion.'

'Unfortunately this is lacking in the industrial and consumer world. Material consumption plays a very important part. Fulfilling of one's own desire is the main focus.' I remembered the days, not long ago, where I placed so much importance on wearing a nice suit to work. 'The world has become cold.'

'The duality we face in Samsara confuses us. We are torn between a higher purpose and our ego. Whereas a higher purpose requires selflessness and self-confidence, the ego, on the other hand feeds "fear" and "ignorance".'

'We have eyes and yet fail to see. Not realizing the true nature of life.' The discussion made me see my life, my future clearly. Dharma had the answers to all my questions.

It was midday and we were hungry. We walked towards the pizzeria we had once visited. It seemed to be a long time ago. We spent the hour enjoying our food and speaking of our plans for the future. I couldn't help realizing, I had to make up my mind about leaving New York, once and for all. I also realized I needed to speak with mom. Would she want to leave her home, would she want to leave all that is dear to her? A CHANGE for her and me, would I be able to leave her behind alone. My heart said "NO". Here was I torn between the people who meant everything to me.

It was late as we began our way back home. Mom was out. Indira walked into the kitchen and made tea. 'You know darling...' I began '...I do have to speak with my mother about our plans.'

'I know it will not be easy. I feel I'm forcing you to leave your mother.' Her eyes reflected the genuine remorse.

'No you're not. The decision is mine.'

'Nevertheless, it will be difficult for you and your mother.'

'I know. I do have a suggestion for her.'

'A suggestion?' she asked with an eyebrow raised.

'Yes. I intend to invite her to follow us.'

'Do you think she would be willing? Oh yes, that would be just wonderful!' she said suddenly being excited at the idea. 'We could all live together.'

'I know. Let's hope for the best.'

Mom came home late that day. We postponed our discussion.

The next morning during breakfast we briefed her. She seemed to be relieved hearing the good news.

'I am so glad for the Tibetan people.'

Before I could present my proposal, she said, 'Honey, I have been meaning to speak to you. Well I have given it much thought.' She began somewhat carefully, 'I know you wish to leave the US and settle in Keajara, although you've said nothing about it.'

I was about to interrupt when she said, 'It's OK dear, I'm sure you would have spoken with me at the right time.' There was a pause. 'I too have given the whole matter a lot of thought. This has been my home for many years and in my age it is difficult to adapt. But things here are not what they were. I'm not saying I have been unhappy here, but if your father were still living, I would have probably moved away long ago. But as a single working parent, I had not many options. I'm older now and I prefer a quieter environment. Furthermore you're my family.'

There was another pause and I could see how uneasy Indira was becoming. 'If it is fine with you, I would like to follow you.'

I couldn't express my relief. 'Mom we are both so happy to hear you say this.'

I walked over to hug her. Indira joined us, tears and all. 'We were about to make the same proposal this very morning.' It was one of the happiest moments in my life.

The next days and weeks were busy ones. We had press conferences and meetings. The media interest was phenomenal. The political message was obvious. The well wishes did not stop coming in, neither did official invitations from Heads of States. Our journey back to Keajara kept delaying. The meeting between the Prime Minister and President Barack Obama was a memorable, my first time at the White House. But like all things, time passed and things did begin to settle down. Keajara began to take its place in the world. For their decision, China was viewed with a more favorable eye in the world. At the same time we were preparing for our journey back. I couldn't bring it over my heart to sell the house and so I left it empty. The packing was however underway and I began finalizing things.

One early spring day a cab was waiting outside. Mom was walking one last time through her beloved house, her beloved home. My heart was breaking seeing her so. She turned around, she noticed my emotions. Putting her arm around my waist she whispered, 'It's alright honey. Everything is fine as it is. I'm just saying my good byes.'

I had to admit, I too shall be missing our dear home. But the decision has been made. As we drove towards the airport, we passed the school I went to, the front gate where mom waited for me, or the playground where I played baseball, it all seemed like yesterday. Someone once said; when a person leaves a place, a part of oneself stays behind.

We spent the rest of the journey in silence. As we got out of the cab, mom took another look at the city, the place she had spent all her life in. She then took my hand softly and asked, 'Honey, could I return for a visit?'

There were tears in my eyes as I took her in my arms and said, 'Mom, you can make as many visits you wish to, and if you wish to return for sure, I shall make sure that all be arranged.'

She smiled with tears in her eyes. 'Thank you.'

I saw how difficult it was for her. I had almost stopped the whole thing if my mother had not said, 'Let's see darling, let's see if I can get used to the life in Keaja-ra. Let us take this step by step.'

After checking in, we passed through security control and boarded the plane.

It was difficult to let go. The memories hold us to the past, like an anchor keeping a ship in its place. To travel to new worlds, to explore, one needs to lift the anchor and fearlessly go into the unknown.

But it is not easy, especially for someone like my mother. She is come into age, she had fought her battles, she is about to leave a world she has known all her life. I loved her more that very moment, for her courage and compassion. Tears began to roll down my cheeks as I watched her looking out of the seat window, looking at her world for the very last time as the plane took off the runway.

No, she never went back home again; she couldn't bring it over her heart to say good bye again. As she later told me, 'The pain would have been too great to bear.'

25

Back in Keajara

We touched down at Delhi International Airport the next morning, a city which never sleeps. Even at such an early hour, life was busting. We saw to it that mom wasn't overwhelmed by the new world. As if anyone could protect oneself of the infinite influences; noises, smells, colors, heat, people. Well we did our best.

Collecting our luggage, we hurried to the exit; a four wheel drive was waiting for us. A very sympathetic and polite man from Tamil Nadu named Narayanan picked us up.

'Good morning Sir, please, please get in. I take care of luggage,' he said.

'Thank you.' It was a relief to have some help.

'Going to hotel Sir?' he asked getting into the driving seat.

'Yes,' I replied.

Somehow he noticed it was the first visit for my mother. 'Not to worry madam. In hotel you can rest well. Very quiet, very safe!' he added with a very polite smile. My mother appeared to be comforted by the words.

He maneuvered the vehicle competently through the busy streets, packed with cars, trucks, buses, people, cows and rickshaws; everyone wanting to go somewhere.

The hotel was only twenty-five kilometers away, but it took us an hour to reach it.

We checked into a five star hotel. I noticed my mother began to relax. After checking in, we were taken to our rooms. I had requested a suite with two bedrooms, just to make sure my mother was nearby. After all we would be in Delhi a few days; my mother could get acclimatized as we go around our business.

The next days were planned for meetings with officials of the Indian government. We were also invited to the Chinese Embassy for talks on future cooperation. The meeting with his Holiness the Dalai Lama in Dharamsala was a special one for me. It was also an emotional one. We were received by Tibetan people, who were in high spirits and great hope, at last to be able to go home. He expressed his thankfulness for our efforts and the great chance the Tibetans were given to begin a new life. As he put it 'It is my hope that all Tibetans see Keajara as their home. I believe it is an answer for our plight these last fifty years. I wish all Tibetans to finally arrive home'. Indira could not hold back her tears.

Mom on the other hand spent most of the time at the hotel, 'acclimatizing' as she put it. She did visit some the interesting places; the India Gate, the Parliament of India, the Rashtrapati Bhavan which was originally built for the Governor General of India, the Connaught Place and the Lodhi Gardens. It gave her an opportunity to breath in a different air. It was her first time away from the States; the cultural shock was preprogrammed, as we heard in the evenings after her trips.

'I have seen it in T.V. but being here is a completely different experience.'

'Another world,' I said.

'It is not the cultural differences, I accept it. No it is the living conditions, the poverty and the obvious difference between haves and have not's.'

'India still has much to do.'

'If India finds its way back to its true self, it would be able to solve all its problems,' said Indira.

'You mean Dharma.'

'She is the mother of Dharma; she should again stand up and lead mankind towards liberation.'

'Indira is right, what has all the trials of socialism or capitalism brought to this nation, except for more pain and suffering.'

'To tread again the path of the great Mahatma, an interesting thought, but you forget the dangers India faces from Pakistan and from China.'

'I am not asking India to be defenseless, no. But she has a chance to turn the wheels of social changes internally. She can again light the candle of Dharma and lead the many millions away from "wanting to have more" towards "being more".' Of course Indira was right. This would solve the problems of many millions, who lead an extremely sad life.

'Many go to temples not really knowing the meaning behind it. They are practicing Dharma, not really seeing the truth behind it. Dharma has been corrupted by the caste system, the political parties and corruption. True Dharma is no more transparent. This is indeed sad.' I could see the great disappointment in her eyes.

'You are right my dear.' Mom tried to console her. 'Now that Keajara is free, now that the world can see this small nation, maybe the world would also see the benefits of Dharma and just maybe, it would follow.'

'Mom is right darling. Maybe by being true to itself Keajara could lead by example.'

We were speaking through our hearts.

This time we flew directly from Leh to Keajara City; a temporary airport had been completed. Our arrival in Keajara was a memorable one. We were welcomed by many happy faces.

Richard greeted us at the airport. He told us of the many celebrations and pujas taking place. One could practically breathe in the air of freedom. He told of the UN peace keepers helping in the buildup phase.

'The Prime Minister is very busy, he couldn't make it.' Richard was full of enthusiasm; I could hear it in his voice. 'I'm very glad young people such as you are here to take over.' And after a short pause, 'You know, I wish to retire. Oh by no means I'm leaving the country.' He spoke slowly as if letting the word sink in. 'Ah yes the country! No, I shall spend my time in spiritual development. It is now up to you; to see to it that Keajara remains a sanctuary for the Tibetans. I have already spoken with the Prime Minister and he concurs.'

I was a little surprised. I wasn't really certain what it meant. 'Richard, I'm not certain what you are trying to tell me.'

'You and Indira have done a great job.'

'I believe I also speak for Indira when I say we will do what we can to support the development of Keajara.' Indira nodded. 'We hope we live up to your expectations. But that doesn't explain what is expected of us.'

'Your performances have exceeded all expectations. But I shall speak no more since the Prime Minister will reveal it himself.' Saying this he led us to the festivities. He spoke of the joy when the news first came in. People all through the country were out in the streets embracing each other and rejoicing. Prayers were performed and festivities were held.

The Prime Minister and the High Lama were present in many of them. They gave speeches of hope, of security, of freedom and of peace. Keajara was not rich in natural resources neither did it play any importance in global politics but it has given hope for the millions of Tibetans who have lost their homes and cultural heritage. It's now seen as a sanctuary. Indeed, the government is planning to accept refugee Tibetans who are willing to live in peace and harmony. A meeting had been scheduled with the High Lama and the Prime Minister.

The next morning at the Prime Minister's office, they greeted us heartily and thanked us for all our efforts.

'As you're aware,' said the Prime Minister, 'a Cabinet already exists. But some of the ministers have tended in their resignation and intend to retire and spend time in meditation. They believe it is time for those younger to take over. I believe this is a good idea. I too intend to hold a general election in the coming year, a first one for us,' he said with a happy and contended smile.

'It's our wish to lead Keajara into the democratic process,' said the High Lama.

'Yes, yes,' continued the Prime Minister. 'But I shall not be candidating for a reelection. I too shall retire to a spiritual life. We agree that suitable candidates are required to continue our work. To preserve the heritage for which we have fought for. We also agree we need someone who has both the spiritual understanding and also conventional wisdom to carry out the task as Prime Minister. I and the Cabinet have unanimously agreed that Indira is the right person for the job. We shall be proposing you as the new candidate in the coming year.'

Indira was apparently surprised to hear this news. She began to protest, but the Prime Minister waved it aside. 'The people know you, they respect you. You have shown great dedication and wisdom. In the meantime you will take over as my deputy. See it as preparation for the office of Prime Minister.'

There was a short pause, as if he was waiting another protest. But none came. Maybe she thought it would be only in vain. He then turned to me. 'We have an offer to make. One we hope you would accept. We would understand if you've other plans.'

Seeing I did not react, he continued, 'We were hoping you would consider remaining in Keajara.' Another pause, still no reaction from me. 'We hope you would see Keajara as your new home and remain here. I believe we know each other long enough to understand ones wishes. I hope I have not made a mistake or put you in an awkward situation.' He paused, waiting for my response.

I didn't know my feelings had been so obvious. I replied, 'You're not wrong in your assumption. I have come to consider Keajara as my home. I do have the intention to live in Keajara.'

'I am happy to hear this,' said the Prime Minister clasping his hands. 'You've become a part of Keajara. I know that ours is a small country. It can by no means compete with the UN and the career perspectives that the UN can offer, but we can offer you a new challenge, an opportunity to build up a nation and lay the stepping stones for a new future.'

'Yes Sir, you are right there.'

'That is why I would like you to consider taking up the position as the Minister of Planning and Sustainability and to candidate for the position as the future Deputy Prime Minister.'

I was somewhat surprised, I didn't know what to say, so I blurted out something like, 'It's a very generous offer sir, thank you sir, I had not expected it sir…'

'If you have an objection or reservations, we can naturally discuss about it…' he left the sentence unfinished.

'No, no, that is not it. Maybe I should explain.' I continued a few seconds later, 'Ever since I left Keajara, I had a very intense wish to return, to be back. I feel at home here. My life at the UN though an important one wasn't sufficient to fulfill the spiritual needs I have found here.'

'I'm glad to hear that,' signaling me to go on.

'I know not where this journey is going to take me, but my heart speaks for me to continue my studies in Dharma.'

'I understand. But I do believe you would find time for both. We all do,' he said with an understanding smile.

I wasn't sure what to say. With an inner assurance that all will be well I answered, 'In that case, I'm happy to accept your job offer.'

'I'm very pleased to hear this.'

I did have another question though. 'Sir, there are many discussions about inviting Tibetans to come and settle down. Our resources are limited, how do we intend to finance the reintegration into the society?'

The High Lama said with a smile, 'Not even in office but already showing great engagement.'

Everyone laughed.

The Prime Minister nodded amusedly saying, 'I would like to ask you for a little patience. We do have a solution. Due to security purposes we would like to keep it silent, at least for the moment. Let's speak more another time.'

A little perplexed about the answer, I prodded, 'Sir, I am not quite sure I understand.'

To this said the High Lama, 'All in time Dr. Cane, all in time, please bear with us a little longer.'

I wasn't sure what to say. Neither the Prime Minister nor the High Lama had ever refused to answer my questions before. It seemed a little strange. I looked at Indira but she too showed no response. Confused and without any other choice, I decided to postpone the discussion for later.

Before the meeting adjoined, the Prime Minister wanted to introduce someone. He asked his secretary to allow the person in. A minute later the door opened and a man, looking very similar to the Prime Minister entered the room. The Prime Minister rose from his chair and walked over to the gentlemen. He embraced him heartily. 'This...' said the Prime Minister '...is my younger brother Mr. Semko Jigme. Semko was also known as Col. Yang. He was the Commanding Officer of the PSB Office in Lhasa.'

Apparently, I was not the only one who was surprised by this revelation. Noticing this, the Prime Minister continued calmly 'Only few knew of this. It was a very delicate and dangerous operation.'

We were all a little speechless and astonished until Richard said, 'An astonishing feat. That explains a lot of things.'

The Prime Minister nodded and continued, 'My father realized long ago that it would take more than being silent to keep Keajara of the Chinese radar. He worked with some influential people in China, those who sympathized with our cause. They helped us to post Semko in a strategically important position. Semko was sent at very early age to China. He went to a normal school and later to university. He then joined the army and rose up in the PSB. With him in the center of the intelligence division in Lhasa, we were able to control and monitor all activities concerning Keajara.'

'This is something one reads in spy novels' said Richard still in a state of disbelief. He then looked at the Col. and said, 'You Sir have done a great deed for your people. I don't know how words can ever express your sacrifice for this nation.'

Semko said in a calm and clear voice, 'Dr. Conners, it was an honor for me to serve my people.'

He then turned to me, Indira and Richard, 'Madam, Sirs, I'm very glad to meet you. I thank you for the dedication, without which we would not be at this point today.'

"He looked tired," I thought.

'I have become old and I have missed my home,' he said smilingly. 'I have now no other wish, but to spend the rest of my days in meditation and prayers.' He reached into his jacket and withdrew a notice book, handing it over to me. 'I hope one day this will be of use. These are my personal notes.' He handed me his diary.

I accepted it and said, 'Thank you.'

'I wish you all the best.' He turned around and he left the room, as silently as he came in. I never saw him again.

I could see I wasn't the only one in a state of trance. The infiltration of PSB at such a high level must have been a mammoth project.

The Prime Minister continued after his brother left the room, 'My father was a man of great vision but he wasn't alone. The oracle and his highness the late High Lama were able to advise him successfully. Of course it wasn't an easy task but with the blessing of the Buddhas we were successful.'

'I believe I'm not alone when I say, your brother has made great sacrifice. I'm also sure, it wasn't easy for him to grow up alone among strangers and to live and work among those who had very little understanding for your plight.'

The Prime Minister answered, 'No, I'm sure it wasn't. But please don't misunderstand me for saying this. We have no wish to see the Chinese as our enemy. In fact we hope one day to live in peace and harmony with all mankind.'

Before the meeting ended, the Prime Minister showed us a piece of paper on which the future cabinets were listed.

Prime Minister's Department and Foreign Affairs
Ministry of Education (both Spiritual and Non-Spiritual)
Ministry of Well Being and Happiness
Ministry of Agriculture
Deputy Prime Minister's Department
Ministry of Planning & Sustainability
Ministry of Internal Affairs and Defense
Ministry of Finance

Looking back, I can only say I had no idea what I was letting myself into. There was much to learn, so much to do. The following days, ministers were sworn in. We were all reminded to always have the people's interest at heart. With a small monthly salary and no other incentives, except a bicycle, we went to work. To be honest, I wouldn't know how to spend my salary, since money had no real meaning here. Everything was shared, food, the work, the leaving quarters, nothing really belongs to anyone.

After a ground laying ceremony and a five month construction period, the new governmental building was completed. It was a two-storey building out of mud and bricks. Other than the size of it, it looked just like any other building in town. The walls were ornamented with paintings of the Holy Beings and holy mandalas. For the opening ceremony a festival was organized. After a puja, the new national anthem and national flag was introduced.

Many came to celebrate that wonderful day. Many governments accepted our invitation and attended the ceremony. We had the honor to welcome Heads of Nations and other delegates. We were very pleased to welcome the Prime Minister of The People's Republic of China, who expressed his countries well wishes.

I felt a new era had begun; a new beginning. I felt hope in the air. I felt at home.

26

A window opened and

I saw a wonderful new world

As months passed we began slowly to build up the nation. We could now openly invite experts into the country to consult us. More importantly, the country became a sanctuary for Tibetans. We had managed to cultivate the vegetation to new heights, built the infrastructure with ecological material. It was necessary as the population has been increasing due to the influx of newcomers.

I and mom settled in, found a home, not imaginable a few years ago. This wasn't part of my plan, neither was my mother's intention to spend the rest of her life in the Himalayas. But it was so. I was very glad to see her becoming accustomed to her new life. She laughed more; there was a twinkle in her eye, something I had not seen a long time since. There was happiness and contentment.

I extended our cottage so that she had a living space for herself; that she was nearby. Mom joined Richard in his daily spiritual activities. Every day I awoke with great motivation and with a happy heart, with the knowledge I'm doing something valuable with my life.

Since the founding of Keajara, many Tibetans saw Keajara as their home. The population was increasing.

Solutions had not been simple. Most of them came out of the blue. Long lost family members became united and friends met again. Everyone helped each other and shared what they possessed. The people joined and helped, everyone chipped in, and everyone was involved. It was not left alone to the government. All worked hand in hand. It seemed to be the most natural thing.

I was on my way to a town one day, a small village. Many Tibetans had come to live there. Whilst coordinating the work I stayed at a small cottage owned by a farmer. One morning during breakfast he said, 'All of us deserve a chance in life, a chance to live a happy life, a chance to know who we are. It begins with the show of love. Love opens doors in us. We begin to embrace the world. I have been fortunate and I'm thankful for that.'

I reflected on what he said and realized that my journey began by me saying goodbye to my old life. I accepted the person I was, the person I am, with all my failures. This gave me peace. It allowed others to accept me for who I am. I understood at that moment that the road to finding one's true self is the most exciting adventure one can have.

He was right, the farmer. I know not how I got there; it might have been providence, a door opened in me, my heart spoke. It began as a whisper. It became obvious that we need others as much as others need us. No one is alone and no one is really lost. We only tend to forget the mystery of compassion, the wonders of giving, the wisdom of companionship. I know not the ways of the universe. Still standing at the beginning, miles ahead of me, years of work to be done; yet there was this deep voice speaking the words of hope, of confidence, of strength. Gone are times of uncertainty, the clouds are clearing and a brave new world is opening in front of my eyes. Happiness engulfed me and a bright smile appeared on my face.

As I was watching the children play, watching the people going about their chores, watching the birds fly, I knew I shall hence fort walk into the horizon and conquer my doubts. Not with force, no. But with love, I shall embrace my fears and release them. With heads held high I shall follow the path of those who had walked before me, of those who had seen the light, who had ascended into the realms of the Enlightened Ones.

One early September morning, an American physicist, one Dr. Andrew Penrose, was waiting for me in my office. He had sent me a letter and asked for an appointment. In his letter he spoke of some important discovery he wanted to share with me. A gentleman in his early thirties, of average stature, wore thick rimmed spectacles. He was wearing a grey pullover and a pair of jeans. Nervously he extended his hand saying, 'Good Morning Dr. Cane.'

'Good morning Dr. Penrose.'

He took a seat in a chair across my table. 'Thank you sir for your accepting my request.'

'Not at all, please how can I be of assistance to you?'

'Well, it is actually a long story, but I think it is important for me to tell you about it. Only I would need a little more time than what was planned.'

I began by saying, 'I'm short of time...', when Dr. Penrose interrupted politely.

'I'm sure you are, but it is very important. You need to understand the reason for my visit,' his request seemed to be very earnest. It was all a little mysterious and I admit I was curious.

'Well, in that case, allow me to inform my secretary to cancel the appointments for the next three hours?'

'Yes, that would be sufficient, thank you and could I propose that we call us by our first names, Andrew.' He extended his hand and I took it by saying, 'Roger'.

'Well to be exact it began a few years back,' as he was speaking he retrieved a bundle of note books out of his shoulder leather bag. 'I was doing some general research, on Albert Einstein's theories. It was just a matter of interest, you see. I wanted to find out on how he came to his ideas. During my research, I explored many aspects of his statements, writings, etc. His emphasis of science and spirituality lead me to seek further. I began to explore the great faiths. Of course I started with the one nearest to me, the Bible, then the Torah and finally arriving to Buddhism. Something about it made me dig deeper. I wasn't a spiritual or religious person before, until I came across the teachings about emptiness, called "Shunyata". It opened my eyes.'

I encouraged him to go on.

'During this, I stumbled into other statements of Einstein on Buddhism and Hinduism. For instance, quote, "If there is any religion that would cope with modern scientific needs it would be Buddhism," or "A human being is part of the whole, called by us "Universe"; a part limited in time and space. He experiences, his thoughts and feelings as something separated from the rest – a kind of optical delusion of his consciousness. This delusion is a kind of prison for us, restricting us to our personal desires and affection for a few persons nearest us. Our task must be, to free ourselves from this prison by widening our circle of compassion to embrace all living creatures and the whole nature in its beauty. Nobody is able to achieve this completely but striving for such achievement is, in itself, a part of the liberation and a foundation for inner security," unquote.' His eyes glowed and his voice sounded enthusiastic.

'You see, Albert Einstein wasn't a big believer of God or religion. He believed more on the laws of nature. A Hindu scientist named Satyendranath Bose and Einstein both came up on the Bose-Einstein theory. Matter is cooled to absolute zero temperature. In this state bosons, which are particles, assume their lowest quantum state. Only then can one observe their behavior, the so-called "macroscopic quantum phenomena".' He paused here a moment to look into his note book. 'My assumption is both scientists had a deep understanding of emptiness, without really knowing it. They were on the right track. Their spiritual convictions helped them to understand the correlation between science and nature. I also believe his theory on relativity has much to do with his understanding of Buddhism.'

I added, 'In the early periods of the sub-continent, they had a perfect understanding of the true existence of nature. It correlates with today's scientific approaches.'

'That is the point I am getting to,' he added.

I interrupted him politely, 'You know in earlier periods there wasn't such descriptions as Buddhism or Hinduism. It was known only as "Dharma", the "Teachings".'

'Dharma?' he asked raising his eyebrows.

'The world we live in is only one of many. What we know is even less. "Dharma" meant more. It meant the wisdom of being enlightened. Dharma engulfs all which we know or understand and all which we do not know or understand, our thoughts, our experiences, the forces surrounding us. It is the truth and the untruth. It is that which binds us inseparably; from the cradle to the grave. It is the source which makes us cross and recross each other's lives, life after life. It transcends time and space. It is the result and the cause; it is the one with compassion and wisdom. Dharma is endless.'

Andrew became silent, as if he had retrieved into some inner-self. A few minutes later he raised his head and smiled. 'I believe I understand what you speak of,' and out of the blue, 'It is about knowing the reason and the causes of our existence, to understand the sense of existing as such and the methods to achieve liberation from an existence which is filled with suffering.'

I was astonished. He had apparently understood me.

'Where was I?' he asked.

'Ah yes, as I continued my research, I crossed topics such as Emptiness and Oneness. Comparing them with modern science theories, I realized that we perceive our reality somewhat prematurely.'

To that I added, 'Our perception of our world is based on our senses. But if we are able to develop finer perception skills, we would be able to accordingly perceive a different world or other dimensions as well. As we are not capable to do this, we rely on modern techniques to explore the deeper part of matter. Enlightened beings rely on meditation. This not only allows them to perceive the finer part of matter, but also the deeper part of the mind.'

He seemed at first to be perplexed at my explanation, but then I saw a spark in his eyes. 'Of course, it all makes sense!'

A sudden shift of position in the chair, a look into his note book and then he saw me in the eye and smiled. At the same time there was this excitement, like a child who couldn't wait to tell his parents his discovery.

'Allow me to begin. It is said in Dharma that everything arises and returns into Emptiness. I call it, "a state of non-duality". It has infinite potential, from which every possible perception can arise from. So in more than one way, you can compare it to a Quantum Field.'

'Please go on Dr. Penrose, so far I'm following you.'

He shifted his sitting position and carried on, 'Everything around us seems to have a location. We need longitude and latitude to be able to pin point the location of a certain object. When we move towards the microscopic world, we realize that the term "location" begins to disappear. Take wave for instance; it has no definite location in space or time. What does that mean? Imagine at the same time, all matter have their source in wave, it can only mean one thing, that matter exist everywhere all at once, since waves are not positionable. It is spread across time and space.' His tone began to be more contemplative. 'I asked myself the question, "How is this possible,

375

how can matter seem to be solid when the basis of matter is not? How can matter be positioned, whereas the positions of waves are not definable?".'

Again he paused and slowly spoke the following words, as if to stress on them. He snapped his fingers. 'There can only be one explanation, it is an illusion, we are in fact living in a world of holography; and what is it that creates these holographic worlds, of course, the human consciousness, the human imagination. This brings me to the next point. Science has discovered that at sub-atomic level the behavior of particles is influenced by the human consciousness,' another pause. 'It has been scientifically proven that the behavior of a particle is not predefined. It is determined by the human consciousness. For us scientists of the today, all this seemed new, but it has been common knowledge in Dharma since a long time.'

I had to interrupt him again. 'So what you are saying is, naturally from a scientific perspective, that what appears to be solid, is actually two sides of the same coin, so to speak; on the one side, a perceived reality and on the other side, the true reality?'

He rose from his chair and walked over to my small window overviewing the inner garden. 'Yes! When I first read about the independence of Keajara, I had felt a great relieve. At last the Tibetan people could live in peace.' He turned around and smiled. I understood how he felt.

'I see I'm drifting of. Where was I? Ah yes, coming back to particles and waves. As you know a lot of work has been done on atoms, especially the density of atoms. It has been proved that 99.999999999999% of an atom is empty space. I call this "the emptiness of atoms". So I ask again the question; "How can everything around us appear to be solid when they are in fact empty of space?".'

'A good question!' I replied without offering an answer.

He continued, 'Well science has an explanation. It calls the solidity a repulsion or push of other sets of atoms. It also says that nothing really touches anything, atoms come close but never touch.'

'So I would ask, what keeps them together?' I said.

'Exactly!' A smile appeared, as if he had found out something.

'It took me sometime to answer this question. The answer was so obvious that I was at first astonished.'

'And it being...?' I waited for him to reply.

'Pressure! It must be the same force which holds everything else together. At the same time I bumped into the two forces in Dharma, the masculine and feminine phenomenon; two forces, with reciprocal and mutual characteristics, with compensating behavioristics. Equilibrium exists when these two forces are in balance. It became clear to me, the mind influences, directly or indirectly the evolvement of matter and pressure to ensure sustainability.'

I understood. 'I believe so too.'

'This brings me to another interesting topic, the quantum field. Einstein called it an electro matter field from which all matter arises. What does that mean? Basically it means that all particles arising from this field have the same basis. That would mean that both the field and particle have the same nature or characteristics. If you recall, a particle reacts to thoughts or observations of a human. There is interaction, communication and inter-connectivity; meaning they speak the same language and have the same background, meaning they are one and the same. So if the Quantum Field exists beyond time and space so does the mind!'

His presentation was so interesting, that I didn't realize how quickly time passed. It was already afternoon and I had the impression that Andrew had more to say.

'I'm very eager to know more, but I must unfortunately stop here. I would like to suggest that we meet again tomorrow, same time, would that be fine with you?'

'Thank you for your patience and for your attention. I apologize for taking too much of your time. Naturally I'm only too happy to accept your invitation.'

We parted. I was very much preoccupied by the things which Andrew had explained. Some were things, which I already knew, others however were new. But it confirmed my conviction to follow the path I have chosen for me.

Somehow I was unable to concentrate the remaining day. That evening, I spoke with Indira during dinner. She found the revelations interesting too and we discussed late into the night. She suggested we persuade Andrew to include his revelations into our spiritual curriculum, to produce clarity about the correlations between spirituality and science. I found it a very good idea.

The next morning at the office, Andrew was punctual, still in his grey pullover and jeans. He seemed to be a little excited, rubbing his fingers. One would think he had discovered something important and couldn't wait to tell someone.

'Good morning Andrew, I hope you slept well?'

'Yes, yes thank you. I slept so well and woke up as if I was new born. How this?'

'I believe it has to do with Keajara. I too had the similar experience when I first arrived.'

He nodded as if he had understood and said, 'I must find out what it is.'

I smirked as I answered, 'All will come in time.'

He took a seat and continued where he left of yesterday as if the interval had not taken place.

'I would like to begin today with the thought of "Oneness". Needless to say you are aware of it, that all things in the universe are interconnected.'

'Remember me speaking of Dharma yesterday?' I asked.

He nodded.

'Well Dharma and the Mind are one.'

'So it does not exist independently of the mind?'

'No, for that matter, nothing exists independently of the Mind,' I answered.

'This only strengthens the view of "onenessness". It is indeed an illusion to believe that we are separate entities or exist separately from the world around us. New discoveries in science are opening to a different idea of the universe. The true nature of both ourselves and the world around us is actually completely unified. This has

379

been proved by Einstein's theory of Quantum Entanglement.'

'I'm not sure if I understand?'

He explained further 'When two particles interact with each other something special happens, a unique connection. A bond is closed. Scientific observations show that when one particle is affected in some way, the other particle reacts instantaneously, irregard of its apparent distance from each other, in the same and exact way. Einstein called it "spooky action at a distance".'

I was about to interrupt him, but he seemed to be intensely occupied with his thoughts; he did not seem to notice my reaction, as if he were in a world of his own.

'So let us go back in time a little, say to the time just before the universe began, the point of time just before what we call the big bang; a point known as the "Singularity". It was when all things in the universe were condensed to one single point, where all potentials of matter and energy were only waiting to explode and spread across time and space. At this point, all things were entangled and connected. Everything existed as one.'

'So what you are saying is that quantum entanglement is a law in time and space facilitating the possibility for phenomena to mix, communicate and interconnect?' I asked.

He answered with a single 'Yes'. Then he took a deep breath before saying, 'I have one more topic to speak of and then I shall like to say why I'm here.'

I nodded silently and he continued. 'There is an experiment called the dual slit experiment. Here the nature of light was tested. Also here something interesting was discovered. What one does is to propel particles of light through slits and record where they land on the other side of a barrier. Something astonishing was observed. Particles which one thought were solid began to behave as waves. That was not all, the particles behaved depending on how they were observed. Those which were not observed showed infinite potential whereas those which were observed became solid, meaning took a state of finite possibility and remained in a defined location.'

'So what you're saying is that the mind controls the behavior of matter beginning at a very subtle state. Buddha said that "Reality is only the projection of the mind." I'm sure you've heard of Nelson Mandela's quoting Henley's poem; "I'm the Master of my fate, the Captain of my soul".'

He looked at me intensely and I noticed something in his eyes. He smiled and said, 'So much wisdom!'

He rose from his chair and walked to the window. 'I would like to say why I'm here.' He spoke slowly without any haste. 'There is a different understanding of the mind in the modern world. I know now that in Dharma, when one speaks of the mind, one is not speaking of the brain. There is where I need your help. What is meant by the term "mind" in Dharma?'

I did not answer him immediately. 'Before I go further, I would like to say, I'm very glad to have met you. You've opened my eyes to a new world.'

He just nodded accepting my compliment.

'Now to answer your question; you're right in your assumption. The term "mind" in Dharma is not that which is understood in the west, rather it is used to address something holy and everlasting. According to the Indian Philosophy matter is not the mind and vice versa. The brain belongs to the earlier category. Allow me.' I opened my drawer and took out a copy of the thangka, which Geshe-La once showed me.

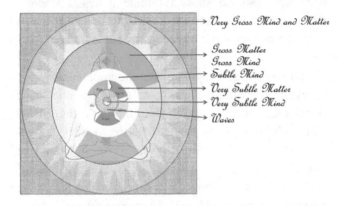

Very Gross Mind and Matter

Gross Matter
Gross Mind
Subtle Mind
Very Subtle Matter
Very Subtle Mind
Waves

'This is a copy of something very old; it helped me once to understand the relationship between mind and matter. You see here the various levels of mind and matter. Actually, there are infinite levels and not all can be shown here, but one could begin to understand the complexity of creation, of Samsara, Karma and the interconnectedness of mind and matter.'

He observed the document carefully. 'Does that mean the very subtle mind is where all begins and ends?'

I was amazed how quickly he understood, I couldn't help being amused. 'Yes, you see, all our actions, be it physical or mental lead to the formation of karmical seeds.'

382

Andrew interrupted saying, 'These seeds cause the creation and cessation of everything around us.'

I nodded again. 'These seeds are situated at the outer layer of the very subtle mind. These seeds remain there until the moment of ripening. When it ripens; it creates a state of consciousness, which we perceive as a reality; also known as a conventional or dualistic world, where matter can be perceived from the most subtle to the grossest of forms.'

'I see!' He seemed to be in a state of total contemplation.

'The very subtle mind is independent of time and space and its nature is clarity. The word "Buddha" comes from an old Indian word "Boodhi" or "Budhi" which means "ultimate comprehension" or "utter clarity". A Buddha is therefore one who has achieved utter clarity.'

'And this mind travels from one life to another, carrying the karmical seeds with it?'

'Yes. There is however something else. In truth the very subtle mind is not mobile; it doesn't move from one location to another, it does not age. Well time and space do not exist at its state of consciousness. It remains in equilibrium. Worlds appear and disappear around it.'

'The mind does not move; it remains in a single position? We perceive nothing more than a holographical production of our world?'

'I'm sure you've heard of the saying "The world is nothing but a dream".' To which he nodded. 'Everything is subjected to change. Worlds arise and decay. At the same time, it is only a state of the mind. The mind dreams and our karmical seeds offer the topics.'

383

'And we assume it to be real.' His voice was almost a whisper, a whisper of amazement.

'Even that what is known as dark energy, dark matter, matter, wormholes, etc., are just phenomena of Samsara which appear in the level of very subtle matter.'

After a few minutes Andrew said, 'So you're saying, science is only observing matter…' He left the sentence unfinished, as if he was speaking to himself.

I could see it in his eyes. How he was beginning to understand. How his thoughts and my words were beginning to interact and interconnect, until I saw how he became "clear".

'I understand…' pausing again '…science will never be able to answer all questions…' pausing again '…unless science explores the spiritual world, just as Dharma does.' He then began to speak without any reluctance, 'Everything is interconnected. The mind is the creator, hence all we see and touch is created by us, by our actions. When the seeds of Karma ripen, we perceive our worlds; the Universe is just another creation, another creation in the continuum of time. At the same time, change is omnipresent. Due to the continual ripening of new karmical seeds, there is no such thing as status quo. The truth is we are trapped in this never ending realm of time and space and the only way out is to open our eyes and see the truth and the truth is, we have to learn to understand Dharma!' Before I could answer he said, 'The line between science and spirituality is actually blur.'

'Andrew, long time ago when people witnessed islands suddenly appear from the sea bed, it was thought to be something supernatural. They were unaware of the laws and mechanisms which lead to such an event. We know today it is caused by volcanic eruptions. Just as volcanism explains the natural causes leading to the creation of an island in a sea, just as you know there is a mechanism which explains the "big bang".'

'Yes, this process is called inflation. About 14.8 billion years ago, there was a sudden fluctuation of the inflation energy which led to the "big bang", which led to the birth of our universe. At the same time something else happened. The natural constants were fixed, the speed of light, the laws of gravitation. These natural constants are the reason for our existence. Likewise there are other natural constants which lead to the creation of other worlds and other universes, therefore the existence of the infinite state of consciousness.'

'Yes and we see on this world how the different climatic conditions for instance lead to the creation of different flora and fauna. What science calls "inflation" is comparable to Karma. This process never ends.'

Andrew did not reply; he remained silent as a few minutes passed. He closed his notebook and looked up, 'I believe I have come to a point in my life, where my questions can only be answered through exploring the spiritual path, would you allow me to stay in Keajara and continue my work.'

I smiled when he said "work". 'Of course you're free to stay here. I have no objections; Keajara welcomes anyone who is willing to work towards peace and harmony.'

I and Andrew spent a lot of time discussing about his "spiritual exploration". We became very good friends.

He later published many of his works. Although initially they were met with skepticism, later the scientific world began to accept his findings. He met a girl, married and settled down. Much of his time he spent with Dharma, with the exploration of the mind and its' potential. He did find the answers he was seeking. He lived to be an old man and left this world as an Enlightened Being.

27

The Portal

Four years passed before Indira and I tied the knot. It took place on a mild summer day, the first day of June, with close friends and relatives. A year later Indira gave birth to a beautiful baby girl, Anna. I adored her. Indira used to say I was spoiling her, but I believed one can't give enough love. At the same time, we were pretty busy, between ensuring the welfare of Keajara and the welfare of Anna. To China we hold a peaceful relationship; the UN still holds a peace keeping contingent at the border, mainly Indian soldiers or soldiers of Indian origin. After the first general election, Indira became the first elected Prime Minister of Keajara, by landslide. I still hold the post as Minister of Planning and Sustainability and deputy Prime Minister.

Over the last two years, thanks to the tremendous efforts of many people around the world, we managed to build up the infrastructure and a strong agricultural basis. It was the people's wish to increase the efforts in the agricultural sector and not in the industrial or technological sector and to continue the tradition of Dharma.

At the same time we had a big influx of Tibetans into the country looking for a home.

I and Indira did not dwindle taking time for meditation and the learning of the Sutras. After spending a term as the Minister of Education, Richard decided to retire. He accepted the life as a monk. My mother followed him and took the oath of a nun. We hardly see them; in fact I had not seen them for many months.

Something worried me. The figures do not tie. One day at the office I decided to ask Indira the reason for the discrepancy.

'I'm at loss,' I said. 'It's about the influx of the Tibetans. Since the last few years, the numbers have been increasing. Only it's not really visible in the population census. Furthermore many Keajarans have just gone missing. Even Richard, my mom or Ananda seem to be missing. I'm not sure I understand this. Is the census accurate? Are Keajarans leaving the country?'

I noticed that my wife wasn't comfortable about me asking her this question, but I was adamant to know the reason.

'Roger, I'm not sure how to explain this to you, but I think it's time to meet the High Lama.'

Astonished and indignant I said, 'You mean you know what is happening, you know the reason and you've not been telling me!'

She said apolitically, 'I'm very sorry, darling, but it wasn't for me to tell. It's a matter of great importance. That is why it's necessary for us to meet Geshe-La.'

I was upset first but I also realized she was the Prime Minister, a function which carries many responsibilities, amongst other things, national security.

A week later we were at the monastery to meet the High Lama.

'Roger, Indira please do come in; please take a seat. How are you and are all things well at home?' he asked with a serene smile.

'We are both very well Geshe-La and all is well at home. Anna is also doing well and she loves school,' I answered, thinking, "I wasn't so enthusiastic going to school at her age, she has that from her mother."

'I'm very glad to hear this.'

He then turned to me and said, 'Roger, I have heard of your concerns and I believe it is time to reveal the most important secret of Keajara. That which makes Keajara so significant for Dharma and for humanity.' I noticed that my heart was beating a little faster. I was suddenly alert and very much excited to know this secret. 'You are about to be revealed a timeless secret. It has been guarded very strictly. Except for the chosen ones, it cannot be shared with anyone.'

He looked me in the eye as he began to tell, 'It is many years since the Lord, Buddha Shakyamuni, turned the wheel of Dharma. During this time he also performed the Tantra Yoga. This he did in the form of Buddha Heruka. The Lord generated twenty four Heruka Mandalas on this world.'

It was late winter and I could see the snow falling outside. I had always liked this room, with its many windows and many colors. It came to my mind that at this very moment, I was also surrounded by a long history and naturally, the past has its secrets.

'These mandalas are "portals" to the pure land of the Buddhas. Buddha Shakyamuni did not destroy the mandalas as it's normally the practice. They still exist. They are visible to the naked eye.' It dawned to me at that moment that many holy places have a reason being known as "holy places". He went on to explain, 'They can be found "as physical location" on this world and the most famous one is the holy Mt. Kailash.'

Indeed, it made sense. How else can one seek a transformation to the pure land of the Buddhas!

'A few hundred years ago...' he went on '...the Great Guru and Bodhisattva, Lord Pathmasambhava, during his pilgrimage to Kailash, halted in Keajara for a rest. He realized during his meditation that the location where this monastery was later built was very powerful. He felt a great presence, a great consciousness. Encountering this experience, he decided to meditate deeper. After many days of single pointed concentration he finally encountered the correct position of another Heruka mandala.'

I interrupted asking, 'Does that mean somewhere in our vicinity is a portal leading to another dimension?'

'Well, yes,' he answered pausing. 'Upon locating this portal he asked a temple to be built around it. He continued his meditation for many months. The realizations during this meditation were the foundation to the secret teachings of accessing the mandala to enable one to then cross over to Buddha Heruka Pure Land, the true Keajra.'

"Many are the secrets in life," I thought. 'Geshe-La, are you saying that there is actually a portal here in this monastery, one which is accessible to mankind, in physical form, visible to the naked eye?'

390

'Ihmmm, yes and no, it is visible to the naked eye but only accessible to the chosen ones. The portal opens only to those with a pure heart.'

'To those with a pure heart?' I asked.

'Yes. Those who wish to achieve enlightenment for the benefit of all beings.'

I understood. 'A pure motivation.'

'This secret teaching, we have guarded with great effort, it is still being practiced and many have been able to cross over to the Pure Land of Buddha Heruka. This is possible through sincere and true practice and through achieving the stage of single pointedness. The people born here and those who find their way to Keajara, most of them bring with them the karmical causes which enable them to easily meditate single pointedly, which you yourself have experienced. I was aware of your capabilities when I first met you, many years ago. That was one of the reasons I asked you to remain in Keajara and encouraged you to continue practicing meditation and the learning of Dharma.'

'I see.' A great feeling of gratitude arose in my heart. 'I'm very thankful for your support.'

Geshe-La smiled. 'When a person achieves the stage of unlimited single pointed meditation, he or she'll begin to practice the secret teachings of Guru Pathmasambhava to open the doors of the portal. That is why, although we have an influx in the population, the growth of the population is sustained.'

'You mean people are leaving this world and are entering the Pure Land Keajra?' I asked.

He simply said, 'Yes. But naturally only if they wish to do so.'

At that moment I experienced great relieve for knowing the reason of missing people. At the same time, an idea did occur to me, if humans were willing, they too had this option. We could end Samsara, we could end suffering, we could end ignorance.

'Geshe-La, how does one, as you say, cross over?'

'Well, during the meditation, one begins to focus inwards. At some point one opens his or her third eye, through which one is able to perceive the portal.'

I felt an excitement in me, not sure what it meant.

Geshe-La explained further, 'A gateway into a world of pure mind. The portal is only visible to ones who have the ability to perceive the endlessness and the beginninglessness of time and space, in other words, one who has realized emptiness directly. It is the awareness of oneness, to be oneness.'

'You mean, the moment when one releases all blockages, encountered by the tranquility of oneness, experiences the constantness of change, one reaches the stage of subtle mindedness,' I added. 'I remember,' I was speaking to myself, 'Boundaries between this world and another are just conventions. When all perceptions of conventions fall away, so do all boundaries and the path to transcendence is open. A separation is only an illusion.'

'Our world is only a reflection of our mind. It is a mirror through which we see ourselves. The hate or love we perceive for others is nothing more than what we carry within us,' he ended by saying, 'the portal is beyond time and space.'

I was very thankful for the revelation; somehow a great weight had been lifted from my heart. Geshe-La rose slowly and bid me good evening. As he was about to leave the room, he turned around and said. 'It is our responsibility to enable access to those seeking the path of liberation.'

We took leave from Geshe-La, I and Indira walked home silently. Many a thought crossed my mind, "...purify your past negative actions with honest repentance, face the future with courage, with self-confidence and a positive mind." I realized it was not easy. It is difficult to let go, to allow things to fall away. The fear of losing is strong. For the moment, I knew I wasn't ready yet for the next step. At the same time I was also somewhat relieved and glad, that I too shall have the opportunity to follow others into the Pure Land of the Buddha. I understood why this information had been kept a secret, especially considering the destruction which took place in Tibet on holy places.

In all of us, there is a center of wisdom and compassion, deeper and greater than what we could imagine, and meditation helps us to reach this center, it helps us to understand. We could reach this source by learning more about ourselves. It is within us, it is our true spiritual guide, our compass. There we shall find the inner peace which we seek, the inner wisdom, which guides us through the turmoil of our lives.

As we explore further towards this center, everyday activities become less important. It reminds us of the fidelity of everyday events. All the answers we seek are within us, waiting to be discovered.

The world around us continually changes, unconsciously we change with it. It is somehow like day and night. I mean, we do take into account that time is somehow passing but we are not really consciously aware of this experience. Instead we choose not to think about change; at the same time we wish for eternal happiness in an ever changing environment. What a paradox!

Eternal happiness cannot be found in an unstable environment. Even the state of "enlightenment" is subjected to change. The difference is, at this state of the mind, duality does not exist. Illusions are not possible. One is constantly in a state of clarity, in a state of oneness; a state of mind in which every experience is a positive one, where change only leads to continuous happiness.

28

Time is a friendly reminder

Many years have passed. Anna has grown into a delightful child. We are both happy to see her grow up in a free, independent and self-confident nation. She just turned eight. After a second term as Prime Minister, Indira decided to not candidate anymore. She concentrated her efforts to help the Librarian in translating old documents. I for my part worked on making Keajara a better place to live in but I did not neglect my studies.

Indira spent a lot of time in the Library. I and Anna used to accompany her often. During one of my visits, I accidently discovered a roll of old writings in "Pali". The Librarian was very surprised of my discovery, but at the same time pleased.

'You have discovered a great treasure. This is a very rare find and the first of its kind to actually document the teachings of the great Bodhisattva Ananda, who was one of the first disciples of the historical Buddha Shakyamuni. Furthermore this is the first spoken words of the great Buddha. It speaks of the four Noble Truths. The roll also describes the sixteen characteristics, which are part of the Mahayana text known as the "Ornament of Clear Realization".' Geshe-La explained further, 'As you can see, the second part of this document shows a drawing of a wheel,' pointing to a sketch of what looked like a ships wheel. Each spoke of the wheel was indicated with a word in Pali. 'I have not seen this before,' he said scrutinizing the sketch. 'It seems to explain how actions originate and how these actions affect rebirth. Very interesting, very profound, this is.' He translated and I drew a picture.

Conviction

Idea Belief

Rebirth Motivation

Karma Thoughts

Physical or Mental Actions

Still explaining, he said, 'It begins with an idea. This same idea becomes a conviction. In due course it becomes a belief, a belief which creates motivations. This emotion turns into a thought and later into an action, an action which creates a possible outcome. Dharma offers a set of ideas which helps us to finally cure all illness, and redeem us from all non-virtuous ideas.'

Coming to the end, he exclaimed, 'Wonderful, wonderful! I'm so happy about this finding. This discovery reinstates our interpretation of Dharma. It has not changed since the last 2,500 years.' During all the years I had known him, it was the first time I had witnessed such emotions.

'I cannot thank you enough for this!' he said heartily. 'With this finding we will be able to speak to the world with more confidence on the validity of Dharma.'

'Why was this roll not discovered or recognized earlier,' I asked a little perplexed.

'Maybe it was or maybe it was overseen. We don't know. Over the past fifty years, we have been receiving many such artifacts. We store them for save-keeping but many go unnoticed or are forgotten. Unfortunately we have not had the manpower to categorize everything.'

'We have to do something about this. I believe we should start a new project to document the artifacts and have them stored properly.'

'I can only agree with you.'

He went on by saying, "For instance, only last week we found another important document. It is from a great Tibetan Master who lived 1,000 years ago. In this document he speaks of the "Truth of cessation".' Geshe-La recited a part of it, "...it is something personal, something magical. It hides no secrecy, nor does it have any connotations of religion. It is no more and no less than an experience of the truth of oneself; a journey undertaken only to return in perfection; in harmony with all things existing."

'So much wisdom,' I replied. 'He regards Dharma as a cure for the illness we face, a means to cure us from attachments and show us the way towards eternal happiness.'

As he was speaking, Indira walked in and we informed her about the document. She too was surprised. We left Geshe-La with high spirits that evening. Despite the precious discovery, I was restless that night. Unable to sleep, I decided to take a walk in the garden. It was very quiet, only the wind was whispering, the trees listening. It was a fresh spring night, a new beginning and nature slowly awakening from its slumber.

Unconsciously my feet took me directly to Geshe-La's quarters. The light was on; uncertainly I knocked on his door, hoping he was still awake. The door opened slightly and a young monk peeped out. He stepped out on the threshold. He asked me if there was anything urgent. I assured him that the matter wasn't urgent and that it could wait until the next morning. As we were speaking, Geshe-La appeared at the doorway. With the door wide open, I noticed other monks in the room.

'I am sorry Geshe-La for disturbing; I didn't realize you had company.'

'Not at all, we have been discussing about your discovery, everyone is very excited.' The other monks nodded smilingly in agreement.

'If you would care to come in?' The monks rose politely and left the room not wanting to disturb us.

'We were also discussing about an old tradition, which we think it is time to be revived. It used to be practiced in Keajara for ordained monks as part of their schooling to plan for longer retreats. The retreats were carried out in secluded areas for longer periods. We have observed that many monks, nuns, other Keajarans and

Tibetans arriving here see the necessity for this, in order to train in single pointed meditation.'

We agreed to work out a plan; we came up with the idea of building a self-sustaining monastery. Later in the week we choose an area, forty five kilometers to the west of Keajara City. It was situated in a small valley nearby a stream, which would supply fresh water. It took three years before the monastery was completed. It enabled many to achieve higher understanding of Dharma and to practice deep meditation techniques. Many came and used the facilities and many were able to achieve higher realization.

Despite the progress we were making in the new nation, there was another issue disturbing my peace of mind. I wasn't really getting any answers from the Prime Minister. It had to do with the finances of Keajara. How was the nation financing itself? The incomes did not explain the expenditures, we were overspending without borrowing. How was that possible? I decided to take it up with the High Lama. So one evening, I paid him a visit.

'I really didn't want to disturb you this late hour, I'm very sorry for this.'

'Not at all Roger, I don't need much sleep, so please take a seat.' He seemed to have noticed my confusion. 'So what is disturbing you?' he asked.

'I don't know how to begin, but maybe it is not so important,' I answered uncertainly.

'Not to worry, please speak your mind.

I decided to come directly to the point. 'Well, it is about the state finances. The numbers do not tie. Actually we should be having problems. The revenue generated by Keajara is very small compared to our expenditure. There are no discriminations in figures neither in the revenues nor in the expenditures. We are not borrowing to cover our spending. Our yearly expenditures are three times higher compared to our revenues. Where is the financial influx coming from?'

He smiled patiently as a loving father would do and proposed, 'Let us pay the main library a visit tomorrow. All will be answered.'

With this I left his quarters.

The next morning we were on our way to the main library. The Librarian welcomed us; after lunch he asked us to follow him. In his room was an entrance leading directly into the main library. Silently we followed him, towards the basement. It was dark, we lit a butter lamp. We descended the staircase and arrived at the bottom, turning right we walked down a corridor. It led us up to an unseeming door. We entered into what looked like a lab. I could smell chemical and various herbs.

The Librarian smiled mischievously as he said, 'This is where Keajara's monetary strength lies. The monks who work in this room are ones who have realized emptiness directly. But there is something special about them. They are able to mold matter physically. What you would call "an alchemist". In other words they produce gold in this room.'

He smiled again as he noticed my astonishment and asked me to follow to the end of the room. There was a large steel door; opening it we entered a room about

250 sqm and four meters high. There they were. The gold bars were staked almost to the roof.

'All this was produced by your monks!'

They nodded.

'A few years ago, when you let me in the secret of the portal to the Pure Land, I had thought nothing else would surprise me. I was wrong.'

Well that explained everything!

29

The Present and the Farewell

Dharma is like the wind, silent but strong. It is ours the choice to follow. It is ever present and ever guiding. Like a ship on high seas, we need only to drop our sails and allow the wind to guide us.

A man living in a cave, unaware of the light outside is buried in darkness. He lives in the conviction that all world is night. It is for him to choose the way outside, it is his to decide to take the first step, to have the courage to seek the light. Alone we can't save the world, but together change is possible. It is an individual and mutual responsibility. Each of us have a free will. Man must decide for himself.

Fifteen years it has been, since I first arrived in Keajara, I not only have found a home here but also a family and Dharma. Indira had opened a window, through which I saw a wholly different world. Our lives are not only our own, we are always bound to others. With each act we create our future. Transcended in time and space, we sail this ocean called Samsara. Conventions are no more real as are the boundaries between noises and sounds. To evolve means to transcend conventions. Separation is only an illusion. The true purpose of our lives is beyond the limitations of need.

Anna now ten years, has grown into an intelligent and self-confident young girl. She is very much her mother. We love her dearly. Indira, apart from being my companion in armor, is my best friend. We are closer now, than ever.

I had left my post as minister. I would not candidate a fourth term. We both decided to spend more time with our child, with Dharma and in meditation. Anna seemed to have a hand for medicine. Her teachers noticed her talent and decided to train her in traditional medicine; her training is not yet complete but she is doing very well.

After completing her studies in Tibetan medicine at her eighteenth birthday, Anna announced her wish to go overseas and do her medical degree, in modern medicine. I used my old contacts at Harvard to enable the admission. Six months later together with her newly found friend Hira, she left to the US, only to return after completing their studies. They settled down and later had a young girl, my granddaughter. They were dedicated to their profession and traveled long miles to nurse the ill.

It's now thirty-five years since I came to Keajara. I have been longer here than I was in the US. I never returned "home" because I had not the longing to do so. We were ready, and it was time to take leave from this world. We had both performed two long retreats, each lasting more than three years. There we had trained our capability in single pointed meditation and the new High Lama was very pleased with our progress and proposed that we consider taking our final journey into the Pure

Land of Keajra. Long intensive discussions followed and we finally decided to take the step and inform Anna and Hira.

The Present

The past came to an end, time had come to bid fare-well.

'Anna, Hira, we have something to say.'

'What is it papa, you sound serious?'

I was not sure how to begin and I hated seeing her so disturbed. 'You know that I and mama have both done our long retreats.'

She nodded.

'Well the High Lama is of the opinion that we have both done great progress. He therefore recommended that we consider our move to the next phase.'

She knew what it meant as tears began to swell up at the corner of her eyes. She had not expected it. The shadow of sadness was apparent on Hira's face.

Indira said, 'My dears, we do know it is difficult for you. It is difficult for us too. We waited to see you prosper. We are very proud of you; of what you're doing. It is so honorable and precious.'

'The High Lama is correct; we are not getting any younger. The time is right,' I added.

Anna was crying and it took quite some time before she could calm herself down. Her mother was at her side.

'When are you planning to leave us?' asked Anna after a while.

Indira replied, 'We will always be there for you, my darling.' She answered in a soft and loving voice. I could see how Indira was trying to keep her composure. 'We intend to leave next week.'

Somehow all that happened after that seemed blur. It was a difficult week, Anna and Hira stayed with us. Leaving Ammu would be even more difficult for me.

It was a Sunday morning. After our early prayers, we said farewell to Anna, Ammu and Hira. With tears we walked away silently towards the monastery.

At the doors the High Lama was waiting. We went inside following him silently. We were first led into a room. Orange robes had been laid out. Changing, we were then led into the library. On the wooden wall where the large thangka of Buddha Heruka and Vajravarahi was hanging, he reached out and pulled at the Vajra. The wall opened. There was a staircase going down to the basement.

We followed him. The stairway was lit with large yak butter lamps. The wooden wall closed behind us. The lamps were bright enough for us to see everything, old drawings of Dakas and Dakinis, of Buddhas and Bodhisattvas on the walls. It was a long walk downstairs. Ten minutes later we arrived at the bottom, with paths leading away into various directions.

'All paths lead to the middle of the monastery, where the portal is situated. Each path has rooms, in which persons like yourselves await their call.'

I asked, 'The "call"?'

'Yes, it is the call towards the great hall. The portal will open and allow you to cross over. Due to the nearness of the portal, the entire complex is under a strong vibration. This will assist you to sustain your concentration during meditation. The vibration here is similar to the vibrations in the red, white and central channels. Therefore your communication with Enlightened Beings shall happen without any disruption, smoothly, until the time has come. Upon passing the portal into the Pure Land of Keajra, you shall continue your meditation until the chakras loosen; the red and white drops will move towards the very subtle mind; finally igniting the great fire eliminating all negative karmical seeds and achieving Buddhahood.'

He paused for a moment to see if we had any questions. We asked none. 'During your period here, you shall be served three meals a day; the meals will be left in your rooms. Otherwise there will be no disturbances. If you need any assistance please use the bell in your rooms. Geshe-La, the first Prime Minister, the Librarian and Richard have left letters for you; before they took their final journey. I for my part would like to say, it has been a great pleasure and privilege to be your friend. I would like to thank you for your efforts and selfless work for Keajara.'

'It has also been a great pleasure for us to be your friend. I thank you. I have one final request. I will leave this manuscript here. Please give it to Anna.'

'It will be my pleasure.'

'Thank you.'

'I shall now take leave and wish you well, good bye my dear, dear friends.'

With these words and tears in his eyes he left. We too were in tears.

A short moment later we entered our room. It was a pleasant and comfortable. It had all the things one would need. But somehow nostalgia caught hold of us and we saw us swaying over memories. Tears began to take the best of us. It was late, there was a clock telling us it was past 10.00 p.m.

The next morning, Indira wanted to write some letters. I for my part wanted to complete my manuscript. We spent the rest of the day doing this. The following day, we decided to read the letters which were left for us. Reading them brought back memories, transported back in time, to the early days. To New York, to the UN, our first meetings and the following years, it was difficult to let go.

30

Home at last

Like all journeys, this too will soon come to an end, only to begin anew. We shall write a new chapter.

The days passed, we were meditating intensely for hours reaching the state of single pointedness.

I had begun to drift very deep. Time stood still and space disappeared. Meditating deeper, visions appeared, first unclear. They were strange, incomprehensible. Slowly it dawned onto me, "matter!" They seemed to be minute particles, atoms!

Realizing this, I remained focused and they began to open, becoming finer. At the same time, great bliss engulfed my heart. This feeling grew greater as I remained focused. The chain of matter seemed to be endless at first. No end perceivable. Yet, this illusion melted away. Particles disappeared and in its place I perceived waves. The waves too began to melt away until only space existed. It this state of equilibrium I remained. In this state all was eternity.

All phenomena began to unknot. The idea of "inherent existence" began to crumble. Engulfed in oneness, feeling lighter than air, being conscious of all things, connected to perfection I remained focused. I sensed clarity, an understanding of how things really existed.

A glow of warmness surrounded my heart; a feeling of peace.

I perceived creation and transformation; motivations arose, transformed into thoughts, thoughts transformed into actions, actions becoming matter, actions resulting in negative and positive Karma, karmical seeds being "archived" and transported from one birth to another.

The experience of the cycle was an emotion which I had not known before; it was a feeling of great tranquility and freedom. As this realization came to a climax, I opened my eyes slowly and saw Indira smiling.

A few moments passed as I came to myself; remaining seated I said, 'I somehow have the feeling I'm hungry.'

She laughed and gave me a piece of bread which I enjoyed silently. I noticed I had a beard.

'A beard? How long have I been in meditation?'

'About thirty-two days,' Indira answered.

She knew what had taken place, there seemed no need for explanation, no words were spoken. I had experienced directly how phenomena were created. I was at one with myself and the universe, at the source of all things, in utter inner peace. I had realized emptiness directly. No more uncontrolled rebirths in Samsara!

Indira helped me up and I took a bath. After dinner I went to a long and peaceful sleep. The next morning I awoke with a clarity which I had not known before. I decided to note down my thoughts and experiences for future generations.

"What we perceive in Samsara are conventional experiences clouded by the duality of things. They appear and disappear as does matter. Our encounters in life are mere perceptions. The profound path shows the way to reach the deepest self, lying within us, to guide us towards liberation. We are responsible for our future, we hold the power to shape our destiny. We are not and can never be victims. We all make our choices; the hard part is living with them. This life which we consider to be precious is nothing but a shadow in time. We are here only for a moment, no more than memories, ashes blown away by the wind of time. Only in the darkest of moments do we learn to seek clarity. Only then do we begin to reach out for answers, to change our destiny, to open the locked doors listening to the music of salvation, where the heart finds peace at last."

Indira fully understanding them said, 'You've realized emptiness directly.'

I asked, 'How do you know?'

She smiled. 'I too realized it only a few days earlier.'

I was very glad to hear this.

'The realization of Emptiness...' she said '...puts our mind in the correct prospective about the true existence of all phenomena. We are freed from the duality of Samsara. We don't think in "right or wrongs", or "ups and downs", any more. We experience phenomena in their true form directly during meditation. Henceforth, during meditation you will not perceive a phenomenon any other way. Only Buddhas are able to perceive all phenomena without any duality at all the times. Henceforth you shall not accumulate any negative Karma. You are free of all egoistical motivation.'

It was a profound experience. The smallest known particle is the "Quark". Its existence is scientifically proved. Furthermore mathematicians have proven there exists nothing $= 0$ at the end of the chain called matter. Science also acknowledges the existence of a pre-stage called wave between "nothingness" and matter.

During my meditation I arrived in these realms, passing them I traveled further.

We continued our meditation and practiced on becoming universal compassion. Samsara unveiled itself before me and bliss and wisdom revealed themselves. There were no friends, no enemies. Attachments freed, walking tall, began a new clarity. No more me, no more you. Being one with all creation, the presence of infinite minds, aware, we became. Abiding, in this state, we did.

Lord Ganesha appeared, the Lord allowed me to abide in his realm until the moment came, an awareness awoke, it penetrated my chakras, and the chakras began to gently vibrate. Everything became light, my body, my thoughts, my emotions, all flowing in unity, a masterpiece of perfect harmony.

As the winds began to carry my mind, a journey into uncharted lands, deeper my consciousness traveled, into infinity, into no space, into no time. All was light, the clouds began to disappear, clarity ruled.

Arriving at the doors of the five Buddhas, the essence of my heart chakra; here they prevailed, the five Buddha Families: Buddha Akshobya, Buddha Ratnasambhava, Buddha Amitabha, Buddha Amoghasiddhi and Buddha Vairochana. Their blessings were like a warm blanket soothing at a cold night. My mind remained in oneness, time had no relevance. The winds gathered in my heart chakra, resonating in perfect harmony as my consciousness traveled deeper. The Buddhas allowed me to pass, doors opening into another world.

At this moment did I become aware of a gentle tone resonating. Softer at first but it became louder; a resonance, a melody of mantras, flowing through me. This was it, the "call", the primal "sound", the source of all "voices" existing since beginninglessness, the "OM".

I was everywhere, all at once, in the past, in the future, in the furthest parts of the universe and here. I could perceive the galaxies, the many dimensions, the infinite voices surrounding us, the vibrations of mother earth, the forces of the magnetic poles, the movement of time and the essence of space. It was as if I was no more, I did not exist, all was one and the oneness was me.

There were no more barriers, no more obstacles. I sensed a consciousness, beside me, a soft and familiar soul. It was Indira. There were no words needed, no more doubts. We understood.

Our bodies began to float. The room was no more, the doors had disappeared, the corridors were gone. We were in the great hall, floating towards the portal.

Embraced by compassion, mother earth welcomed us, experiencing great bliss. At this moment we dematerialized and appeared in the Pure Land of Keajra.

There in the realm of realms, the center of all things existing, in the finiteness of what is infinite, we perceived a realm of pure consciousness, of pure wisdom, of pure compassion. We became aware of the unknown, in the middle of the infinite beings, in the state of meditation; all serving the great endeavor, the path of paths.

At this moment we felt the presence of the great union, the beginning and the end of wisdom, the beginning and the end of compassion, the father and the mother. Home at last!

The End

9 783000 526152